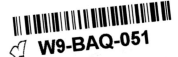

Squirrel's New Year's Resolution

Pat Miller

Illustrated by

Kathi Ember

SCHOLASTIC INC.
New York Toronto London Auckland
Sydney Mexico City New Delhi Hong Kong

For Baby D.
Grandbaby to be.
PM

To my wonderful "family" of friends. Thanks for all your help.
I resolve to return the favor.
Love, Kathi

ISBN 978-0-545-43406-5

12 11 10 9 8 7 6 5 4 3 2 11 12 13 14 15 16/0

Printed in the U.S.A. 08

First Scholastic printing, December 2011

The artwork for this book was rendered traditionally using acrylics.
The design is by Lindaanne Donohoe.

Squirrel pinned up her brand new Nut-of-the-Month calendar. “It’s January first,” the radio said. “A great day to make a resolution.”

"Make a resolution?" wondered Squirrel. "How do you do that? Bear might know." She went to see Bear at the Lonewood Library.

"Happy New Year!" he said.

"Same to you, Bear. Do you know how to make a resolution? Is it like making a snack?"

Bear laughed. "Resolutions are more important than snacks."

"More important than snacks?" said Squirrel. "What *is* a resolution?"

QUIET
JAN
1
BOOK
RETURN
Happy
New
Year!
RESOLVE
BETTER YOU

“A resolution is a promise you make to yourself to be better or to help others,” Bear said. “When we begin a new year, we make a fresh start.”

“Wow. Did *you* make a resolution?” asked Squirrel.

“I did,” Bear answered. “I resolved to teach others how to read. I’m going to teach Skunk as soon as she gets well.”

THE
YOUR
ANIMAL
HOW
THE
New Year
Traditions
JAN
1

"Oh, no, Skunk is still sick," Squirrel thought, as she hurried to Skunk's house for a visit. She forgot all about making a resolution.

Skunk was sick of being sick.

"I'm stuck in bed until Dr. Owl says I'm better," said Skunk. "I would rather be learning to read. That's my New Year's resolution."

PINE SCENT
Learn to Read!
Eau de You
P.U.

Squirrel knew how to cheer up her friend. She hid at the foot of the bed. She popped up and shouted, "Boo!"

Skunk giggled. Hide-and-skunk was her favorite game. Squirrel popped up again. "Boo!"

And again. "Boo!" By now Skunk was laughing hard.

Just then Dr. Owl came by. “Skunk, I can tell by your laughter that you are feeling much better,” he said. “Now you can visit Bear. Just make sure you have a healthy lunch first.”

"Lunch!" thought Squirrel. She headed toward the Hidey Hole Diner. "Maybe someone there can help me with my resolution."

On her way she met Mole and Turtle. Mole was holding a map close to his nose.

"What are you doing?" asked Squirrel.

"Turtle and I resolved to plant a garden," said Mole. "But I can't find a good place to dig with all these trees."

EAT
AT THE
Hidey
Hole
DINER
LUNCH
SPECIALS
EVERY
DAY
MAP
WOODS

"Wait here," said Squirrel. She dashed up an oak tree and looked down. She spied Wildcat Creek and on its bank, a perfect place for a garden.

Squirrel scampered down and led Mole and Turtle through the woods to the edge of the creek. She helped them stake out string for the borders of the garden.

"Thanks, Squirrel. I will start digging right after lunch," said Mole.

"Lunch!" thought Squirrel, and she rushed away. She still hadn't thought of a resolution.

At the diner, Squirrel chose a stool next to Porcupine. He looked grumpy.

"What's wrong?" asked Squirrel.

"I resolved to be less grumpy. So I'm trying to laugh more. But I can't think of anything funny."

MENU
Hidey Hole
Diner

"I can help you think of something funny. Like, why did the squirrel run back and forth across the road?"

"I don't know, why?" asked Porcupine.

"Because she was nuts!" laughed Squirrel.

Porcupine laughed, too. "I get it! That reminds me. What's striped and bouncy?"

"Tell me," giggled Squirrel.

"Skunk on a trampoline!" said Porcupine. Squirrel laughed herself right off the stool.

Porcupine said, "That's a good one! I'd better write these down." Off he went to find paper and pencil.

Squirrel felt left out. "Porcupine has a resolution. So do Bear and Skunk and Mole and Turtle," she thought. "I'm the only animal in the forest who hasn't made a New Year's resolution."

New Year's Special
Cabbage Stew
MENU
Hidey Hole Diner

Rabbit came to take Squirrel's order. "Would you like to try my New Year's Special?" asked Rabbit.

"Sure," said Squirrel. "Maybe it will help me make a resolution. I wish I knew how."

"Think of a way to improve yourself. Or a way to use what you're good at to help others," said Rabbit.

Squirrel ate her lunch special and thought hard.

Just then, Skunk came in. “I need a healthy lunch! Thanks to Squirrel, I’m feeling better!”

“Sit with me, Skunk,” Bear called. “I see you brought our first book.”

Turtle and Mole came in next. "What do you have for two thirsty animals who just started a garden?" said Mole.

"Squirrel found a terrific place for it," said Turtle.

Porcupine hurried in. "Do you know why Bear said 'Caw, caw?'"

Before anyone could answer, Porcupine said, "He was learning another language!" All the animals laughed.

"I didn't know you were so funny," said Mole.

"Me, either," said Porcupine. "Squirrel got me started."

Whip
MENU
Hidey Hole
Diner

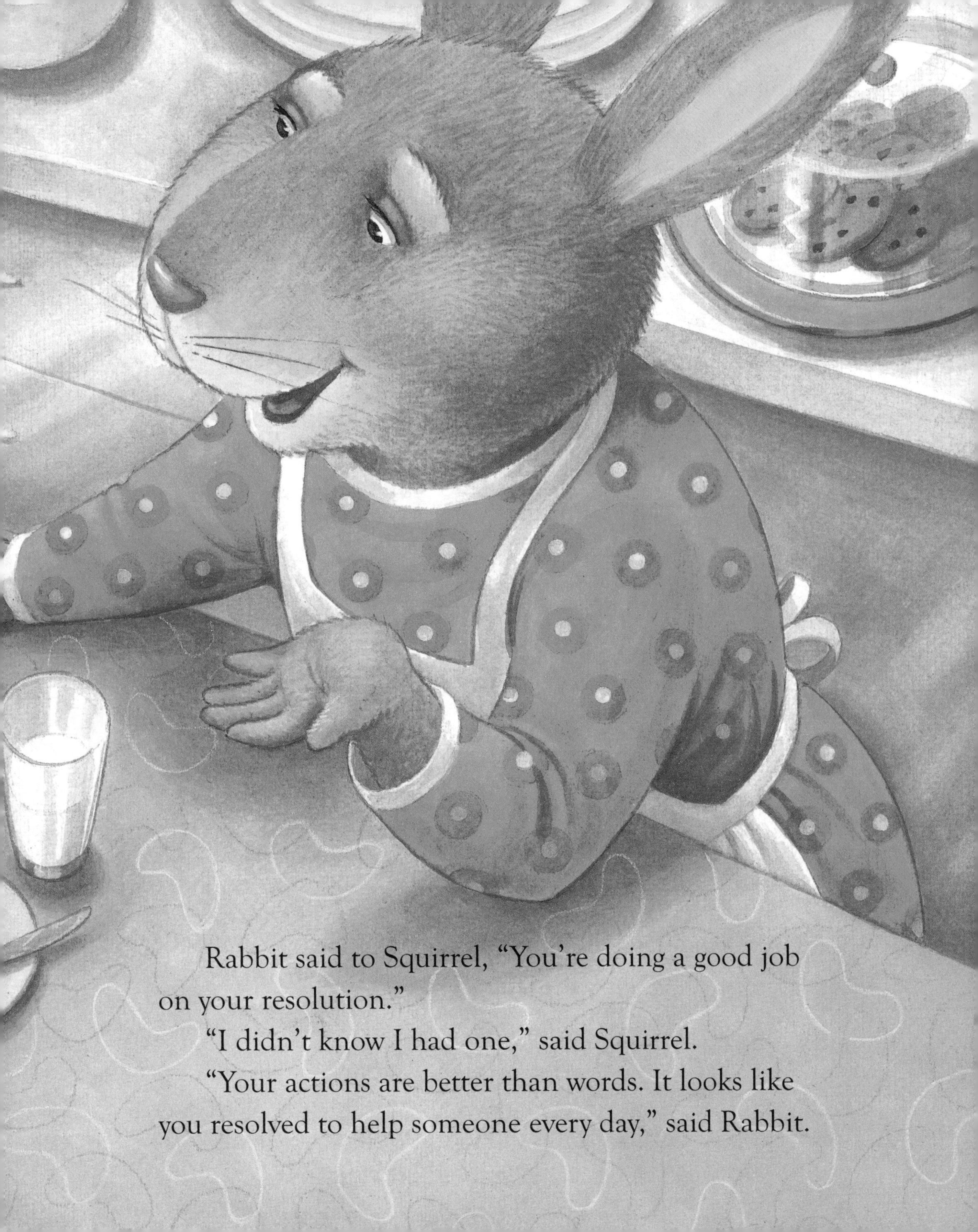

Rabbit said to Squirrel, “You’re doing a good job on your resolution.”

“I didn’t know I had one,” said Squirrel.

“Your actions are better than words. It looks like you resolved to help someone every day,” said Rabbit.

Happy New Year!!

“Really?” asked Squirrel. “I did it! I made my very first resolution!”

“Hurray for Squirrel!” shouted all the animals.

It was going to be a very happy New Year.

HUME STUDIES

ISSN 0319-7336

Volume 45, Number 1–2
Special Book Issue

EDITORS' NOTE

DISCUSSION OF JAMES HARRIS,
HUME: AN INTELLECTUAL BIOGRAPHY

DISCUSSION OF STEFANIE ROCKNAK,
IMAGINED CAUSES: HUME'S CONCEPTION OF OBJECTS

Founded by John W. Davis in 1975

Published by The Hume Society

DISCUSSION OF DONALD C. AINSLIE, *HUME'S TRUE SCEPTICISM*

DISCUSSION OF JACQUELINE A. TAYLOR, *REFLECTING SUBJECTS: PASSION, SYMPATHY, AND SOCIETY IN HUME'S PHILOSOPHY*

ERRATUM

Acknowledgments

The editors acknowledge the generous support of the University of Texas at Austin, University of Alberta, University of California, Irvine, and University of Calgary. We also acknowledge the assistance of Corina David as copy-editor for this issue.

HUME STUDIES
Volume 45, Number 1–2, 2019, pp. 1–2

Editors' Note to Volume 45, Special Book Issue

This volume of *Hume Studies* is a special double-issue devoted to discussions of four recent books on Hume: *Hume: an Intellectual Biography*, by James Harris; *Imagined Causes: Hume's Conception of Objects*, by Stefanie Rocknak; *Hume's True Scepticism*, by Donald Ainslie; and *Reflecting Subjects: Passion, Sympathy, and Society in Hume's Philosophy*, by Jacqueline Taylor. The latter three discussions began as Author-Meets-Critics sessions at the 43rd International Hume Conference in Sydney, Australia, and the present volume keeps the AMC format: each discussion starts with a short précis of the book from the author, followed by comments from three respondents, and concludes with the author's reply. The selection of books under discussion offers, we hope, a good selection of scholarship on Hume over the last decade. Although the rich outpouring of recent scholarship means that no selection could cover everything, the volume aims to offer at least a sample of the variety of topics, approaches and styles now available. Many readers will already be acquainted with one or more of the books included in here; our hope is to provide fresh perspectives on familiar views, as well as prompting new discoveries among both established scholars and students.

The editors would like to express our thanks to all the authors included here, many of whom worked hard to turn informal remarks into written pieces, while others wrote comments especially for this volume. It is with great regret that we were unable to publish this volume in time to thank the late Barry Stroud personally. But we are very honored that one of the last pieces he worked on will appear here: his comments on Donald Ainslie's account of Humean scepticism. It seems a fitting coda for a great and generous scholar of Hume and scepticism that his last contribution to *Hume Studies* is a discussion of the work of a new generation. We would like to thank Sarah Stroud for her help in preparing Barry's copy and approval to publish. We trust that he would be pleased with the results—and hope that you will find this volume a useful and agreeable companion to recent literature.

Ann Levey,
Karl Schafer,
Amy Schmitter

Hume Studies
Volume 45, Number 1–2, 2019, pp. 3–5

Précis of *Hume: An Intellectual Biography*

JAMES A. HARRIS

My purpose in *Hume: An Intellectual Biography* was to write the first comprehensive account of Hume's career as an author, beginning with what we know about his education at Edinburgh, and ending with "My Own Life," the brief autobiography that Hume wrote shortly before he died. Where Ernest Mossner, in his classic *The Life of David Hume,* was explicitly concerned with the man rather than with the ideas, I was concerned with the ideas, and the arguments, rather than with the man. Hume's biography was of interest to me insofar as, but no further than, it shed light on Hume's intellectual development. In many respects, Mossner's achievement as a biographer remains deeply impressive, and anyone wanting to gain a full impression of Hume as an individual certainly needs to read his book, as well as mine. But in one crucial respect, I believe, Mossner was deeply mistaken. Mossner was determined to present Hume as an outsider, continually subject to snubs and humiliations, and almost universally misread and misunderstood. I was concerned, by contrast, to present Hume's authorial career as a triumphant success. As I explain in my response to my critics below, I fixed on the persona of the man of letters as the key to understanding Hume's writings taken as a whole, and I gave an account of Hume's life as man of letters that was intended to bring out his central place in the literary worlds of mid eighteenth-century Scotland, England, and Europe. Thus, I emphasised his friendly intellectual engagements with his contemporaries, and I argued that, in the case of Hume, "Enlightenment" was the creation of a kind of discursive space in which fundamental disagreement about speculative and practical matters could be both polite and constructive.

Closely related to this way of presenting Hume's relationship with the intellectual world in which he lived and worked was a particular approach to the question of Hume and religion. Hume's religious skepticism was, I fully accepted, both unique and a supremely important part of his legacy, but it did not set Hume dramatically against the spirit of his age in the way

James A. Harris, Department of Philosophy, University of St Andrews, Edgecliffe, The Scores, St Andrews, KY16 9AL.
Email: jah15@st-andrews.ac.uk

that Mossner and many others have claimed. It was no barrier, for instance, to close friendships with several ministers of the Church of Scotland, nor to productive argument with men outwith Scotland such as Richard Price and Josiah Tucker. I attempted to set Hume's religious thought, in the first instance, in a complicated Scottish context in which traditionalist Calvinist orthodoxy was being challenged by a self-consciously "moderate" faction in the Church. This conflict had consequences for many aspects of Scottish cultural and intellectual life, and it impacted sharply on Hume on more than one occasion, for instance when he applied for academic positions in Edinburgh and Glasgow, and when he was trying to establish himself in Edinburgh in the 1750s. Hume was, in an important sense, an ally of the moderates, but it was also true that he shared the skepticism of the orthodox about the possibility of the kind of compromises the moderates wanted to make between religion and modern philosophy. I suggested that one way to read the *Dialogues concerning Natural Religion*—begun, of course, thirty years before its publication in 1779—was as a response to this intellectual predicament. I was doubtful, then, that it makes sense to think of Hume as hostile to something called, simply, "religion." Religion was not, for him, a monolith. It was a complex and variegated phenomenon, that had played and continued to play many different roles in the emotional, moral, and political lives of human beings. It was also—as Hume revealed in the *Natural History of Religion*—a phenomenon with deep roots in human nature, and so was something that a skeptic about human rationality was bound to accept as almost certainly a permanent feature of any conceivable human society.

Part of the point of understanding Hume's career as that of a man of letters, and of seeing that career as having been a success, was to move beyond the idea that Hume's failure to secure an academic appointment was in some sense the defining disappointment of his life. Much writing about Hume is done by academic philosophers, and it is natural for them to suppose that Hume wanted to have the same kind of career as they have. In my book I argue that there is no reason to think that that supposition is true. For one thing, Hume gives no sign in his letters that he was particularly disappointed at not becoming a professor of moral philosophy. For another, when one considers what being a professor of moral philosophy actually entailed at a Scottish university in the eighteenth century, this is not surprising. Students were, as Hume himself had been, boys in their early teens, and a large part of the job was a kind of moral pedagogy that it is difficult to imagine Hume having much of a relish for. Even a man as fundamentally serious as Adam Smith left academia as soon as he possibly could. Hume's skepticism is relevant here too, because it was, among other things, skepticism about the practical efficacy of philosophy. It was skepticism about the ability of philosophy to do much, if anything, to alter and improve an individual's fundamental dispositions and enjoyments. It was skepticism about the ancient conception of philosophy as a kind of medicine for the mind. It was, in other words, skepticism about the very possibility of moral philosophy as most of Hume's contemporaries conceived of it.

The lack of success of the *Treatise*, taken together perhaps with Hume's failure to get a university job, did not, on the view I developed in the book, constitute a crisis that prompted Hume to move from "philosophy" to something else. It did not cause him to give up on serious intellectual pursuits and pursue fame and wealth instead. Hume's career as man of letters was, instead, the application of a philosophical style of reasoning—skeptical, disengaged, impartial, interested in the identification of general laws lying below the apparent chaos of human behaviour—to an extraordinarily wide range of subjects. Hume regularly referred to the entirety of the contents of *Essays and Treatises on Several Subjects*, which included all of his essays on politics and political economy, as his "philosophy." He regarded the history of England as an opportunity for the exercise of the same "philosophical spirit" as had been put to work in his other writings. Hume was a man with many interests. Nothing seemed to be, in principle, alien to philosophy in his capacious understanding of the word. For reasons I mention below, I was unable to convince myself that there was anything systematic about the way Hume moved from one subject matter to another. My book was an attempt to consider each of his intellectual endeavours on its own terms, and to offer some suggestions about what, exactly, Hume might have been trying to do as he wrote in this way about human nature, about morals and manners, about British party politics, about political economy, about English history, and about religion.

Hume Studies
Volume 45, Number 1-2, 2019, pp. 7-16

Hume as Man of Letters: Comments on Harris's *Hume: An Intellectual Biography*

CATHERINE JONES

James A. Harris suggests, in the "Introduction" to his intellectual biography of David Hume, that we should take seriously Hume's description of himself in "My Own Life," composed in April 1776, as having intended from the beginning to live the life of a man of letters. Harris uses the category "man of letters" both to characterise Hume's intellectual career as a whole, and to address the question of how to approach the relation between Hume the philosopher, Hume the essayist, and Hume the historian. In this article, I will discuss Harris's claim that Hume "is best seen not as a philosopher who may or may not have abandoned philosophy in order to write essays and history, but as a man of letters, a *philosophical* man of letters, who wrote on human nature, on politics, on religion, and on the history of England from 55 BC to 1688."[1] I will begin by outlining who or what the man of letters was in early modern Europe. I will then consider one aspect of Harris's presentation of Hume as man of letters: Hume's style. I will conclude with some reflections on the genre of biography, and Harris's methodology in particular.

The earliest published work explicitly dedicated to the character and career of the man of letters was the Italian Jesuit writer and historiographer Daniello Bartoli's *Dell'huomo di lettere difeso et emendato* (1645), which was translated into English by Thomas Salisbury as *The Learned Man Defended and Reform'd* (1660). Peter Burke, however, convincingly suggests that in the twelfth century, for the first time since late antiquity, a "clerisy" became visible to the world outside the monastery; these specialists in knowledge were known as "men of learning (*docti, eruditi, savants, Gelehrten*)" or "*men of letters (literati, hommes de lettres)*." Such men were not confined to a clerical elite, but included "a group of learned laymen," usually either physicians or lawyers, who found their place within the medieval university, as well as status

Catherine Jones is Professor of English at the School of Language, Literature, Music and Visual Culture, University of Aberdeen, King's College, Aberdeen AB24 3UB, United Kingdom.
Email: c.a.jones@abdn.ac.uk

in the world outside it (enhanced in time by the foundation of corporate groups, such as the London College of Physicians [established in 1518], which were concerned to maintain a monopoly of knowledge and practice against unofficial competitors). Bartoli's treatise, Burke argues, represents a strengthening of group identity in the mid-seventeenth century rather than a new formation.[2]

Men of letters in early modern Europe defined themselves as citizens of the Republic of Letters, a term that goes back to the fifteenth century, but that was employed with increasing frequency from the mid-seventeenth century onwards.[3] The term embraced, as Françoise Waquet describes, first existing institutions of learning, then the scholarly community as a whole, and finally, that part of it which is interested in "letters" more or less broadly understood.[4]

The Oxford English Dictionary defines the "man of letters" as "a man of learning, a scholar; a professional writer, *esp.* one having a variety of literary or intellectual interests."[5] It gives as the first recorded use of the term a diary entry of the English *virtuoso* John Evelyn (1620–1706). Visiting the Library of the Vatican, in Rome, on his second tour of continental Europe (1643–1647), Evelyn wrote on 18 January 1645:

> The Library is doubtlesse the most nobly built, furnish'd, and beautified in the World, ample, stately, light and cheerfull, looking into a most pleasant Garden: The Walls and roofe are painted; not with Antiqu[e]s, and Grotesc's (like our Bodlean at Oxford) but Emblemes, Figurs, Diagramms, and the like learned inventions found out by the Wit, and Industry of famous men. . . . There were likewise the Effigies of the most Illustrious men of Letters and Fathers of the Church, with divers noble statues in white marble at the entrance, viz. Hippolitus and Aristedes.[6]

Evelyn was committed to erudition as well as to "practical" *virtuoso* activities.[7] The interest that he displays, while travelling on the Continent, in both the literary remains of scholars and memorials to them, suggests his affinity with the "men of Letters" of his own and earlier generations.

Hume uses the term "man of letters" in the sense of "a man of learning, a scholar," in his letter to the anonymous physician of March or April 1734. He is describing the character of the individual he hoped would help him recover from the crisis of emotional and physical distress that he had suffered in 1729:

> The Favour I beg of you is your Advice, and the reason why I address myself in particular to you need not be told. As one must be a skillful Physician, a man of Letters, of Wit of Good Sense, and of great Humanity to give me a satisfying Answer, I wish Fame had pointed out to me more Persons, in whom these Qualities are united, in order to have kept me some time in Suspense.[8]

Hume characterizes his correspondent as exceptional, anticipating the character of the ideal physician—who is "ornate" in his politeness, gentility, and liberal learning, and "skillful" in his practice—elaborated later in the eighteenth century by John Gregory (1724–1773) and William Cullen (1710–1790) in their lectures to medical students at the University of Edinburgh.[9] Hume goes on to describe how his intense studies over the past five years have broken his health.

The term "man of letters" takes on a somewhat different meaning when Hume uses it to describe his own ambitions. In a letter to James Oswald of Dunnikier of 29 January 1748, for example, Hume writes of his decision to accept the offer of a further term of employment as Secretary to General St Clair, which will involve travel to Austria and Italy, specifically to the Courts of Vienna and Turin: "I shall have an opportunity of seeing Courts and Camps; and if I can afterwards, be so happy as to attain leizure and other opportunities, this knowledge may even turn to account to me, as a man of letters, which I confess has always been the sole object of my ambition."[10]

By the mid-eighteenth century, the Republic of Letters could be said to be epitomised by the French salon, which brought together in exquisite tension men and women, print and conversation, sense and wit, philosophy and amusement.[11] To be admitted to the Paris salon was the ambition of many men of letters; but, as Hume's correspondence makes clear, other locations on the Continent also offered British travellers the opportunity to develop their identities as men of letters. The courts and camps of Vienna and Turin held out for Hume the prospect of gaining greater experience of "the Operations of the Field and the Intrigues of the Cabinet," requisite for one of his ambitions, the writing of "History."[12]

Harris discusses Hume's breakdown and letter to the anonymous physician in chapter 1 of his biography ("Pursuits of Philosophy and General Learning"), and the letter to Oswald and his term of employment as St Clair's secretary in chapter 4 ("The Achievement of Independence"). Harris highlights in chapter 1 the important information found in the letter to the physician, that Hume, with his college education at Edinburgh University and an abortive period as a law student behind him, "found his choice inclining 'almost equally . . . to books of reasoning and philosophy, and to poetry and the polite authors.' What it suggests is that it would not be right to imagine the young Hume to have been fascinated by philosophy and by philosophy alone" (42). Chapter 4 brings out the urgency of Hume's pursuit of a moderate quantity of capital from employment that would allow him to devote himself entirely to a life of letters. On 9 February 1748, shortly before departing for the Continent, Hume wrote from London to Lord Kames of "an inward reluctance to leave [his] books, and leisure and retreat."[13] And yet, as Harris describes, he not only appears to have "wholeheartedly entered into the social life of Turin"; he also wrote a new essay, "Of National Character" (first published in *Essays, Moral and Political,* third edition [1748]), "[p]erhaps inspired by what he had seen on his journey to Italy" (242). Here the biographical context illuminates Harris's reading of the text; Harris also speculates on the possible influence of the ideas of Montesquieu on Hume's essay (243–44).

Harris emphasizes the centrality of breadth of learning to the identity of the eighteenth-century man of letters, an emphasis that fits Hume's career well, given the variety of his writing on a range of subjects—politics, economics, aesthetics, civil history, and the history and philosophy of religion. "To call yourself a man of letters," Harris writes in the "Introduction" to his biography, "was to distance yourself both from the academic specialisms of the university and from the narrow and pedantic obsessions of the gentleman *érudit*" (15).

The generalist orientation of the man of letters was perceived as desirable in eighteenth-century Britain because, as Lawrence E. Klein observes, it "tend[ed] to the development of the whole person and ke[pt] the person and his social relations in view. It fixed knowledge in a firm ethical and social grid, flagged by such key words as 'judgment' and 'taste.'"[14] This was also the case in France, as Roger Chartier shows in his essay "L'Homme de Lettres," cited by Harris (477n66). Chartier takes as his starting point Voltaire's article "Gens de Lettres" of 1757, published in the *Encylopédie* (1751–72) of Denis Diderot and Jean le Rond d'Alembert:

> On ne donne point ce nom [gens de lettres] à un homme qui avec peu de connaissance ne cultive qu'un seul genre· Celui qui n'ayant lû que des romans ne fera que des romans; celui qui sans aucune littérature aura composé au hasard quelques pieces de théatre, qui dépourvû de science aura fait quelques sermons, ne sera pas compté parmi les gens de lettres.[15]

What was inimical to politeness in learning was damned in Britain and France as pedantry. The word "pedant," observed William Smellie in the first edition of the *Encyclopaedia Britannica* (1771), "is used for a rough unpolished man of letters, who makes an impertinent use of the sciences, and abounds in unseasonable criticisms and observations."[16]

In his study of the changing conditions and conceptions of authorship in the eighteenth century, Dustin Griffin divides the men of letters of the period into "authors by profession" and "gentleman authors."[17] Harris, however, rightly observes that Hume does not fit neatly into either category (477n75). Hume needed money; but, in Harris's words, "[Hume's] idea of himself was as a man of letters unconstrained by any practical demands, whether professional or political, or, for that matter, moral" (18).

Harris convincingly argues that Hume sought to model his identity as a man of letters on Alexander Pope (1688–1744), "the first writer in English to alter the balance of power between author and publisher and achieve financial success on his own terms" (16). In his account of the circumstances surrounding the genesis of Hume's *A Treatise of Human Nature* (chapter 2, "Anatomist of Human Nature"), Harris also makes the intriguing suggestion that Hume may have taken inspiration from Pope's *An Essay on Man* (1733–34). Harris goes on to contrast the approach of Hume and Pope to the study of human nature with fine discrimination (83). Less plausible is Harris's assertion (477–78n75) that money mattered more to Hume than it did to Samuel Johnson (1709–1784), author of *A Dictionary of the English Language* (1755), who famously observed on 5 April 1776, "No man but a blockhead ever wrote, except for money."[18]

Hume's style has been the focus of a number of important studies over recent decades. These include Adam Potkay's *The Fate of Eloquence in the Age of Hume;* Susan Manning's *Fragments of Union: Making Connections in Scottish and American Writing;* and Anthony La Vopa's *The Labor of the Mind: Intellect and Gender in Enlightenment Cultures.* Harris, however, is the first to consider Hume's style across his career, and in the framework of an intellectual biography. Style mattered greatly to Hume, Harris argues, "because, as a man of letters, he did not write as a specialist only for fellow specialists. He sought, and found, a very large readership among the educated men and women of his day, in Britain, and in Europe more widely" (23). Harris's careful consideration of how Hume made his arguments in different genres is a particularly valuable aspect of his biography.

In his account of the rise of a culture of conversation in the eighteenth century, John Mee suggests that Hume sought to create in his essays an "elegant" world through a partnership between the "learned and conversable," on the model of Joseph Addison's and Richard Steele's *Spectator* (1711–12).[19] Like Mee, Harris draws attention to the links between Hume's essays and the Spectator (chapter 3, "Essayist"). But where Mee emphasizes the reorientation of learning in Hume's essays "away from scholasticism and towards the ordinary relations of the everyday world and vernacular language,"[20] Harris characterizes the kind of conversation that Hume wanted to engage in as "philosophical" because of its interest in underlying general explanatory principles, and because of the impersonality of its tone (23).

Of particular importance to Hume's sense of his task as writer of essays, Harris argues, was the woman reader: "Hume was interested in the extent to which women could help with the process of 'importing into company' the choicest discoveries made by the learned. . . . Any man of letters, therefore, who desired success with the public at large must first win over his female readers" (159). Harris describes how, in several of his essays, Hume explicitly addressed himself to women: "'Of Love and Marriage' explained to women 'what it is our sex complains of most in the married state.' 'Of the Study of History' recommended the study of history to women 'as an occupation, of all others, the best suited to their sex and education'" (159). Hume's condescension towards women in these essays is striking, but it is nonetheless important to bear in mind, as La Vopa argues, that, against the backdrop of one of the most pervasive conventional discourses in early eighteenth-century Britain, Hume conducts a positive reevaluation of women: "When he chides them for their preference for 'secret history,' the stories of behind-the-scenes intrigues and scandals, he aims to endow them with a knowledge of public history they can share with men."[21]

Harris offers a compelling account of Hume's conception of "proper historical style," and of his attempts in the *History of England* (1754–62) to balance a striving for impartiality with a desire "to emotionally engage the reader with the fate of history's victims, both great and small" (31). Harris suggests that Hume sought to reduce political debates to their most essential and abstract principles by balancing the best case that could be made on one side, against the best that could be made on the other, and then presenting a considered judgment as to the strengths and weaknesses of each argument. "Sometimes," Harris observes, "[Hume] presented arguments that were not made on one or other of these occasions, but that might have been made had the parties been more reflecting than they actually were" (339–40). Hume's method would be criticised by Thomas Babbington Macaulay, in an essay on "History" published in the Edinburgh Review in May 1828, for distorting facts to suit general principles.[22] Walter Scott, however, recognized the value of Hume's approach, and incorporated reflections in the style of Hume in novels such as *Waverley: or, 'Tis Sixty Years Since* (1814) and *Old Mortality* (1816). "Ah that Distance!" Scott wrote privately in 1826, "what a magician for conjuring up scenes of joy or sorrow, smoothing all asperities, reconciling all incongruities, veiling all absurdness, softening every coar[se]ness, doubling every effect by the influence of imagination."[23]

By the time *Waverley* had burst upon the publishing scene in the early nineteenth century, the term "literary character" was in use as an alternative to "man of letters." Isaac Disraeli, for example, had published *An Essay on the Manners and Genius of the Literary Character* in 1795, on the habits and lifestyle of intellectuals. Thomas Carlyle, however, would revitalize the earlier term by depicting the "man of letters" as the modern manifestation of the heroic type in *On Heroes, Hero-Worship, and the Heroic in History* (1840). In his chapter on "The Hero as Man of Letters"—on Johnson, Rousseau and Burns—Carlyle proclaims the quasi-religious sanctification of authorship:

> Fichte discriminates with sharp zeal the *true* Literary Man, what we here call the *Hero* as Man of Letters, from multitudes of false unheroic. Whoever lives not wholly in this Divine Idea, or living partially in it, struggles not, as for the one good, to live wholly in it,—he is, let him live where else he like, in what pomps and prosperities he like, no Literary Man; he is, says Fichte, a "Bungler, *Stümper*."[24]

Not until the late nineteenth century, with the instigation in 1878 of John Morley's series, *English Men of Letters*, did the phrase "become nearly synonymous with the concept of a professional author (what we now call a "public intellectual") and widely used as an honorific for a writer who had achieved literary distinction as well as financial success."[25]

In the "Introduction" to his biography, Harris gives particular attention to late nineteenth-century explanations of Hume's career as articulated by, amongst others, Leslie Stephen (in his *History of English Thought in the Eighteenth Century* [1876]). "Hume began as a philosopher, the story went," Harris writes,

> but in the *Treatise* reasoned himself into a position which made philosophy look as though it had destroyed itself under the pressure of systematic skeptical argumentation. Therefore, he turned from philosophy to subjects which could be treated purely empirically, such as politics, political economy, and history, but in each case the work that he produced was evidence that, as Stephen put it, his power as a destroyer was much greater than his abilities as a creator. (7)

This "story," Harris notes, would have a long reach into the twentieth century, informing, for example, Lytton Strachey's claim, in *Portraits in Miniature* (1931), that Hume had completed all his important works by the time he was twenty-six.

Stephen was the author of the "Old" (1859–1900) *Dictionary of National Biography's* entry on Hume, as well as the editor of the whole project. "The Old *DNB*," as H. C. G. Matthew describes, "exemplified the 'man-of-letters' tradition and it rewarded its practitioners with fulsome coverage of their predecessors."[26] By the early twentieth century, however, biography was seen as "the literary emblem par excellence of Victorianism, a product faithful to the old era's habit of misapplied and exaggerated hero worship, with all its attendant hypocrisy and evasiveness."[27] The 1920s and 1930s saw the emergence of new biographical theory and practice.[28] Virginia Woolf, for example, satirized the necessary conventionality of the approach to biography of her father, Leslie Stephen, as editor of the *Dictionary of National Biography,* in her mock-biography *Orlando* (1928), her fictional life of Vita Sackville-West. She also mocked Stephen's idea of the eighteenth century as the age of Addison, Dryden, Pope and Swift, articulated in *English Literature and Society in the Eighteenth Century* (1904). Woolf responds in kind to what might be perceived as these writers' dismissive views of women by silencing them, such as when she excises Pope's words:

> Then the little gentleman said,
>
> He said next,
>
> He said finally, *
>
> *These sayings are too well known to require repetition, and besides, they are all to be found in his published works.[29]

Woolf thus sought to redress the balance of literary history by giving, in Jane de Gay's words, "short shrift to the writers whom Stephen had deemed central."[30]

In a letter to Vita Sackville West of 3 May 1938, Virginia Woolf wrote: "My God, how does one write a Biography? Tell me. I'm fairly distracted with Fry papers. How can one deal with facts — so many and so many and so many? Or ought one, as I incline, to be purely fictitious? And what is a life? And what was Roger? And if one cant say, whats the good of trying?"[31] Harris's answer to Woolf's question of how to write biography is to focus on the ideas rather than the man, the arguments made in defense of the ideas, and the language in which the arguments were couched. Such a focus, as Tim Stuart-Buttle observes, risks underplaying "the tension between Hume's carefully constructed literary persona (cool, detached and impartial to the point of ambivalence) and the character occasionally glimpsed in his correspondence (passionate, opinionated and contemptuous of the intellectual shortcomings of others)."[32] Yet by setting all of Hume's works in biographical and historical context and bringing to light the major influences on Hume's intellectual development, Harris enables us to reassess Hume's contribution to each of the fields that he entered, and to gain greater understanding of the nature of his engagement in the eighteenth-century Republic of Letters. *Hume: An Intellectual Biography* is a seminal work of scholarship, engagingly written and meticulously researched.

NOTES

1 Harris, *Hume,* 2.

2 Burke, *A Social History of Knowledge,* 19, 21, 28. In his use of the term "clerisy," Burke follows Samuel Taylor Coleridge, *On the Constitution of Church* and *State,* and Ernest Gellner, *Plough, Sword and Book.*

3 Burke, *A Social History of Knowledge,* 29.

4 Waquet, "Qu'est ce que la République des Lettres?"

5 *Oxford English Dictionary, s.v. "man of letters."*

6 Evelyn, *The Diary of John Evelyn,* 2: 300–01.

7 Hunter, "John Evelyn in the 1650s," 67–98.

8 David Hume to a Physician [Dr George Cheyne], March or April 1734, in *Letters* 1: 12. Harris argues that the most likely identity of the "skillful Physician" was George Cheyne (1671–1743), author of *The English Malady* (1733), "a pioneering study of depression" (77).

9 [Gregory], "Observations on the Duties and Offices of a Physician"; Thomson, *An Account of the Life, Lectures and Writings of William Cullen, M.D.,* 1: 504. See also Rendall, "The Reputation of William Cullen."

10 David Hume to James Oswald, 29 January 1748, in *Letters,* 1: 109.

11 Goodman, *The Republic of Letters.*

12 David Hume to James Oswald, 29 January 1748, in *Letters,* 1: 109.

13 David Hume to Henry Home, Lord Kames, 9 February 1748, in *Letters,* 1: 111.

14 Klein, *Shaftesbury and the Culture of Politeness,* 5–6.

15 Voltaire, "Men of Letters," 7: 599.

16 *Encyclopædia Britannica: or, A Dictionary of Arts and Sciences,* s.v. "pedant," 3: 464.

17 Griffin, *Authorship in the Long Eighteenth Century,* 84–88, and chap. 11.

18 Boswell, *Boswell's Life of Johnson,* 3: 19.

19 David Hume, "Of Essay Writing"; Mee, *Conversable Worlds,* 62.

20 Mee, *Conversable Worlds,* 62.

21 La Vopa, *The Labor of the Mind,* 189.

22 Macaulay, "History," 7: 217.

23 Scott, *The Journal of Sir Walter Scott,* 127–28.

24 Carlyle, *On Heroes, Hero-Worship, and the Heroic in History,* 135–36.

25 Peterson, *Becoming a Woman of Letters,* 3.

26 Matthew, *Leslie Stephen and the New Dictionary of National Biography,* 20, 27–28.

27 Altick, *Lives and Letters,* 289.

28 Marcus, "The Newness of the 'New Biography,'" 193–218.

29 Woolf, *Orlando,* 193.

30 de Gay, *Virginia Woolf's Novels and the Literary Past,* 154.

31 Virginia Woolf to Vita Sackville West, 3 May [1938], in *The Letters of Virginia Woolf,* 6: 225.

32 Tim Stuart-Buttle, review, *EHR,* 132, no. 556 (June 2017), 719–20 (720).

WORKS CITED

Altick, Richard D. *Lives and Letters: A History of Literary Biography in England and America.* New York: Knopf, 1965.

Bartoli, Daniello. *Dell'huomo di lettere difeso et emendato.* Venice, 1651.

Boswell, James. *Boswell's Life of Johnson.* Edited by George Birkbeck Hill, revised and enlarged edition by L. F. Powell. 6 vols. Oxford: Clarendon Press, 1934.

Burke, Peter. *A Social History of Knowledge: From Gutenberg to Diderot: Based on the first series of Vonhoff Lectures given at the University of Groningen (Netherlands).* Cambridge: Polity, 2000.

Carlyle, Thomas. *On Heroes, Hero-Worship, and the Heroic in History.* Edited by Michael K. Goldberg. Berkeley: University of California Press, 1993.

Chartier, Roger. "L'Homme de Lettres." In *L'Homme des Lumières.* Edited by Michel Vovelle, 159–209. Paris: Éditions du Seuil, 1996.

Coleridge, Samuel Taylor. "On the Constitution of Church and State." In *The Collected Works of Samuel Taylor Coleridge. Vol. 10.* Edited by John Colmer. 1829. Princeton: Princeton University Press, 1976.

de Gay, Jane. *Virginia Woolf's Novels and the Literary Past.* Edinburgh: Edinburgh University Press, 2006.

Disraeli, Isaac. *An Essay on the Manners and Genius of the Literary Character.* London, 1795.

Encyclopædia Britannica: or, A Dictionary of Arts and Sciences. Edited by William Smellie. 3 vols. Edinburgh, 1771. s.v. "pedant," 3: 464.

Evelyn, John. *The Diary of John Evelyn.* 6 vols. Edited by E. S. de Beer. Oxford: Clarendon Press, 1955.

Gellner, Ernest. *Plough, Sword and Book: The Structure of Human History.* Chicago: University of Chicago Press, 1988.

Goodman, Dena. *The Republic of Letters: A Cultural History of the French Enlightenment.* Ithaca and London: Cornell University Press, 1994.

[Gregory, John]. *Observations on the Duties and Offices of a Physician; and on the Method of Prosecuting Enquiries in Philosophy.* London, 1770.

Griffin, Dustin. *Authorship in the Long Eighteenth Century.* Newark: University of Delaware Press, 2014.

Harris, James A. *Hume: An Intellectual Biography.* Cambridge: Cambridge University Press, 2015.

Hunter, Michael. "John Evelyn in the 1650s: A Virtuoso in Quest of a Role." In *Science and the Shape of Orthodoxy: Intellectual Change in Late Seventeenth-Century Britain,* 67–98. Woodbridge: Boydell Press, 1995.

Hume, David. *The Letters of David Hume.* 2 vols. Edited by J. Y. T. Greig. Oxford: Clarendon Press, 1932.

Hume, David. "Of Essay Writing." In *Essays, Moral and Political.* Vol. 2. Edinburgh, 1742.

La Vopa, Anthony. *The Labor of the Mind: Intellect and Gender in Enlightenment Cultures.* Philadelphia: University of Pennsylvania Press, 2017.

Klein, Lawrence E. *Shaftesbury and the Culture of Politeness: Moral Discourse and Cultural Politics in Early Eighteenth-Century England.* Cambridge: Cambridge University Press, 1994.

Macaulay, Thomas Babington. "History." In *The Complete Works of Lord Macaulay,* 12 vols. London, 1898.

Manning, Susan. *Fragments of Union: Making Connections in Scottish and American Writing.* Basingstoke: Palgrave, 2001.

Marcus, Laura. "The Newness of the 'New Biography': Biographical Theory and Practice in the Early Twentieth Century." In *Mapping Lives: The Uses of Biography.* Edited by Peter France and William St Clair, 193–218. Oxford: Published for the British Academy by Oxford University Press, 2002.

Matthew, H. C. G. *Leslie Stephen and the New Dictionary of National Biography.* Cambridge: Cambridge University Press, 1997.

Mee, Jon. *Conversable Worlds: Literature, Contention, and Community 1762 to 1830.* Oxford: Oxford University Press, 2011.

Peterson, Linda H. *Becoming a Woman of Letters: Myths of Authorship and Facts of the Victorian Market.* Princeton: Princeton University Press, 2009.

Potkay, Adam. *The Fate of Eloquence in the Age of Hume.* Ithaca: Cornell University Press, 1994.

Rendall, Jane. "The Reputation of William Cullen (1710–1790): Family, Politics, and the Biography of an 'Ornate Physician.'" *Scottish Historical Review* 93, no. 2 (2014): 262–85. https://doi.org/10.3366/shr.2014.0219

Salisbury, Thomas. *The Learned Man Defended and Reform'd.* London, 1660.

Scott, Walter. *The Journal of Sir Walter Scott.* Edited by W. E. K. Anderson. Oxford: Clarendon Press, 1972.

Stephen, Leslie. *English Literature and Society in the Eighteenth Century.* London: Duckworth, 1904.

Stephen, Leslie. *History of English Thought in the Eighteenth Century.* 2 vols. London, 1876.

Thomson, John. *An Account of the Life, Lectures and Writings of William Cullen, M.D.* 2 vols. Edinburgh, 1832.

Voltaire, [François-Marie Arouet] de. "Men of Letters." In *Encyclopédie; ou, Dictionnaire raisonnée des sciences, des arts, et des métiers par une société des gens de lettres.* 17 vols. Edited by [Denis] Diderot and [Jean le Rond] d'Alembert, 7: 599–602. Paris, 1751–65.

Waquet, Françoise. "Qu'est ce que la République des Lettres? Essai de sémantique historique." *Bibliothèque de l'Ecole des Chartes* 147 (1989): 473–502. https://doi.org/10.3406/bec.1989.450545

Woolf, Virginia. *The Letters of Virginia Woolf.* Edited by Nigel Nicolson and Joanne Trautmann. 6 vols. Hogarth Press, 1990.

Woolf, Virginia. *Orlando.* Edited by Rachel Bowlby. Oxford: Oxford University Press, 1992.

Hume Studies
Volume 45, Number 1–2, 2019, pp. 17–27

All Style, No Substance? Comments on Harris's *Hume: An Intellectual Biography*

ANDREW SABL

This meticulous work, the product of years of scholarship and effort, contains a great deal to admire. It rightly rejects the frame, still common in philosophy departments, of Hume as someone who, after writing the *Treatise*, "abandoned philosophy" (with the possible exception of the *Dialogues concerning Natural Religion*) for the sake of lesser inquiries like politics and history. It convincingly portrays Hume's vast classical learning as devoted, in the end, to modern conversations and modern purposes, not to the pursuit of ancient wisdom as directly therapeutic for individuals (194). It deftly places Hume's work not in a narrow Scottish or English context, but in the larger conversation of European letters, proving that Hume himself sought a central place in that conversation. It traces Hume's pervasive anti-Providentialism throughout works that are not usually read as evidence for it, drawing a portrait of Hume as the "disenchanted" thinker *par excellence* (382). Impressively mastering a great many works, it demonstrates how Hume endorsed central insights of the Tory historians Robert Brady and Thomas Carte, while rejecting their Tory conclusions. And it is outstanding on the details of Hume's multiple revisions and the contexts that evoked them, in particular on the ways in which the libertarian and anti-Scottish "Wilkes and Liberty" movement provoked both despairing letters to friends and substantial revisions to Hume's *Essays* and *History of England*.

All that said, I do differ substantially with the book's approach. Its emphasis on historical context, however welcome with respect to some of the questions above, leads it to assess Hume's work in narrow ways that often obscure the substance of what Hume was trying to say. Its determination to characterize Hume's "philosophical" project as a matter of promoting thoughtful, polite discourse, rather than as a search for enduring truths, both distorts

Andrew Sabl is Professor in the Department of Political Science, University of Toronto, 3018 Sidney Smith Hall, 100 St. George Street, Toronto ON M5S 3G3, Canada. Email: andrew.sabl@utoronto.ca

Hume's own proclaimed purposes and slights his permanent contributions. To focus on my own fields of expertise, Hume's history and political science: Harris's central thesis obscures the extent to which Hume sought a political science that would establish reliable laws (corrigible through "experience," i.e. data) and wanted to produce a history that would not just defuse partisan myths of his time, but also be worth reading far into the future. Yet more specifically: in evaluating Hume's *History* mostly through the lens of how it subverted Tory and Whig myths, Harris's work ends up unable to see—indeed, determined to deny—that Hume replaced those myths with a substantive *account of political authority* to which history, time, and experience remained central.

In general, I worry that this book makes Hume's life seem both more adverbial than it was, and more ephemeral. It portrays a Hume more devoted to promoting polite, judicious ways of thinking, conversing, and writing than to establishing—through systematic thought and empirical evidence—durable, often difficult, truths.

I. Contexts and Excluded Middles

Following Duncan Forbes, Harris is determined to read Hume's political works "in terms of their various contexts, intellectual and political" (13). (One short footnote dismisses David Miller and Frederick Whelan, widely considered very thoughtful scholars of Hume's political theory, on the grounds that they slight these contexts [476n59].) But what does this mean? Some intellectual historians stress the need to understand how the meaning of words change over time, or to appreciate that the questions that motivated past thinkers may have been very different from the allegedly "perennial" questions, really questions of our own time, that we are inclined to attribute to them. Harris, however, does not stress such problems of intellectual translation or understanding. His understanding of context is actually very different and surprisingly committal: "Hume *was not engaged* in the business of filling out an intellectual vision in abstraction from the world around him. He was acutely sensitive to the complexities of his time and place, and wrote, and corrected, out of a desire to show how philosophy might illuminate some of the deeper problems *faced by the age in which he lived*" (25, emphases added).

If forced to plump for one alternative or the other—Hume as aspiring to pure, abstract ratiocination, or else as minutely responsive to current events—one might, indeed, choose the latter. But these hardly exhaust the options. Hume might, like many philosophers and historians today, have *alternated* between months or years spent on intense scholarship, and other intervals spent engaging in political and social disputes. (E.C. Mossner's famous biography certainly leaves that impression.) More to the point, Hume's determination to apply the "experimental method of reasoning" to moral subjects might have led him to see "the world around him" as the necessary matter for thought whose validity would then transcend what he found in that world, in his own time and place. Hume might have been using his experience of his world, and his reading of its past, as sources of data—Hume was an early adopter of that word's modern sense—from which to derive general, though necessarily preliminary and corrigible, propositions in what came to be called moral, social, and political theory (or, in a different mode, social science). The question is not whether Hume paid attention to the world, but how and to what purpose. Put differently: while Harris focuses on instances in which observing the events of the world led Hume to edit and amend his texts, we might just as profitably ask how that process of observation enabled Hume to draft the parts of his work—the great majority—that he did not see the need to amend, and that still endure.

II. Polite Manners vs. Theoretical Matter

Rejecting (rightly and convincingly) the thesis that Hume's entire *oeuvre* should be glossed as pursuing the project outlined in the *Treatise,* Harris maintains that all of Hume's work was philosophical in a different sense, involving intellectual style. What unifies Hume's works, Harris claims, is not a unified body of thought, but the "disengaged, skeptical, philosophical frame of mind of their author" (viii). What it means to be *philosophical* (Harris's emphasis) is, more specifically,

> to rise above the everyday and the particular and, from that vantage point, to identify and characterize general principles that were otherwise hard, if not impossible, to discern. This is philosophy understood not as a body of doctrine or a subject matter, but rather as a habit of mind, a style of thinking, and of writing, such as could in principle be applied to any subject whatsoever. (18)

Harris provides excellent examples of Hume himself both declaring and practicing an attachment to general principles that rise above particular examples; that was one thing Hume meant by "enlarg[ing]" one's perspective (20).

Yet there is something oddly missing from Harris' account of Hume's general principles—in the case of history, for examples, principles "able to explain long-term and large-scale social, political, economic, and cultural change" (20): namely, their substance. Nowhere does Harris clearly state what he thinks the fundamental principles of Hume's politics and history *are,* or whether they proved valid—actually and demonstrably better at explaining political and historical events, or more useful in telling us how to shape events so as to further good outcomes, than alternatives. On the contrary, all his summaries of Hume's fundamental principles are essentially negative (though accurate as far as they go). Harris documents, for example, that Hume faulted Harrington for his thesis that power followed property (Hume argued that opinion also matters [178f.]), and that Hume faulted the ancient constitution thesis, variously put forth by Whigs and opposition Tories, for imagining that English liberties could be traced back to the Saxons when their foundations were modern (see chapters 6 and 7). This way of thinking, however, leaves it difficult to discern what Harris thinks Hume *discovered* or *established.* If opinion matters, *how* does it matter: how can someone seeking political insights make sense of how opinions—in particular those of right to power—are likely to arise and change? If modern societies' liberties have a modern foundation, how should we understand that foundation, perhaps so as to see when those liberties are crumbling, or to be able to form a strategy for shoring them up?

This evasion of substance seems to be by design. Harris strongly implies that he takes Hume's politeness to *be* his contribution. Even the point of seeking general principles seems to be a kind of misdirection. Hume, on Harris's portrayal, sought to defuse passionate convictions—especially partisan ones—not by establishing general principles, but rather by encouraging the reader to seek general principles, and then proceeding to show how elusive, and inherently controversial, such principles are. (Thus, Harris says that the Political Discourses promised "theorem[s]" but did not deliver them: Hume's project was "to 'start difficulties'. . . with the intention of stimulating surprise, puzzlement, and reflection in his readers" [282].) In describing Hume's engagement with, and pervasive moderation of, the partisan political and historical positions of his time, Harris portrays this not as necessary framing, the best practice of a rhetorician who must start from the audience's premises rather than his own, but as something like the pinnacle of Hume's achievement as a thinker:

> *The philosophical spirit* [of Hume's *History of Great Britain,* later *History of England*] expressed itself most clearly of all in those passages in which Hume sought to reduce political debates to their most essential and abstract principles, by balancing the best case that could be made on one side against the best that could be made on the other, and then presenting a considered judgement as to the strengths and weakness of each argument. (339, emphasis added)

There is nothing wrong with moderation. The above formulation, however, strikingly portrays Hume's final conclusions as stemming from his own good judgment, his native *phronesis*—not from an intellectual inquiry aiming at discovering and applying on general principles, an inquiry that (always? Harris seems to think so) produces nothing but antinomies.[1] In this respect, Harris believes that the *Dialogues concerning Natural Religion* resembled "all of Hume's works" in being "an attempt to help the reader to stand back from everyday practical concerns, and to consider the matter at hand in terms of its general principles" (456). And Hume's works, like the *Dialogues,* are apparently supposed to yield this happy effect of seeing things in terms of "general principles," even though—or better, precisely *because*—reasoning based on general principles yields no determinate conclusion. Hume's goal, on Harris's portrayal, is to induce reflection—not to communicate knowledge.

Harris repeatedly writes of Hume's attempt to draw his readers—perhaps, eventually and by long-term diffusion, educated society as a whole—into a philosophical *conversation* or *community* among people whose principles might differ quite fundamentally (see, e.g., 24, 30, 263, 298f., 305–306). Writing of the *Political Discourses* (part of what we now call the *Essays*), Harris writes:

> [Hume's] goal, usually, was to raise questions and provoke further thought, not definitively to establish a theoretical postulate. It mattered that he was *not* elaborating

> a systematic theory of commerce . . . . His intention would seem to have been to turn commerce into a subject of reflection and conversation for those who did not themselves have a direct interest in one or another of its branches (30, emphasis in original).

Consistent with this, Harris, on that page and others, is at pains to deny, as much as possible, the degree to which Hume's contributions to his many fields were original and exceptional. "Very often in *Political Discourses*," Harris writes, "the core argument of an essay was not Hume's own invention" (30). Hume's self-portrayal of himself in the *Treatise* as a "solitary revolutionary, occupied with tasks that no one before him had seen were there to be undertaken" is portrayed as both fictive and slightly embarrassing (213). Also consistent with this, Harris clearly prefers the "engaging and solicitous" tone of what became the two *Enquiries* to the *Treatise's* "aggressive self-assertion" (221). Finally, Hume's *History of England,* as we shall see, is portrayed as an artful synthesis-*cum*-denaturing of existing Whig and Tory tropes. Far from drawing from history his own set of conclusions, Hume essentially ends up saying (Harris believes) that history can teach us nothing. The result is to portray Hume's achievements as primarily those of a synthesizer and popularizer. He is always, in Harris's eyes, the "ambassador from the dominions of learning to those of conversation" (159 citing Hume, "Of Essay Writing," *Essays*, 535)—and never the prime minister of the former, making fundamental contributions to learning itself.

Harris's endorsement of the idea that "philosophy is not a discipline that is worth pursuing if it loses touch with the language and concerns of the ordinary educated reader" (232) sounds benign; I share Harris's frustration with the kind of analytic philosophy that aspires to match science in its technical precision and ability to make progressive discoveries. Taken literally, however, this claim is quite radical. Do we really value *only* the kind of philosophy that can be understood by polite readers picking up an essay in the evening? After all, Hume's conviction that easy philosophers would have more lasting fame than abstruse ones was one of his ideas that was as most obviously time-bound as it is clearly wrong. We no longer read Aristotle more than Cicero, and it now seems a bit silly that Hume thought "*Addison,* perhaps, will be read with pleasure, when *Locke* shall be entirely forgotten" (232, citing EHU 1.4; SBN 7).

Of course, Harris endorses Hume's final aspiration to render his work *both* rigorous and accessible, to "unite the boundaries of the different species of philosophy, by reconciling profound enquiry, with clearness, and truth with novelty" (223, citing EHU 1.17; SBN 16). Harris, however, seems mostly to care about the second part. To cite a political example: Harris notes (237) that the essay "Of the Original Contract" shrinks Hume's *Treatise* attack on consent theory "almost to the point of perfunctoriness"; the shrunken version is far less philosophical and implies that contract theory can be disproven solely by common sense. Harris seems quite unconcerned, however, that the result is to render the argument far from sound, with many striking insights but also clear gaps in reasoning that undergraduates quickly note. In general, it seems quixotic to try to capture accurately Hume's life as a man of letters while abstracting from such questions of substance. Such abstraction will make it impossible to tell the difference between someone who *successfully* combined rigor with accessibility, and someone who tragically (or even defensibly) sacrificed much of the former for the latter's sake.

The determination to portray Hume as overwhelmingly concerned with anti-dogmatism and polite disagreement likewise makes it hard to understand how he could have striven to make his historical writing a permanent achievement. Harris cites Hume's remark, in a letter to John Clephane, that there was "no post of honour in the English Parnassus more vacant than that of history" (308). But Harris does not consider Philip Hicks' convincing argument that Hume really meant it—that he aspired to be read, like Thucydides with respect to Greece, or Tacitus with respect to Rome, as the classic historian of England and in English, permanently and perennially instructive.[2] On the contrary, he portrays Hume, much as Forbes did, as chiefly concerned with smoothing over contemporary partisan squabbles. In describing "how Hume wanted his history writing to be read," Harris stresses not his findings, or even his method, but his impartial ethos: he wanted it read "as the work of one who was a member of neither party, and who was able to identify the faults, as well as the merits, of both" (387). And again: "[w]hat Hume wanted his reader to be impressed, and amused, by was the way he played his predecessors off against each other, making Tory points against Whig orthodoxy" (405). This does not describe the attitude of someone who was aware that the squabbles of party politics were evanescent—who, indeed, worked mightily to render them so—while hoping that, once those squabbles had been dispelled, the positive contribution of his work might endure. Deftly deconstructing the debates of the day is a fine thing, but no path to Parnassus.

None of this is to deny that Hume aspired to disagree, politely, with those who differed with his claims and conclusions. It is to suggest that the reason we still care about Hume concerns the genius behind those claims and conclusions, and the arguments on which they rested. Hume's civility towards critics and his zeal to recommend such civility towards others were admirable traits—but rather more common, less worth remembering, than the substance of what he discovered.

I suspect that one reason that Harris slights Harris's permanent contribution to the study of human subjects is that he doubts that such are possible. He seems to think of moral subjects as matters of rhetoric and debate all the way down. (This would explain another excluded middle: Harris prefers to portray Hume as addressing a variety of contemporary problems rather than as devoting his whole life to pure philosophy—but does not consider that he might have sought, and discovered, enduring contributions to what became political science, political economy, or history.) But then we are reduced to thinking of Hume as solely a man of his time, comprehensible and admirable if one enters deeply into the purposes of eighteenth-century Britons or Europeans and not otherwise.

III. Custom and Fundamentals: Crown and Charter

In answering the question posed above—if politics rests on opinion, on what does opinion rest?—the common (and correct) first stab at a Humean answer is "custom." Opinions rest on mental habits, and habits on repeated experience. This suggests in turn that of all the potential sources of authority that Hume mentions in the *Treatise*, the most solid (when one can get it) is "long possession": people feel allegiance to the regime that they, and others on whose experience they draw, are used to. In *Hume's Politics*,[3] I have read the *History of England* as essentially an extended reflection on this: on the fundamental conventions defining authority, and the limitations on authority, that arise from historical experience. On my view, for which I cannot properly argue here, the fundamental conventions that Hume regards as having arisen in England are hereditary monarchy—eventually, a monarchy limited by law—on the one hand, and Magna Carta on the other. The latter allowed for the rise of parliament, at first very limited in its powers but over time increasingly strong, culminating in what was in Hume's time still a mixed and balanced regime (though one Hume well knew to be unstable).

Again, Harris seems deeply committed to denying that Hume's work contains this systematic account of authority *or any other.* If Hume's program was to cultivate polite conversation and respect for intellectual adversaries by showing that appeals to general principles are both necessary and aporetic (notwithstanding Harris's denial that Hume's intention was to draw therapeutic effects from ancient philosophical schools, he clearly portrays Hume's work as deliberately therapeutic in this more indirect, and more modern, way), then it would be impossible for Hume to have stood behind any law-like, general, and non-intuitive explanation of politics, history, economics, or culture. Even a tentative law, corrigible by further experience, would undermine the suspense of judgment, the benign and polite self-doubt, that Harris takes to be Hume's central goal. On this account, even if Hume did think he had discovered general truths, he would have had to hide them, lest his readers come to think that they know something important.

Beyond Harris's general determination not to find in Hume systematic doctrines of any kind, however, there are more specific reasons that Harris' approach prevents him from doing justice to the role of monarchy and Magna Carta in Hume's thought—to the extent of barely mentioning that they play any role at all.

First, Harris assumes (perhaps drawing the assumption from the "Cambridge School" of historical analysis) that *the* big constitutional question in Hume's age—perhaps all ages—concerns the form of government: republic or monarchy? Thus, when Harris rightly glosses Hume as being relatively indifferent to the question of forms of government, or at least determined to draw complex and nuanced conclusions on the subject (see the excellent discussion around 341–42), he concludes that Hume was therefore indifferent to constitutional questions.[4] This places beyond the reader's notice Hume's determination to treat the nature, origin, and limits of all authorities, whatever they may be: his account of how various bodies have each come to embody a certain measure of authority, and in what respects none of them exert effective, recognized authority in certain areas regarded as beyond their scope. Thus, Harris portrays Hume as thinking Magna Carta "less than revolutionary" because it "contained no establishment of new courts, magistrates, or senates, nor abolition of the old," only forbidding "such tyrannical practices as are incompatible with civilized government, and, if they become very frequent, are incompatible with all government" (398, citing *History* 1:487, App. II). The obvious rejoinder is that when such prohibitions become an unquestioned limitation on what government may do, that is a slow constitutional revolution—not in government's form but, just as important, in its permissible scope.

Harris' approach to the *History* is also hindered by what seems to be misplaced interpretive charity. Probably because he regards the principle of hereditary monarchy as faintly ridiculous, Harris is determined to read Hume as believing that the Glorious Revolution put it in its place once and for all, making it a matter of parliamentary sufferance rather than constitutional principle. The result is one of the book's few demonstrable misreadings. Here is Harris:

> Hume saw it as obvious that something dramatic and quite novel happened in 1688–9. The Revolution, he wrote, 'forms a new epoch in the constitution,' it 'made a new settlement,' and it did so in so far as it established a *new precedent*, that of 'deposing one King, and establishing a new family,' thereby 'put[ting] a period' to the principle of hereditary succession (338, emphasis in original).

But the text in question says nothing about abolishing the principle of heredity; quite the contrary. Here is Hume (in the standard edition, not appreciably different from the one Harris cites, *History* 6: 531):

> By deciding many important questions in favour of liberty, and still more, by that great precedent of *deposing one king, and establishing a new family*, it [The Glorious Revolution] gave such an ascendant to popular principles, as has put the nature of the English constitution beyond all controversy. . . .
>
> To decry with such violence, as is affected by some, the whole line of Stuart; to maintain, that their administration was one continued encroachment on the incontestible rights of the people; is not giving due honour to that great event, which not only put a period to *their* hereditary succession, but made a new settlement of the whole constitution. (Emphases added.)

Hume here states quite clearly, not that the revolution "put a period" to hereditary succession, but that it ended the continuation of that succession in the Stuart line—in favor of establishing the hereditary succession of a new line (a succession that persisted not only through Hume's day, but even through ours). In "Of the Protestant Succession" (note the language), Hume imagines advocates of continuing the Hanover line on the one hand, or restoring the Stuart line on the other. The Stuarts' partisan, naturally, places the constitutional advantages of heredity—which Hume, both there and in his own voice, argues are very considerable—above even parliament's claims to authority. Even the Hanoverians' defender, however, does not defend Parliament's power to place the Crown where it will. On the contrary, this imagined advocate stresses the benefits of Parliament's having chosen a monarch "*in the royal line*"—thus preventing non-royal "ambitious subjects" from aspiring themselves to the job—and rendering "the crown *hereditary* in his [the Prince of Hanover's] family" (*Essays*,

506; emphases added). Thus, Harris fails to see the whole point of the Revolution as Hume saw it. It did not abolish the central constitutional principle of hereditary monarchy, but rather settled it on a firmer footing by establishing a family that shared Britons' accustomed (Protestant) religion, and balanced that principle against the privileges and powers of Parliament.

Hume was, in fact, deeply attached to hereditary monarchy and saw its having become slowly embedded in British constitutional habits as a key reason for the peace and order that Britons had come to prize. Because he is determined to downplay the role that hereditary monarchy played in Hume's history-based praise of Britain's constitution, Harris is forced to portray Hume's historical judgments as less consistently reasoned and more haphazard than they are. To take just one example: in describing why Hume rejected Thomas Carte's defense of Richard III (*qua* courageous, prudent, and just, exercising the "power and pride of conquest"), Harris writes that "Hume was not prepared to violate the conventions of Whig history to that extent." But he does not explain why Hume endorsed those conventions in this case: in fact, he condemned Richard because of the enormity of his departure from hereditary succession. "Never was there in any country an usurpation more flagrant than that of Richard," wrote Hume, "or more repugnant to every principle of justice and public interest" (H 2.508). Richard III's admitted "courage and capacity . . . would never have made compensation to the people for the danger of the precedent" of that departure from hereditary right (H 2.518).

Once again, I suspect that Harris avoids attributing this view to Hume out of attempted interpretive charity. Those living in parliamentary regimes are taught to regard the idea of limiting parliament's sovereign authority—even, perhaps especially, its constitutional authority—as both incoherent and pernicious. Yet a more sober look at absolute parliamentary supremacy (or any other doctrine of absolute sovereignty for that matter) reveals that it cannot resolve some obvious paradoxes, most notably the question of whether a sovereign parliament may pass a law stipulating that future parliaments may not change that law. The necessary conclusion, a cliché among philosophers of law but apparently no one else, is that no parliament—no authority whatsoever, in fact—can be sovereign both at all times and over all things. One might even conclude that any sound doctrine of law must at some point be—like Hume's—an "acceptance" theory, appealing not to the formal prerogatives of the allegedly supreme law-making body, but to that body's convention-based ability or inability to have the laws it passes recognized as binding.[5]

Another act of interpretive charity, I think, accounts for Harris' portrayal of Hume's history as self-effacing. Harris glosses Hume's *History* as concluding that "the past had no political significance. Politically speaking, it was the present, and the future, that mattered. History should be left to historians" (406). To be sure, Harris is quite right that the justification of any constitution, for Hume, was interest: that constitution's ability to embody authority and uphold justice in ways that made all those subject to government better off. He is also right that Hume saw modern politics as not needing "the kind of support from history that both Whigs and Tories usually supposed it to need" (321)—history consisting of myths of royal prerogative flouted, or ancient liberties and privileges eroded, of romantic Lost Causes or providentially progressive change. However, Hume saw politics as requiring *another* kind of support from history, the kind that showed how politics goes better when conventions of authority, and of the limits on authority, develop over time and grow stronger the longer they continue. Interest explains why we are all better off when we recognize some convention of authority. History explains which one, and why we are better off embracing the conventions we have than aiming at new ones—since the latter attempt is likely to split the country into partisans of more than one convention, none of which is universally acknowledged.

Harris clearly thinks it a compliment to Hume to portray him as saying that the past does not bind us, that politics is wholly up to us in the present. I would question that. Would we really want all the fixed points we use to plan our lives—our property in our homes and effects, our rights against arbitrary interference, our ability to assert a private realm where others' political whims cannot reach, our accustomed sense of what counts as just and unjust—to be subject to reversal at the whim of a sovereign legislature? If we do say yes, I submit, we do not really mean it. Those of us who defend absolute sovereignty in theory do so on the tacit assumption that it will encounter limits in practice beyond which sovereign action is unthinkable. It is because so much of politics is not up to us, not generally a conceivable object of political action, that our lives in all realms other than politics are sometimes tolerable.

IV. Hume's Achievement

Befitting a work that sees Hume's main purpose as "philosophical conversation" (24), Harris's book ends with Hume's life. It does not assess his works' enduring impact, even in the generation or two just after his death. Conversations, after all, die with the conversationalist. Taking Hume at his final word as someone devoted to *literary* fame[6] would have suggested a different perspective, one concerned to ask what of Hume is still read with profit today, and why.

Those seeking in Hume an exemplary citizen of Europe's republic of letters, determined to ask big questions without answering them, and priding himself on his style, his impartiality, and his skill at puncturing the excesses of dogma, can do no better than to appreciate the figure that emerges from this book: judicious, sociable, public-spirited, mostly harmless. Those inspired by Hume as a hero of the human intellect who is still considered a canonical author of political theory, a pioneer in political economy and social theory, and indeed, a great innovator in pure philosophy, will have to seek out one of the many future biographies that will no doubt be spurred by Hume's remarkable genius.

NOTES

1 Similarly, Harris portrays Hume as trying to "encourage 'the philosophical spirit'" in readers of his *History* by trying "to get him or her thinking in terms of the fundamental principles that underlay and animated the events portrayed in the narrative, and to encourage recognition of how finely balanced the arguments were in favour of, on the one hand, the partisans of liberty, and, on the other, the partisans of the crown" (340). Again, the purpose of getting people thinking about fundamental principles is to educate them *away* from seeing politics as something that such principles can clearly illuminate, much less guide.

2 Hicks, *Neoclassical History and English Culture.* Harris cites this work globally but does not really take up its argument. On the contrary, on 193, he glosses Hume's "Sceptic" persona in the Essays—often, and not unreasonably, taken as a proxy for Hume himself—as aspiring to the "mortification of self-love and ambition." This is telling, since the passages Harris cites describe a project of inclining people towards social and away from sensual passions, but nowhere mention mortifying ambition—elsewhere praised by Hume as "greatness of mind"—much less the "love of literary fame" that Hume called his "ruling passion" ("My Own Life," in *Essays,* xl). Harris, at 459, chooses to efface this self-styled love of fame, stressing instead an earlier passage (xxxii–xxxiii) in which Hume names a "passion for literature" (not literary fame) as his ruling one. Harris's problem is that an intellectual who aspires to enduring fame must belief himself capable of a permanent contribution to human knowledge—as Hume, in fact, did.

3 See Sabl, *Hume's Politics.*

4 Without specifically defining what he means by constitutional questions, Harris' language repeatedly suggests (e.g. at 184, 250) that assessing constitutions means, more or less exclusively, assessing the nature and worth of different forms of government.

5 See Suber, *The Paradox of Self-Amendment.*

6 See above, note 2.

WORKS CITED

Harris, James A. *Hume: An Intellectual Biography.* Cambridge: Cambridge University Press, 2015.

Hicks, Philip. *Neoclassical History and English Culture: From Clarendon to Hume.* New York: St. Martin's, 1996.

Hume, David. *Essays Moral, Political, and Literary.* Edited by Eugene Miller, revised ed. Indianapolis: Liberty Fund, 1987.

Hume, David. *The History of England from the Invasion of Julius Caesar to the Revolution in 1688.* 6 vols. Ed. William B. Todd. Indianapolis: Liberty Fund, 1983.

Sabl, Andrew. *Hume's Politics: Coordination and Crisis in the History of England.* Princeton: Princeton University Press, 2012.

Suber, Peter. *The Paradox of Self-Amendment: A Study of Law, Logic, Omnipotence, and Change.* New York: Peter Lang International Academic Publishers, 1990.

Hume Studies
Volume 45, Number 1–2, 2019, pp. 29–36

Hume as an Essayist: Comments on Harris's *Hume: An Intellectual Biography*

MIKKO TOLONEN

I was a Leverhulme visiting fellow at the University of St Andrews in 2012–13 when James Harris was working on *Hume: An Intellectual Biography*. At the time, I expected his book to take decades to finish due to the daunting nature of the task. During those years there were periods when we sat daily discussing Hume at the National Library of Scotland and its near vicinity. As a result of those conversations, we also wrote and published an article about Hume in the Scottish context.[1] I look back to those days with warmth. I wanted to say this to point out that I am not impartial towards Harris, who I consider a friend, nevertheless, I am not responsible for what is advanced in James's book, and thus I can comment on it. James Harris succeeded in his undertaking much faster and better than what I expected—and my expectations were high.

The focus of this paper is on Hume's essays in a broad sense. The topics I will engage with include writing an intellectual biography, style, method, political perspectives, religion, and what I call "a defense of the unity thesis" in Hume, in contrast to Harris's argument that, surprisingly bluntly, claims that there is no real continuity throughout Hume's works.

What is it that you do when you write an intellectual biography? To me, it seems that the responsibility is overwhelming because you are not engaging in a regular scholarly debate, or what Quentin Skinner encourages us to do in historical research. The goal in Skinnerian intellectual history is not to put forward a "refereed perspective," but to find a *new* perspective which often means purposely arguing against what others have said. The objective is thus to formulate a novel, justified stance on some particular aspect of political thought. This approach is apt also due to the practical reasons. We do not have access to the past as such that would enable us to formulate an "objective" perspective on intellectual history qua facts.

Mikko Tolonen is Associate Professor of Digital Humanities, University of Helsinki.
Email: mikko.tolonen@helsinki.fi

Hence, we are always engaged in a hermeneutic undertaking of a dialogue between previous interpretations and what we take away from our reading of the original sources, trying to find some new angle to a debate that is justified within some context of previous scholarship.[2] If we share this idea of what intellectual history is, then we are willing to allow that even going to the extremes of the argumentative style will advance our understanding of the past, as long as the perspective is contextualized. This, I believe, can be contrasted to some extent to what Harris does in his book, which is about carefully considering the different sides of previous arguments in scholarship and formulating a position based on it. In a sense, the question then is whether it is possible to act as a referee and write an intellectual biography that would be more objective than other studies of Hume's intellectual development, to be flagged out as the general point of reference.

To illustrate what I mean in Harris's case, let us consider the influence of Mandeville on Hume, a topic that I have been keenly interested in in my own past, and which Harris takes to be a relevant part of his story about Hume. When I attended my first Hume Society conference in 2005, I was afraid to defend the position of Hume as a Mandevillean thinker, because it was an unorthodox stance in the Hume Society at the time. Has this thinking about Mandeville's positive influence on Hume now become orthodox? I am not entirely sure about it. The reason why I am pointing this out is just to illustrate the nature of the game when one begins to write an intellectual biography—it is a tricky business to canonize different perspectives, because scholarship is consistently on the move. Whether we want it or not, this process of canonizing different perspectives, is also what separates a "regular" study of Hume's intellectual development from an intellectual biography.

Balancing Act

Over the years there have, of course, been several different accounts of David Hume's thinking. He has commonly been presented as the author of the *Treatise*. It is therefore understandable that much emphasis in contemporary Hume scholarship has been on metaphysics, as well as on epistemology. This overemphasis on merely one side of Hume needs to be challenged and alternated with a more balanced view of a person, who was in fact a multifaceted intellectual. This, I believe, is a view that Harris and I share, and it is the reason why he has written an intellectual biography of Hume.

What, in my opinion, should be understood is that the very need for a reassessment of Hume's thought is complex, and not a mere matter of antiquarian interest. The main reason why a new interpretation is needed is that a more balanced understanding of the coherent historical nature of Hume's thinking, and of his skepticism in general, should change the current view of Hume as a philosopher. Easier said than done. Thus, the motive for publishing yet another book on Hume is not simply a desire for historical accuracy in a biographical sense, nor the mere need to take his essays and the *History of England* more seriously. The claim made is that, hitherto, we have been unable to grasp the nature of his thinking and how his works are connected. Let us reflect on how Harris accomplishes this task.

What mattered a great deal to Hume was, of course, style. Being an essayist is inherently linked to the question of style—and I refer not only to what Harris states about style and Hume, but also to how Harris himself writes. Harris captures the relevance of style, perhaps better than anyone else hitherto, in the part of the book entitled "Achievement of independence." I believe that Hume himself would have been pleased with this interpretation of what it means to be a man of letters; a crucial topic to understand the relationship between the *Treatise* and the rest of Hume's writings. This is a brilliant feature of the book—how Harris is able to deal with Hume's intellectual enterprise in general—and I believe it is precisely what he writes about essays that captures this.

Another example of what Harris can do with his writing is the magnificent way in which he follows and makes sense of the political details of eighteenth-century Britain. I cannot recall reading such a clear-headed account of the political context of the Scottish Enlightenment. In Hume scholarship, the political developments of the eighteenth-century Britain and Scotland, starting with the union debates, continuing with local political upheavals, and advancing towards arguments about militia are too often left for those studying political theory, without an attempt to bridge Hume's philosophical views and political thought. In Harris's hands, the matter is somewhat different, for example a chapter entitled "Lessons of a Jacobite rebellion" continues one of the great virtues of Harris's book, linking different matters of real-life politics to Hume's works. The so-called newer essays from the later 1740s are covered very thoughtfully, and this, again, is a real pleasure to read. These are the parts that bring to mind the late Nick Phillipson's intellectual biography of Adam Smith, which is quite different in nature to Harris's Hume, but yet another fine example of the Scottish tradition of writing intellectual biographies on the main figures of the Scottish Enlightenment.

Yet, Harris is not really aiming to make overarching points about Hume, which is somewhat disappointing. He has chosen to treat Hume's essays, for example, by analysing them individually, often commenting on them one by one. These analyses are elegantly written, as Harris explores different political and other contexts, frequently in great detail. But perhaps the idea was to leave these larger arches of interpretation of Hume to his latest book that Harris has already been able to publish (and which I am yet to read)?[3]

Simultaneously, Harris also demonstrates that Hume was an experimentalist of borrowed methods, attempting explicitly to deploy a Newtonian experimental method to morals in his *Treatise*, and then switching to writing essays in the way adopted from Joseph Addison, for example. Aiming to do what Newton did in science, in morals, and then turning to writing *Spectator*-like essays, was of course explicitly underlined by Hume himself, but it has not often been realized that this constituted a pattern for this young man seeking fame. Harris is subtle in making these points, but at the same time, he captures the essence of Hume, what the person was about. He did his own thinking, but on many occasions, he borrowed the form from elsewhere. Regarding Hume the essayist, Harris apparently believes that Hume was really negotiating the middle way between extreme opposites. I would be inclined to claim that, at times, this was more of a rhetorical strategy: he put forward both sides of the argument, at least seemingly, but stood more firmly on one side rather than the other. This is not always easy to detect, but still possible in my understanding. For example, if we read carefully what Hume actually says in his "Of the Rise and Progress of the Arts and Sciences" and the later "Of Government" essays, it seems evident that Hume presents the virtues of both republic and monarchy, but he is really underlining the relevance of hierarchy in eighteenth-century political institutions related to matters such as politeness and sociability. The tendency in modern scholarship has of course been to understand Hume's perspective in the exact opposite way, thinking that what we have at hand is a eulogy of democracy with some added and outdated remarks about monarchy—this question of the moral consequences of politics for Hume is a mater far from settled in scholarship, and thus something that is difficult to be refereed in an intellectual biography.

As I have pointed out, refereeing historical authority is a tricky business. All the same, there really is no anatomy in history-writing, merely justified and plausible arguments that can build a case. Regarding Harris's strategy for dealing with Hume the essayist, his idea to start with the early memoranda is good. The downside of commenting on everything chronologically, however, is that he does not seize opportunities to make more substantial intellectual claims: he sets the context for many potential claims, but he does not set out the arguments as clearly as I, at least, was hoping for. The question of the relevance of hierarchy, evolution of civil societies, and civilized monarchy that I mentioned above, is one such matter.

Let us think about Harris's method of finding all possible relevant contexts for Hume's texts. There are numerous contexts, of which many are impossible to reconstruct, as Harris with his experience well knows. Thus, he ends up with a certain number that are open to interpretation. To me it seems that with just a little adjustment, one could also put forward an explicit interpretation in intellectual history in a Skinnerian sense, which is somewhat different from intellectual biography with this higher aim of "correctness." In the case of Hume the essayist, one possible interpretation of an intellectual historian, for example, would be to aim to understand Hume's emphasis on the already mentioned civilized monarchy by placing his early essays in their Court Whig context, and thus considering Hume as something of an anti-republican thinker, instead of someone trying to find a middle-ground on these issues. There would then be other material that one could connect to this claim in Hume's *Treatise*, a view also supported in other essays and his historical writings. This would be an argument in intellectual history, as opposed to intellectual biography (if there is such an invisible wall). In any case, the aim should be to say something more about continuity and unity in Hume. I do not really believe that Harris is putting forward this kind of interpretation about the nature of Hume's political thought in the book: he prefers to entangle all the contexts of Hume's different works and thus does not put forward any kind of "unity" thesis. I would like him to rethink this aspect to some extent, and offer more extended interpretations.

I would have also expected a stronger link between the discussion on trade and commerce, and the nature of political organisation. As it stands in Harris's interpretation, the discussion on forms of government, civilized monarchy, and *Political Discourses* are not really connected, which I think they should be. Harris's account of *Political Discourses,* although admirably covering different real-life political contexts, is somewhat technical and detailed. I very much agree with Harris's understanding of the relevance of civilized monarchy in Hume's essays: its role is hard to exaggerate. It is more a question of connecting this to everything else that is going on.

Essays, History, and Religion

Another question about continuity in Hume that I would like to put forward here concerns the relationship between many of the essays and Hume as a historian. I would claim that Hume's writing of history begins with the essays. These are the kinds of transition at which Harris is usually very good, making his points without a further need to underline them. It is no accident that Hume read all of the ancient authors, quantifying and making a statistical interpretation about population, for example. This is very much backed up by what was going on at the University of Edinburgh at the time. Hume, in his reading of ancient texts and other histories in his own historical scholarship, is no different from what other historians did in this context. We do not have Hume's commonplace books on his own calculations, but he must have kept them. A significant piece of evidence in this respect is what the others were doing: in the ancient vs. moderns debate between Hume and Robert Wallace, Wallace had professor Charles Mackie on his side. At the University of Edinburgh, they were rechecking all the ancient works to confirm and question the calculations that Hume put forward in his essay on ancient populousness.

The population debate constitutes evidence that also sheds light on the relevance of methods that Hume was using in his scholarship. As noted above, many of his choices concerned the application of particular methods that others had developed relating to some specific subject matter like history or morals. These are exercises in a particular field, almost like brilliant student exercises in a classroom: one can witness Hume's engagement in this with respect to Newton, Mandeville, Hutcheson, Montesquieu, Wallace and Mackie, and Kames. As we very well know, the subject matter that Hume aimed to approach extended from human understanding to morals and politics and history. While this extensive scope of "science of man" is well known in Hume scholarship, this curiosity and the aspect of borrowing methods and tools from others while experimenting with ways how human sociability can be studied has not received much attention. This kind of experimentation is an aspect of continuity that could perhaps have been underlined more strongly in Harris's *Hume*.

With regard to the reading of Hume on religion in general, I agree with Harris that the atheist line in current Hume scholarship needs to be balanced. Nevertheless, I would have liked him to have made more of religion, in the sense that it is a political issue, very much a subject matter of the essays. Harris seems to me to be following Sandy Stewart's line to some extent in his discussion on experimental natural philosophy.[4] I was hoping to see more (in terms of pages) here, because the material is vast, and the possibilities to see more continuity in Hume rather obvious.

Hume was a system builder, who in the end, devoted a great deal of time and pages to discussing what could be categorized as natural history (muscles, Linnaean taxonomy) and what could not (taste in art, religion), as well as the reasons for such categorization. *Dialogues concerning natural religion* deal with system building to the same extent as the *Treatise* and the essays. This desire for hierarchy and systematization is possibly also one core reason why he ended up making unfounded and unfortunate racist comments, which have been the focus of much recent debate. Again, instead of separate works, I see lines of unity that run through everything that Hume wrote.

Another small point that concerns me somewhat is the role given to Montesquieu in Harris's attempt to understand Hume's intellectual development leading up to the *History of England*. I understand that, of course, much of the discussion was shaped by reactions to Montesquieu, and his influence was strongly felt in Edinburgh at the time. I do not believe that Hume's sense of what can be achieved based on experimental science on human nature really changed in Hume's later career as much as Harris believes, and not because of Montesquieu.

Unity and Speculation

One main conclusion Harris reaches is that it is wrong to obsess about Hume being a thinker with a unified theory or plot that runs through all of his works. In his view, there is no "one Hume," and efforts to find unity in his works are in vain (cf. Harris, 12–13). Harris's method thus affects how he reads the relationship between the *Treatise* and the essays. I do not agree with Harris on this. I see no difficulty in emphasizing a continuum between Hume's *Treatise* and the essays, for example.

In fact, I would be very careful about disclaiming unity throughout Hume's works. At the same time, I agree with Harris's account that previous efforts to explain Hume's intellectual life through the scope of the first book of the Treatise, and to ascertain whether the rest of his works unleash a somewhat extended plan of his early philosophy, have been rather futile. Yet, to the best of my understanding, there is clear coherence and continuity in Hume, which is also apparent in Harris's book.

If one assumes that Hume was a profoundly "historical theorist," in whose thinking a particular conception of time and social change played a substantial role, one could say that his moral theory and moral philosophical perspective are largely historical, in the sense that there is continuity—not from philosophy to history, but from history to philosophy. When we aim to contextualise Hume's philosophical works as part of his overall project, there is room for reinterpretation. Consequently, if one were to take a different approach, not the normal path from philosophy to history and letters, but vice versa, one might detect the strong continuity in his thinking.

The implication here is that there is more stability in Hume's *Treatise*, essays and historical work than is displayed among natural law thinkers, for example, who also wrote on philosophy and history (such as Hobbes and Pufendorf). Earlier, history was written with the didactic purpose of learning about society. That is to say that one was able to pick and choose elements of history from different times and places. For Hume, the historical horizon was more modern, in the sense that Reinhart Koselleck has taught us.[5] The implications on developing an idea of evolution of sociability ranging from principles of human understanding to political organization that includes a perspective of history was very different from Hobbes and Locke. This is poorly understood in Hume scholarship in general. It is an aspect that needs to be brought into all current discussions on Hume and history, especially with regard to the question of government, authority, and opinion. But in order to do this, we need to use our scholarly imagination to cross a few bridges for which we have no direct textual evidence as such.

Harris follows the Hume scholarship line of non-speculation on issues for which there is no concrete evidence. However, in all honesty, Harris also enjoys speculating about what Hume did with his life. This is a biographical interest. For example, speculation about Hume's desire to understand the world and growing up on a farm is, of course, biographical rather than intellectual setting for the book. I would also call Harris's reading of the *Letter from a Gentleman*, and the relationship between Coutts, Kames, and Wishart surprisingly speculative given the context. My point is that there is nothing wrong with this, because it is more difficult than one might think to separate the two and not to weigh what might have been the case.

Conclusion

We are very fortunate that James Harris has devoted so much of his career thinking about Hume's intellectual development. If we focus on Hume's essays, which was my main aim, what Harris has achieved is to make a substantial contribution to our current understanding of Hume as an essayist. Through Harris's hands, Hume the man of letters becomes alive, and it is easy to understand the relevance of style, method, different political debates, and crucially, religion in Hume's intellectual development. I have made comments about the difficulty of writing a balanced intellectual biography, and what it entails. Yet, from the perspective of Hume scholarship, a general intellectual biography was certainly needed to complement Mossner et al.[6] It is an incredible achievement by James Harris to be the first to accomplish this, and to put, for example, Hume's essays in their overall intellectual context that includes a perspective of Hume on human understanding. Naturally, there is no systematic plot followed by Hume in all of his intellectual life, yet there is much coherence in the undertaking of science of man, and the connections between his different works need to also be teased out.

NOTES

1 Harris and Tolonen. "Hume In and Out of Scottish Context."

2 Skinner, "The Practice of History and the Cult of the Fact," 8–26.

3 Harris, *Hume: A Very Short Introduction.*

4 Stewart, "Hume's Intellectual Development, 1711–1752."

5 Koselleck, *Futures Past.*

6 Mossner, *Life of Hume*; Norton, "An Introduction to Hume's Thought"; Emerson 'The "Affair" at Edinburgh and the "Project" at Glasgow; Forbes, *Hume's Philosophical Politics.*

WORKS CITED

Emerson, Roger L., "The 'Affair' at Edinburgh and the 'Project' at Glasgow: The Politics of Hume's Attempts to Become a Professor." In *Hume and Hume's connexions.* Edited by M. A. Stewart and John P. Wright, 1–22. Philadelphia, PA: Pennsylvania University Press, 1994.

Forbes, Duncan, *Hume's Philosophical Politics.* Cambridge: Cambridge University Press, 1975.

Harris, James A. *Hume: An Intellectual Biography.* Cambridge: Cambridge University Press, 2015.

Harris, James A. *Hume: A Very Short Introduction.* Oxford: Oxford University Press, 2021.

Harris, James and Mikko Tolonen. "Hume In and Out of Scottish Context." In *Scottish Philosophy in the Eighteenth Century, Volume I: Morals, Politics, Art, Religion.* Edited by G. Graham, A. Garrett, and J. Harris, 163-195. Oxford: Oxford University Press, 2015.

Koselleck, Reinhart. *Futures Past: On the Semantics of Historical Time.* New York, NY: Columbia University Press, 1979.

Mossner, Ernest. *The Life of David Hume,* 2nd edition. Oxford: Oxford University Press, 1980.

Norton, David Fate. "An Introduction to Hume's Thought." In *The Cambridge Companion to Hume.* Edited by David Fate Norton, 1–32. Cambridge: Cambridge University Press, 1993.

Skinner, Quentin. "The Practice of History and the Cult of the Fact." In *Visions of Politics, Volume 1: Regarding Method.* 8–26. Cambridge: Cambridge University Press, 2002.

Stewart, M. A. "Hume's Intellectual Development, 1711–1752." In *Impressions of Hume.* Edited by Marina Frasca-Spada and P. J. E. Kail, 11–58. Oxford: Oxford University Press, 2005.

Hume Studies
Volume 45, Number 1–2, 2019, pp. 37–45

Reply to My Critics

JAMES A. HARRIS

I am very grateful to Catherine Jones, Andrew Sabl, and Mikko Tolonen for taking the trouble to read my book *Hume: An Intellectual Biography* so carefully, and for responding to it so thoughtfully and constructively. I thank the editors of *Hume Studies* for the honour of having the book discussed in the journal that matters most to any Hume scholar. I would also like to take this opportunity to thank the organisers of the 2017 Hume Society Conference in Providence, and especially Aaron Garrett and André Willis, for inviting me to take part in a discussion of the book there. My critics on that occasion were James Moore and Dario Perinetti, both of whom gave me much to think about. Before I begin my responses to Jones, Sabl, and Tolonen, I feel that I need to draw the attention of the reader to the fact that what is at issue here is a book that was published in 2015. I finished work on it, in fact, in the autumn of 2014. As I write, that is almost seven years ago, and since then I have continued to think about the character and shape of Hume's intellectual development. Indeed, I have in the meantime written another book about Hume.[1] This new book is much shorter. It does not differ from the earlier book in any very significant way, but there are nevertheless some things that I have changed my mind about, and so it is possible that my replies to my critics here say more about my current views than about the views I held as I wrote the book under discussion. I hope that this does not make my critics feel that I am guilty of moving the goal-posts while the game is still being played.

Reply to Jones

One of the things that I was most interested in as I wrote *Hume: An Intellectual Biography* was how to characterize what might be termed Hume's literary persona. I wanted to find a

James A. Harris, Department of Philosophy, University of St Andrews, Edgecliffe, The Scores, St Andrews, KY16 9AL.
Email: jah15@st-andrews.ac.uk

way of describing what, in some languages, would be called his *authorship*, the nature of his ambition as a writer, how he addressed his readers, the voice he adopted in his appeal to their attention.[2] I was sure that a clear and categorical distinction needed to be made between Hume's literary persona and the characteristic ambitions, and mode of address, of the Anglophone philosopher of today. Of course, Hume thought of himself as philosopher, and often engaged with his reader as a philosopher, but, it seemed—and still seems—to me, it would be a serious mistake to assume without reflection that the kind of thing Hume understood philosophy to be was the same as the kind of thing we understand philosophy to be now. My suggestion, at any rate, was that "philosophy" was for Hume more a style of thought, and of writing, than a discrete subject matter, and that the best way to understand his project as a writer is to see him as taking up the persona of the "man of letters" and attempting to give that persona a distinctively *philosophical* inflection. I am very glad that Catherine Jones accepts this as a fruitful way of characterizing Hume's authorship. What she makes clear in her comments is that there is much more to say than I said in the book about the history of the man of letters, and much more to say also about Hume's particular version of this literary persona.

I suggest in my book that, as a way of bringing Hume's literary ambitions into clearer focus, it is helpful to compare and contrast them with his almost exact contemporary Samuel Johnson. Both sought a kind of independence and autonomy that it had not been possible for authors in English to achieve before the eighteenth century—though both had before them the example of Alexander Pope, and the way he dramatically altered the balance of power between author and bookseller. Money was, of course, the key to independence, but money mattered in very different ways to Hume and Johnson, and Jones is quite right to pick me up for suggesting in a note that money mattered more to the Scot than to the Englishman. That claim is at odds with what I remark on elsewhere, the fact that financial support from his family meant Hume did not, as Johnson did, need to write in order to eat. Hume's path to independence as a man of letters was considerably smoother and more agreeable than Johnson's. From the start—or, almost from the start, once he had put the crisis of the late 1720s and early 1730s behind him—Hume had a sense of security, a sense of himself and of his place in the world, that Johnson, with his fits of anger and his bouts of depression, seems always to have lacked.

Thomas Carlyle wrote about this difference in *The Edinburgh Review* with compassionate exactness in a passage that I am glad to have the excuse to quote here:

> Greater contrast, in all things, between two great men, could not be. Hume, well-born, competently provided for, whole in body and mind, of his own determination forces a way into Literature: Johnson, poor, moonstruck, diseased, forlorn, is forced into it "with the bayonet of necessity at his back." And what a part did they severally play there! As Johnson became the father of all succeeding Tories; so was Hume the father of all succeeding Whigs, for his own Jacobitism was but an accident, as worthy to be named Prejudice as any of Johnson's. Again, if Johnson's culture was exclusively English; Hume's, in Scotland, became European;—for which reason too we find his influence spread deeply over all quarters of Europe, traceably deeply in

> all speculation, French, German, as well as domestic; while Johnson's name, out of England, is hardly anywhere to be met with. . . . Both were, by principle and habit, Stoics: yet Johnson with the greater merit, for he alone had very much to triumph over; farther, he alone ennobled his Stoicism into Devotion. To Johnson Life was as a Prison, to be endured with heroic faith: to Hume it was little more than a foolish Bartholomew-Fair Show-booth, with the foolish crowdings and elbowings of which it was not worth to while to quarrel; the whole would break up, and be at liberty, *so soon*.[3]

There is much to quibble with here, but when it comes to the larger issue, Carlyle seems to me exactly right. As Jones notes, Carlyle's lecture on "The Hero as Man of Letters" instances Johnson, along with Burns and Rousseau, as an example of the man of letters as "heroic soul," devoted, "in his squalid garret, in his rusty coat," to revealing quasi-religious truths to which his age has made itself dead. This particular kind of hero "is he who lives in the inward sphere of things, in the True, Divine and Eternal, which exists always, unseen to most, under the Temporary [and] Trivial."[4] Hume is not mentioned in his lecture, but he is present in it all the same, as an exponent of the prevailing skepticism that put men like Johnson, Burns, and Rousseau so fatally at odds with their time. In Carlyle's terms, Hume was in tune with his age in a way that Johnson was not. This is an exaggeration, maybe, but it is no more an exaggeration than Ernest Mossner's picture of Hume as prophet almost entirely denied honour in his own country.

As foreign as skepticism to Carlyle's heroic man of letters is the irony that inevitably goes along with skepticism. The man of letters as hero struggles to excavate deep truths in order to remind his contemporaries of what they need to know about human existence. The skeptic holds that such truths are beyond our grasp, and that even the most tentative assertion is shadowed by uncertainty, so that it is never quite clear exactly what it is that one is entitled to mean, and never quite clear how to understand others. It is natural for the skeptic to try on different voices, and to set personae against each other, in the hope that the presentation of discord and disagreement will ensure that nothing is taken as a pretention to certainty. Hence, I think, Hume's deployments of the dialogue form, and the way—to which I return below—he *staged* arguments instead of trying to conclude them. Jones echoes a frustration expressed by Tim Stuart-Buttle in his review of my book, a frustration at my decision to concentrate on the ideas rather than the man, and at my consequent neglect of the tension between Hume's detached literary persona and the passionate and opinionated character occasionally seen in his letters.[5] The sense that I myself got as I worked with Hume's letters was that they were just as much acts of authorship as his books. I did not feel that they told me very much at all, if anything, about the opinions and sentiments of the "real" Hume. They seemed to me to be very often, if not always, exercises in personification, full of ironies that I was in no position to gauge, and jokes that I only occasionally understood.

Reply to Sabl

"The Eighteenth was a *Sceptical* Century," Carlyle claimed, and, he continued, in the word "scepticism" "there is a whole Pandora's Box of miseries. Scepticism means not intellectual Doubt alone, but moral Doubt; all sorts of infidelity, insincerity, spiritual paralysis."[6] I do not think that skepticism was for Hume the kind of existential malaise that it was not only for Carlyle, but for many others in the nineteenth century, but I do think, along of course with many who have written on Hume, that an account of his skepticism is an essential part of any attempt to characterise Hume's cast of mind.[7] In the first instance, it seemed to me as I wrote *Hume: An Intellectual Biography*, skepticism was for Hume a certain attitude towards intellectual endeavour. It expressed itself in what might possibly have been a compulsion to expose fallacies and contradictions in the arguments of everyone and anyone, be they antiquarians, university professors, religious apologists, or political pamphleteers. In many of his writings, as I read them, Hume seems to have been concerned more with bringing puzzles and problems to the reader's attention than with offering the reader a decisive argument in favour of this or that position on the matter at hand. This is especially clear, I think, in the way in which Hume adopted and adapted the essay form. Hume's essays very often stage a confrontation between two well established moral or political contraries, with the aim of getting the reader to think beyond those contraries, and to see the issue in a new light. They seldom, if ever, purport to solve a problem so that the reader need think about it no longer. In his writings on the human understanding, Hume's interest is in the tools we have at our disposal in order to answer the questions we find ourselves wanting to ask about ourselves and the world around us, and what he wants to show us is how ill-suited those tools are to providing us with certainty about anything. Right at the end of Book 1 of the *Treatise*, and possibly also in part 12 of the *Dialogues*, Hume turns skepticism back on itself. Hume's skepticism is not the end of thought, but the impetus for thought to continue.

Andrew Sabl evinces a certain disappointment, both at my interest in Hume as man of letters, and at my determination to show skepticism to be at the heart of Hume's particular way of being a man of letters. Sabl sees me as neglecting Hume's effort to establish durable truths, particularly in what is now called political science. In this connection, it seems to me that there is a distinction to be drawn between what a present-day political scientist, or indeed a present-day philosopher, can extract from Hume's works for the purposes of advancing present-day debates, and what Hume's intentions were as he wrote those works. I read Sabl's book *Hume's Politics* with great pleasure and profit.[8] It is one of the best accounts I know of what a genuinely Humean theory of political authority, and political obligation, looks like.[9] But I do not believe that Sabl's account of what can be learned from Hume, and from *The History of England* in particular, tells us very much about what Hume took himself to be doing. Reading against the grain, so to speak, is often a fruitful way to read. But it is one way of reading among others, and, for the purposes of *Hume: An Intellectual Biography*, I was reading Hume in a different way. There is good evidence, it seems to me, that Hume himself was skeptical about the possibility of a science of politics. Yes, he wrote an essay with the title "That

Politics May Be Reduced to a Science," but he himself wrote little that advertised itself as proof "that politics admit of general truths, which are invariable by the humour either of subject of sovereign."[10] In another essay, he remarked that he was "apt . . . to entertain a suspicion, that the world is still too young to fix many general truths in politics, which will remain true to the latest posterity."[11] It is significant, I think, that Hume generally wrote about politics using the essay form. It is also significant that his one longform work on political subjects was a narrative history, and not an "account of the general principles of law and government, and of the different revolutions they have undergone in different ages and periods of society" of the kind promised by Adam Smith at the end of *The Theory of Moral Sentiments*.[12]

This is not to deny that Sabl disagrees with me about how to interpret Hume's intentions in his—Hume's—treatment of specific topics and events. Actually, I am not sure that we are as far apart about, for instance, Magna Carta as he suggests in his comments. My view—certainly my view now—is that while Hume was skeptical of the short-term consequences of what happened at Runnymede in 1215, he did not deny that, in the end, the principle that the crown is bound by laws was hugely significant in English history. His point was merely that it took a very long time for what was in the first instance a tactical victory for the barons to turn into something of advantage to the people as a whole. On the other hand, it might be that Sabl and I do disagree at quite a fundamental level about Hume's attitude to the revolution of 1688–89. I just do not recognise Hume in Sabl's distinctly Burkean claim that the great achievement of that revolution was to have settled the principle of hereditary power on a firmer footing. It could not be clearer, it seems to me, that what Hume saw in the replacement of James II with William and Mary was the inauguration of a new era in English, and eventually British, politics. (I do not see that to interpret Hume this way must be to read him as claiming that politics is wholly up to us in the present.) However, the more important point here has to do with what I take to be the remit of an intellectual biographer. I do not think that it is the job of someone writing an intellectual biography to make judgments about the nature of their subject's enduring impact on the world of letters. Certainly, I took myself not to be obliged to spell out what in Hume is still read with profit, and why. It is probably true that Hume wrote in order to be read not only by his contemporaries, but also by posterity. But is it clear that we remember him for things he wanted to be remembered for? Can we be sure that we profit from his writings in ways he intended? My guess is that he would be surprised, and probably disappointed, to learn what philosophers and others have, and have not, taken from his works over the past 250 years.

Reply to Tolonen

Mikko Tolonen, too, displays a measure of frustration at the way I treat Hume's interventions in the intellectual disputes of his day. He suggests that Hume's claim, in many of his writings but especially in his essays, to be promoting compromise and moderation should not always be taken seriously. Hume had definite views, Tolonen suggests, and this can be seen in his writing if one reads carefully enough. For instance, there is, according to Tolonen, a discernible anti-republicanism in Hume's political thought. Now, the first thing to note here is that this claim is at odds with Sabl's claim that Hume set out to establish a system of political science. When Hume speaks in the voice of someone concerned to show that politics may be reduced to a science, he limits himself to the claim that general truths are more easily established with respect to republican forms of government than with respect to monarchies. Secondly, though, there is the question of what the dialectical situation was in British political argument in the middle decades of the eighteenth century. Is it true to say that to take up at least some of the language of the Court Whigs, and also to argue that liberty can be as real under absolute monarchy as under any other form of government, was, in this time and place, implicitly to take a stand against *republicanism*? Answering that kind of question is precisely the kind of thing that I *do* think is part of the remit of the intellectual biographer. One way—perhaps the only way—to get a sense of what Hume's intentions might have been is to pay attention to the state of play, at this time, in the debates that Hume engaged with. Then one can ask what, given that the intellectual climate was like *that*, a text like *this* might have been meant to do. Influential work on eighteenth-century British political thought by John Pocock and others has focused on the continuing importance of the language of neo-Machiavellianism, but I am—now, at any rate—unconvinced that this entails that the great question of the age was between republicanism and anti-republicanism. In fact, it seems to me, what to a very significant extent continued to structure political argument was a dispute between those, broadly speaking, sympathetic to the ideas of Locke, and those, equally broadly speaking, sympathetic to the ideas of Sir Robert Filmer. Both positions were "anti-republican." How Hume negotiated a way between these opposites has yet to be properly examined.[13]

Another important issue raised by Tolonen concerns Hume's intellectual engagement with Montesquieu. Tolonen suggests, not unjustly, that I give the impression that whereas—as no one has made clearer than Tolonen himself—Mandeville was Hume's chief intellectual companion in the early stages of Hume's intellectual development, it was Montesquieu who played this role later on. There was, to be sure, more to say about Hume and Montesquieu than I said in *Hume: An Intellectual Biography*, and no doubt what I did say there was unsatisfactory because too brief. I hope to have made it clear, though, that in the case of neither Mandeville, nor Montesquieu was significant impact upon Hume's thinking the same thing as "influence." In both cases, there was important disagreement, as well as important agreement, and it may be that the right thing to say is that the role these writers played for Hume was that of exemplars of the right way, in general, to think about moral and political subjects. Both, from Hume's point of view, struck the right tone, both were refreshingly free of illusion, neither was disposed to blink in the face of the realities of moral and political life. It is a striking fact that, as we can tell from the 1741 and 1742 volumes of *Essays, Moral and Political*, Hume was clearly thinking about politics in what we might call a "Montesquieuian" way *before* he read *De l'Esprit des Lois*. That might be because of what he had been able to glean from Montesquieu's early work. But it might equally be just a coincidence, a matter of two men developing roughly the same cast of mind, at roughly the same time. (Hume was not the only Scot of his time who in the early and mid 1740s thought himself into an intellectual position that anticipated

Montesquieu: Kames was another, and it may be that there is much more to say about the Hume-Kames relationship than I was able to say in my book.) The right thing to say might be that Montesquieu, like Mandeville, gave Hume the confidence fully to develop thoughts that he was already having. In any case, I remain committed to Montesquieu's importance to Hume, and I am keen to see what Tolonen will say on this matter in his own future work.[14]

A more fundamental dissatisfaction expressed by Tolonen concerns my reluctance to entertain the idea that there are substantial connections to be drawn between Hume's various works. As I explain in the introduction to my book, my approach to Hume's intellectual development took its point of departure from a dissatisfaction with the idea that everything that Hume wrote was, in some sense or other, a part of the science of man announced at the beginning of the *Treatise*. One way of putting what is wrong with this is approach is that it makes life too easy for the history of philosophy as currently practised in the Anglophone world. It means that a text like the *History of England* can be written about in almost complete ignorance of an extremely complex context provided by the large number of other histories of England published in the decades before Hume began his own historical work. As I have indicated above, knowledge of that kind of context seemed to me to be essential to the task of figuring of what Hume's intentions might have been. Of course, it was the same man who wrote the *Treatise*, the *Essays*, the *History*, and so on, and of course he did not wipe his mind clean of all that he had previously written when he began a new work. But, still, it does not seem to me that it helps very much, in approaching the *Essays* or the *History*, to know that the person who wrote those texts also wrote *A Treatise of Human Nature*. I have the sense that Hume was a fox, not a hedgehog. His was a restless mind that wanted to move on to new things, not a mind that returned again and again to the same ideas and debates. Tolonen asserts that Hume was a system builder. My response to that is that I just do not see any evidence for it, not in anything that Hume himself said after 1739, nor in the shape of his *oeuvre*. Smith was a system builder. So, perhaps, was Thomas Reid. But I do not think Hume was, any more than Johnson was, or Voltaire.

Conclusion

I want to add only that I do not regard my book as in any sense the last word about Hume's intellectual biography. It could not but be a speculative piece of work, because, as I emphasise in the book itself, there is so little surviving evidence for an intellectual biographer to work with. We have no diaries, almost nothing in the way of notebooks, and, comparatively, a very small number of letters. We have Hume's works themselves, but Hume was generally reticent when it came to programmatic statements about what he thought of himself as doing in those works. The *History of England* had no preface or introduction. "Of Essay Writing" was withdrawn in 1742, never to be published again. Section 1 of *An Enquiry concerning Human Understanding* is, to say the least, difficult to interpret. So, there is ample room for reconstructions of Hume's intentions, and of the development of his career as an author, very different to mine. There is also, surely, more to discover about every phase of Hume's life. Hard work in libraries and archives has the potential radically to change our understanding of what Hume was about as a philosopher and as a historian.[15] I look forward to reading new intellectual biographies of Hume in the years to come.

NOTES

1 Harris, Hume: *A Very Short Introduction.*

2 I take this understanding of the word "authorship" from Clare Carlisle's biography of Kierkegaard, *Philosopher of the Heart.*

3 Carlyle, "Boswell's Life of Johnson," 111.

4 Carlyle, *Selected Writings*, 235–36.

5 Stuart Buttle provides his own interpretation of aspects of Hume's intellectual biography in his deeply interesting book *From Moral Theology to Moral Philosophy: Cicero and Visions of Humanity from Locke to Hume.*

6 Carlyle, *Selected Writings*, 250.

7 For a powerful interpretation of Hume's skepticism, published too late for me to make use of it in *Hume: An Intellectual Biography*, see Ainslie, *Hume's True Scepticism.*

8 See also Spencer, "Hume's Magna Charta and Sabl's Fundamental Constitutional Conventions," and Sabl's "Reply to my Critics."

9 Sabl's book is profitably read together with Sagar, *The Opinion of Mankind.*

10 Hume, *Essays and Treatises*, I: 17.

11 Hume, *Essays and Treatises*, I: 91.

12 Smith, *Theory of Moral Sentiments*, II: 399.

13 For a preliminary survey of the territory, see Harris, "Of the Origin of Government."

14 All future work on Hume's engagement with Montesquieu will need to take account of Pye, "Histories of Liberty in Scottish Thought."

15 For one example of what such work can achieve, see Perinetti, "Hume at La Flèche." New studies of Hume's context will also alter our understanding of aspects of Hume's thought: see, for instance, Silvia Sebastiani's current work on the Scottish science of man and its implications for the theorization of racial difference, in, e.g., Sebastiani, "Monboddo's 'ugly tail.'"

WORKS CITED

Ainslie, Donald. *Hume's True Scepticism*. Oxford: Oxford University Press, 2015.

Carlisle, Clare. *Philosopher of the Heart: The Restless Life of Søren Kierkegaard.* Harmondsworth: Penguin, 2019.

Carlyle, Thomas. "Boswell's Life of Johnson." *Critical and Miscellaneous Essays.* 5 vols. IV: 23–113. London: Chapman and Hall, 1862.

Carlyle, Thomas. *Selected Writings.* Edited by Alan Shelston. Harmondsworth: Penguin, 1971.

Harris, James A. *Hume: A Very Short Introduction.* Oxford: Oxford University Press, 2021.

Harris, James A. "Of the Origin of Government: Afterlives of Locke and Filmer in an Eighteenth-Century British Debate." *Intellectual History Review*, forthcoming.

Hume, David. *Essays and Treatises on Several Subjects.* 2 vols. London, 1777.

Perinetti, Dario. "Hume at La Flèche: Skepticism and the French Connection." *Journal of the History of Philosophy* 56 (2018): 45–74.

Pye, Tom. "Histories of Liberty in Scottish Thought, 1747–87." Ph.D. dissertation, University of Cambridge, 2018.

Sabl, Andrew. *Hume's Politics: Coordination and Crisis in* The History of England. Princeton: Princeton University Press, 2012.

Sabl, Andrew. "Reply to my Critics." *Hume Studies* 41 (2015): 91–102.

Sagar, Paul. *The Opinion of Mankind: Sociability and the Theory of the State from Hobbes to Smith.* Princeton: Princeton University Press, 2018.

Sebastiani, Silvia. "Monboddo's 'Ugly Tail': The Question of Evidence in the Enlightenment Science of Man." *History of European Ideas* 48 (2022): 45–65.

Smith, Adam. *The Theory of Moral Sentiments.* 6th edition. 2 vols. London, 1790.

Spencer, Mark G. "'Distant and Commonly Faint and Disfigured Originals': Hume's Magna Charta and Sabl's Fundamental Constitutional Conventions." *Hume Studies* 41 (2015): 73–80.

Stuart Buttle, Tim. *From Moral Theology to Moral Philosophy: Cicero and Visions of Humanity from Locke to Hume.* Oxford: Oxford University Press, 2019.

HUME STUDIES
Volume 45, Number 1–2, 2019, pp. 47–50

Précis of *Imagined Causes*

STEFANIE ROCKNAK

By Hume's own account, his most ambitious project, the *Treatise on Human Nature,* was a notoriously immature undertaking, choked with immutable difficulties.[1] Perhaps as a result of this immaturity, and perhaps because, as Kant suggests above, Hume is perpetually misread, his view on objects remains obscured. What are they? Are they ideas? Impressions? Mind-independent objects? All three? None of the above? To date, scholars have not provided a unified, much less exhaustive, answer to these questions. Rather, four somewhat fragmented interpretations have been circulating in the literature. We may characterize them (in partial response to Marjorie Grene)[2] as follows: 1.) The phenomenonalist reading, where objects *are* impressions (for example, Grene, "The Objects of Hume's *Treatise*"; Bennett, *Locke, Berkeley and Hume*; Steinberg, "Hume on the Continued Existence and the Identity of Changing Things"; and Dicker, "Hume on the Intermittent Existence of the Objects of the Senses"); 2.) The intentional reading, where objects are the objects of thought (for example, Salmon, *The Central Problem of Hume's Philosophy*); 3.) The realist reading, where objects are mind-independent things (for example, Wilson, "Is Hume a Skeptic with Regard to the Senses?"; Flage, *David Hume's Theory of Mind*; Costa, "Hume and Causal Realism"; Strawson, "David Hume: Objects and Power"; Wright, "Hume's Causal Realism: Recovering a Traditional Interpretation"; 4) The imagined, but non-causal reading, where objects, to varying degrees (depending on the scholar at hand) are imagined, but are not imagined as causes (for instance, Price, *Hume's Theory of the External World*; Kemp Smith, *The Philosophy of David Hume*; Wilbanks, *Hume's Theory of Imagination*; and Waxman, *Hume's Theory of Consciousness*).

This book presents a new interpretation of Humean objects, where I focus on just Book 1 of the *Treatise*. In the course of doing so, I show that although in places, Hume surely does suggest that objects are impressions, or are intentional, or are imagined but are not imagined as

Stefanie Rocknak is a Professor of Philosophy at Hartwick College, Oneonta, NY.
Email: rocknaks@hartwick.edu

causes, these intermittent uses of the word "object" do not reflect Hume's more comprehensive position. Nor does Hume think that objects are mind independent things; he is not a realist.

Rather, throughout Book 1 of the *Treatise*, Hume struggled with two positions on the nature of objects. On the one hand, Hume believed that despite what we, in our common, that is, "vulgar" state of mind, or alternatively, in our more sophisticated "philosophical" state of mind, *think* that objects are, what we actually and *always* do, is imagine that objects are the causes of our various and interrupted perceptions. Objects are nothing more than complex, imagined *ideas*, as such, they are perceptions. Moreover, objects are necessarily imagined (as causes) because they constitute certain conditions of possibility for experience, making them functions of what we may refer to as a "transcendental" faculty of the imagination: "we *always* imagine that there is some cause that separates or unites [objects]" (T 1.3.2.2; SBN 74; emphasis added). In this very general respect, Hume anticipates the Kantian transcendental turn.

But Hume also seemed to think that we *only* imagine causes (although unwittingly) when we reach a certain "philosophical" level of thought. Thus, when we imagine a cause of a set of interrupted and varying perceptions—where we believe that this cause is a real mind-independent thing—we are "philosophers," as they are described at the end of 1.4.2 ("Of skepticism with regard to the senses"). However, such philosophers are *not* aware that they are imagining causes. Instead, they mistakenly think that they are using *reason* to conclude that objects are real, mind-independent things. As a result, on this second reading, imagining causes is a natural, although unacknowledged, *culmination* of human thought, as opposed to being something that all of us, *always*—although unknowingly—do.

The tension between these two positions on objects manifests itself in Hume's much discussed account of personal identity, presented in 1.4.6 of the *Treatise*. In fact, Hume openly acknowledges this tension in the Appendix to the *Treatise*. Here, he suggests that the philosophical account of perfect identity is *mistaken*, while his account of transcendentally conceived of perfect identity is correct—at least in regard to the "self." However, this is not a definitive solution to the conflict. In fact, this conflict is never resolved in the *Treatise* (nor anywhere else in Hume's work).

Regardless of this rift in his thought, it may be shown that Hume thought that *some* objects are imagined to be causes in a manner that is more "justified" than others. Generally speaking, this justification turns on how empirically grounded the given imagined cause is in sense impressions. This "grounding" occurs much in the same way that Hume thinks we come up with an idea of an abstract, general idea. A *particular* object is imagined as the cause of a set of resembling impressions and/or ideas that exactly represent impressions. This imagined cause indirectly represents one of those impressions, making it "real"—in a manner to be explained in great detail in this book. Accordingly, Hume writes off the "antient" (T 1.4.3; SBN 219–24) and "modern" (T 1.4.4; SBN 225–31) conceptions of objects, as well as notions of "immaterial souls" (T 1.4.5; SBN 232–50) as *un*justified. *These* philosophical "objects" are perverted cases of imagining causes; their "objects" do not represent (indirectly or not) any impression and/or any idea that exactly represents an impression, and thus, they are completely incomprehensible. Meanwhile, the "philosophical" position presented at the end of 1.4.2 (SBN 187–218) may be interpreted as the generic, *justified* version of imagining causes.

In the course of showing that some ideas of particular objects are justified, we see that some causal inferences are justified. This justification is a function of the constancy and coherence that obtains of our impressions, and ideas that exactly represent our impressions. As such, justified causal relations reflect "reality" much in the same way that justified ideas of particular objects reflect reality. Relatedly, we see that Hume must be interpreted as an "agnostic' in regard to the mind-independent existence of objects and causality, contrary to the recent tendency to interpret Hume as a "skeptical realist."

In the course of this analysis, we review seven kinds of belief at work in the *Treatise*, five kinds of reason, three kinds of causation, Hume's two systems of reality, and two fundamental kinds of objects, that is, those that may be identified with impressions and ideas that exactly represent impressions, and those that admit of what Hume refers to as a "perfect identity."

NOTES

1 Norton, *Cambridge Companion to Hume*, 349.

2 "The Objects of Hume's *Treatise*."

WORKS CITED

Bennett, Jonathon. *Locke, Berkeley and Hume: Central Themes*. Oxford: Oxford University Press, 1971.

Costa, Michael J. "Hume and Causal Realism." *Australasian Journal of Philosophy* 67, no. 2 (1989): 172–90. https://doi.org/10.1080/00048408912343751

Dicker, Georges. "Hume on the Intermittent Existence of the Objects of the Senses." Paper presented at the *153rd Creighton Club Conference*, Hobart and William Smith Colleges, 2007.

Flage, Daniel. *David Hume's Theory of Mind*. London: Routledge, 1990.

Grene, Marjorie. "The Objects of Hume's *Treatise*." *Hume Studies* 20, no. 2 (1994): 163–77.

Hume, David. *A Treatise of Human Nature*. Edited by D.F and M. J. Norton. Oxford: Oxford University Press, 2002.

Hume, David. *A Treatise of Human* Nature, 2nd ed. Edited by L. A. Selby-Bigge, revised by P. Nidditch. Oxford: Oxford University Press, 1978.

Norton, David F., ed. *Cambridge Companion to Hume*. Cambridge: Cambridge University Press, 1993.

Price, H. H. *Hume's Theory of the External World*. Oxford: Oxford University Press, 1940.

Salmon, Christopher V. *The Central Problem of Hume's Philosophy*. New York: Garland, 1983.

Smith, Norman Kemp. *The Philosophy of David Hume; A Critical Study of its Origins and Central Doctrines*. New York: Macmillan, 1941.

Steinberg, Eric. "Hume on the Continued Existence and the Identity of Changing Things." *Hume Studies* 7, no. 2 (1981): 105–20. https://doi.org/10.1353/hms.2011.0584

Strawson, Galen. "David Hume: Objects and Power." In *The New Hume Debate*, rev. ed. Edited by R. Read and K. Richman, 31–35. New York: Routledge, 2007.

Waxman, Wayne. *Hume's Theory of Consciousness*. Cambridge: Cambridge University Press, 1994.

Wilbanks, Jan. *Hume's Theory of Imagination*. The Hague: Martinus Nijhoff, 1968.

Wilson, Fred. "Is Hume a Skeptic with Regard to the Senses?" *Journal of the History of Philosophy* 27, no. 1 (1989): 49–73. https://doi.org/10.1353/hph.1989.0006

Wright, John P. "Hume's Causal Realism: Recovering a Traditional Interpretation." In *The New Hume Debate*, revised edition. Edited by R. Read and K. Richman, 88–99. New York: Routledge, 2007.

Hume Studies
Volume 45, Number 1–2, 2019, pp. 51–58

Comments on Rocknak's *Imagined Causes*

DONALD L. M. BAXTER

Stefanie Rocknak has written an ambitious and challenging book[1] in which she argues for a new interpretation of Hume's account of how we come to believe in external objects, and what it is we believe in. I am hampered by the fact that she and I seem to agree on so little. Thus, my criticisms run the danger of simply not seeing what she is up to.

A preliminary terminological point: where Rocknak uses the word "object," I will often use the word "body," since I think Hume sometimes uses "object" in a more general sense that includes perceptions.

If I understand correctly, Rocknak's Hume argues that we come to believe in bodies through a special kind of causal reasoning. We reason what must exist in order to cause sequences of sense impressions with constancy and coherence and in order to explain the fact that the impressions have these characteristics. Our conclusion is that bodies must exist and we come to the idea of body via an exercise of our transcendental imagination. Bodies are imagined causes, as she puts it: secret causes that we have never experienced and can never experience (118). To quote her,

> [B]y using a special kind of reasoning from causation—which is not based on experience—we "infer" that some continuous and distinct object must be the cause of the impressions . . . in order to explain the constancy and coherence that our impressions do clearly admit of. For how else, the idea is, could my impressions of say, a mountain, be constant and coherent, no matter how many times they are interrupted, unless there is some continuous and distinct object, causing those impressions? (117)

As near as I can tell, the rhetorical question here is what guides her interpretation.

Donald L. M. Baxter is Professor Emeritus of Philosophy at the University of Connecticut, 344 Mansfield Rd, Unit 1054, Storrs, CT 06269-1054, USA.
Email: donald.baxter@uconn.edu

I myself do not see how the vulgar could feel the pull of the question when they first generate the idea of body as a result of tricks of the imagination. In my view, the idea that bodies cause impressions is much further downstream when the philosophers get into the picture, not at the origin of the idea of body (see T 1.4.2.43–46; SBN 209–12).

In any event, I will focus on some passages in Hume that Rocknak interprets as descriptions of this process of transcendental reasoning and imagining, and will give alternate interpretations.

First is the discussion in T 1.3.9.3–4 (SBN 107–108)[2] of the two systems of realities (58–60). Rocknak takes the first system of realities to consist of impressions and memories of impressions, and takes the second system of realities to consist of transcendentally imagined causes of the first system. I have trouble squaring this interpretation with the context. It seems to me that Hume is just continuing the previous discussion of everyday causal reasoning. The first system of realities consists of the things we sense or remember sensing, and the second system of realities consists of the things that we believe exist because the ideas and memories transport our minds to causally related ideas and enliven them. Our belief in Rome, if we have not experienced that city, is an enlivened complex idea consisting of ideas with a customary association with impressions of words or stories about Rome. The enlivened ideas that compose the complex idea are copies of impressions of ordinary experience. If Hume is switching from a discussion of causation as customary conjunction to a special sort of transcendental causation, he is doing it without any warning and without any need. Rocknak seems to be inferring from the fact that we do not see and feel the realities in the second system, that they cannot be seen and felt, and can only be grasped by the transcendental imagination. But this inference seems inconsistent with the fact that Hume is continuing his discussion of how observed constant conjunctions and present impressions lead to belief in things not currently sensed. Because the constant conjunctions have been observed, both types of things have been observed. There is no indication that he has switched to talking of things that cannot be sensed.

Second is Hume's discussion in T 1.3.2.2 (SBN 73–74) of the inconstant relations (97). As I read Hume, he is in the process of arguing that only ordinary causation enables us to infer the existence of objects we are not currently sensing. When we have observed that things of one type are always accompanied by things of another type, and we have an impression of something of the first type, we infer the existence of something of the second type that we are not currently sensing. In contrast, neither identity nor spatial or temporal relations support this inference. That I see something here now does not allow me to infer that something exactly resembling it, and uninterruptedly connected to it, did or will exist. That I see something here now does not allow me to infer that something else far away (that is, remote) or nearby (that is, contiguous) exists. If I can make such inferences, it is only because of causal connections of the currently sensed things with the currently unsensed. For instance, if I infer that there was previously something just like what I see now and uninterruptedly connected with it, it is because there is a causal explanation of why such things are durable and not momentary.

Rocknak, on the other hand, takes this passage to support Hume's commitment to the exercise of transcendental reasoning in inferring a product of the transcendental imagination.

She says that "'remote' seems to mean, *distinct* from, i.e., *independent* of, our perception," and dismisses the obvious meaning of distant, even though spatial relations are under discussion (95). She then takes the 1.3.2.2 passage on identity to pre-sage the T 1.4.2.31–36 (SBN 201–205) passage about attributing identity to an interrupted succession of exactly resembling impressions, and says it is about imagining a secret cause—one with perfect identity—of the resembling impressions. All this seems out of keeping with the express overall purpose of Hume's discussion here. And again, it seems clear he is talking about ordinary causation, not transcendental causation.

Third is Hume's discussion at the beginning of T 1.4.2.18–19 (SBN 194–95) of constancy and coherence. Hume is concerned to explain why we attribute to body continued existence unperceived, as well as existence distinct from mind and perception. His answer is that these attributions are the effects on our imagination by interrupted successions of certain impressions that exhibit constancy, and interrupted successions of certain impressions that exhibit coherence. A succession is constant if each member exactly resembles any other. A succession is coherent if there is a sequence of changes between its members just like other sequences of changes in a number of other successions. A constant succession of impressions is interrupted if between some of its members are impressions with little resemblance to them. A coherent succession of impressions is interrupted if instead of some of its members are impressions not normally found in such sequences of changes.

In a complicated story, Hume says that the imagination takes distinct impressions in a constant sequence to be identical, and masks the absurdity by taking the imagined single lengthy impression to sometimes exist unperceived. Similarly, the imagination takes the missing impressions in a coherent succession to exist unperceived. Hume explicitly talks of impressions here. However, Rocknak takes this to be mere "terminological carelessness." She says we cannot imagine that an impression exists unperceived because impressions are not imagined and are perceived (108). However, Hume explicitly addresses such an objection at T 1.4.2.37–39 (SBN 205–207) and takes himself to have answered it. That seems a lot of care to expend in support of terminological carelessness. Rocknak's section is entitled "Impressions Are Never Imagined," but imagining something about an impression is not the same as imagining the impression.

At T 1.4.2.20–21 (SBN 195–98), Hume discusses how coherence leads to a belief in continued and distinct existence. The gist is that we imagine unobserved impressions to exist in order to preserve the regular sequence of changes that we are used to observing. Hume calls this a kind of causal reasoning. It is not garden variety causal reasoning because we suppose more regularity than we have actually observed. For instance, when we have our back to it and so are not looking, we suppose the door to be swinging when we hear the familiar creak. The explanation is what one might call regularity inertia—seeing some cases of a regularity impels one to imagine constant conjunction even when the conjunction has only been inconstantly observed.

Rocknak adds the word "mysterious" to Hume's word "kind" when he speaks of a "kind of reasoning from causation" (T 1.4.2.19; SBN 195) (115). She takes Hume to be introducing transcendental causation between imagined causes and the impressions we have. But there is no mysterious transcendental causation here. Hume has told us what he means—regularity inertia.

In four parts, Hume explains how a constant succession of perceptions causes belief in the idea of body (T 1.4.2.25; SBN 199–200). Rocknak says that a detailed explanation of this system is lacking in the literature, but see my own explanation in Saul Traiger's *Blackwell Guide*.[3] In any event, Hume says that when we have an interrupted succession of exactly resembling impressions, we take each of them to be identical with the next. The interruption is clear evidence, however, that each is a new existence, distinct from the last. We are uneasy with this contradiction and resolve it by supposing that the identical impression which we suppose there to be, exists sometimes perceived and sometimes unperceived. The vivacity of the impressions lends vivacity to this supposition and we believe it. This process takes place on the supposition that our perceptions are our only objects, so that examples of the impressions at issue are what "the common man means by a hat, or shoe, or stone" (T 1.4.2.31; SBN 202).

Understanding this account requires understanding what Hume means by "identity." Identity, for Hume, is the "invariableness and uninterruptedness of any object, thro' a supposed variation of time" (T 1.4.2.30; SBN 201). Hume explains how "a single object, plac'd before us, and survey'd for any time without our discovering in it any interruption or variation, is able to give us the notion of identity" (T 1.4.2.29; SBN 201). It does so because of an irresistible fiction of the imagination whereby for any "unchangeable object" we take it "to participate of the changes of the co-existent objects, and in particular that of our perceptions" (T 1.4.2.29; SBN 200–201). The object we are surveying, which is clearly steadfast, we take nonetheless to be also successive. Steadfastness is contrary to successiveness. So we alternate viewing the object as a single, steadfast thing, and as many successive things. This alternation between regarding the object as one thing and regarding it as many things is the idea of identity. "Here then is an idea, which is a medium betwixt unity and number, or more properly speaking, is either of them, according to the view, in which we take it" (T 1.4.2.29; SBN 201).

Hume gives this strange account because he is concerned to explain how identity can be an inconstant relation. Constant relations are ones that "depend entirely on the ideas, which we compare together," whereas inconstant relations are "such as may be chang'd without any change in the ideas" (T 1.3.1.1; SBN 69). Identity, Hume says, is an inconstant relation. We may think of something at one time and something exactly resembling at another, and without any change in our ideas alternately imagine that they are identical or imagine that they are distinct. After all, identity is something we can be unsure of. It is not a relation of ideas.

However, this banal fact about identity raises a very difficult metaphysical problem, what I have termed "Hume's difficulty concerning identity."[4] If we can suppose that things A and B are identical and then go on to suppose that they are distinct, then we can suppose that the identical thing we have taken them to be is distinct from itself. But that seems to be supposing an obvious contradiction. How can we conceive of identity as an inconstant relation while avoiding this obvious contradiction? How can we conceive of one thing as, for all we know, two? How can we conceive of two things as, for all we know, one? These would require us to be able to conceive of a genuine medium betwixt unity and number. In his discussion of identity, Hume finesses the problem by appealing to the fiction by which we alternately conceive the object as one single thing or two distinct things. I have argued that Hume merely evades and does not solve the profound problem he has raised, and no-one else has solved it either. The closest approach is F. H. Bradley's concept of identity-in-difference, but Bradley himself calls it "a clear make-shift" that does not resolve the contradiction and "is not the truth about reality."[5] Analytic philosophers do not even see the problem because they confuse it with Frege's puzzle about identity.

I have said that understanding Hume's explanation of our belief in body from a constant, interrupted succession of impressions requires understanding his idea of identity. Understanding his idea of identity requires understanding the difficulty with identity being an inconstant relation, and the apparent need for a medium betwixt unity and number. Understanding why his purported solution appeals to the idea of time requires understanding that a steadfast and invariable object is one, and a succession is many. That is why the idea of identity is an idea of an invariable and uninterrupted object through a supposed variation in time. In this way, the object is supposed to be both one, in virtue of its steadfastness, and many, in virtue of its duration.

As Rocknak recognizes, the whole edifice of this interpretation depends on a proper understanding of what a steadfast object is supposed to be for Hume. Something is steadfast when it is a single thing coexisting with a succession of things.[6] Rocknak tries to topple the edifice by critiquing my interpretation of what Hume means by "steadfast." She takes "steadfast" to have two senses for Hume. In one sense, she says a steadfast object for Hume is an interrupted succession of exactly resembling impressions—in other words, a succession with constancy (137). In the other sense, she says that a steadfast object is a continued and distinct imagined secret cause of such a succession (138). As near as I can tell, both these claims are based on confusion. Rocknak uses "constant," "uninterrupted," "invariable," "continued," and "steadfast" interchangeably (131, 134). However, such readings cannot be sustained.

First, "constant" has a special use for Hume in this discussion, as I have noted previously. Constancy is the exact resemblance of the impression before losing sight (or touch, etc.) of something, and the impression after regaining sight of that thing.

> These mountains, and houses, and trees, which lie at present under my eye, have always appear'd to me in the same order; and when I lose sight of them by shutting my eyes or turning my head, I soon after find them return upon me without the least alteration. My bed and table, my books and papers, present themselves in the same uniform manner, and change not upon account of any interruption in my seeing or perceiving them. (T 1.4.2.18; SBN 194–95)

Constancy is the exact resemblance of impressions in an interrupted succession. Sometimes the interruptions are impressions of the indistinct play of after images that one gets when ones eyes are closed, for instance. So, an example of a constant sequence would be impressions of one's books interspersed with impressions of one's after images.

Steadfastness is something different. To show this, let me appeal to things Hume says about what can give us the idea of time. Note that a succession of impressions with constancy can give one the idea of time. There is, after all, "a perceivable succession of changeable objects" (T 1.2.3.7; SBN 35): the succession changes from impressions of books to after images. Note, second, that "an unchangeable object, since it produces none but co-existent impressions, produces none that can give us the idea of time" (T 1.2.3.8; SBN 36, my emphasis). Hume just below calls such an object "stedfast and unchangeable" (T 1.2.3.11; SBN 37). The impression it produces is steadfast as well—that is, not successive. Thus, an example of constancy of impressions can produce the idea of time. An example of steadfastness of impression cannot. So constancy is not to be confused with steadfastness.

Nor is steadfastness continuity in the sense in which Hume uses it at the beginning of T 1.4.2. Hume talks of attributing "CONTINU'D existence" as short for attributing "CONTINU'D existence to objects, even when they are not present to the senses" (T 1.4.2.2; SBN 188). But an object can be steadfast even when perceived, such as when it is producing "none but co-existent perceptions" (T 1.2.3.8; SBN 36), or when one is surveying "a single object, plac'd before us . . . for any time without discovering in it any interruption or variation" (T 1.4.2.29; SBN 201). So, something can be steadfast when it is not continued in Hume's special sense. Likewise an altering body that one sees interruptedly can be continued in Hume's special sense, even when it is not steadfast.

Rocknak justifies these confusions as the only way to understand Hume's talk of steadfastness, invariableness, and uninterruptedness. She says that there is clear evidence that we never have a steadfast perception (130–33).

First she cites T 1.3.2.2 (SBN 74) and says, "Hume explicitly tells us here that we do not perceive an object that is both invariable and uninterrupted; such an idea is a 'conclusion beyond the impressions of our senses'" (131). But Hume is only saying that when an object goes out of sight or touch and then returns, we cannot be sure it is the same object again, unless there are some causal reasons why it must be. We appeal to causation to tell us about the existence of things we are not currently sensing. Hume is not talking about secret objects that it is impossible to sense.

Second, Rocknak appeals to T 1.4.6.2 (SBN 251) in which Hume says "there is no impression constant and invariable" (131). However, Hume's previous sentence is, "If any impression gives rise to the idea of self, that impression must continue invariably the same, thro' the whole course of our lives; since self is suppos'd to exist after that manner." Hume is only denying the existence of such a life-long impression, not generally asserting that there is no impression coexisting with any succession. Rocknak responds to this argument by citing Hume's mind as theater analogy including, "They are the successive perceptions only that constitute the mind" (T 1.4.6.4; SBN 253) (132). But this is not inconsistent with what I say. Any steadfast impressions would be part of the bigger succession of perceptions in the mind. Being steadfast is being a single thing coexisting with a succession. It is certainly not being a single thing that exists for all eternity in no succession.

Rocknak concludes by saying, "Hume is not excluding just the possibility of an impression of the self that somehow, would last the course of our lives. Rather, he is ruling out the possibility of any impression of an invariable and uninterrupted self" (132). But this claim is not relevant to my point that some single perceptions co-exist with some succession. My defense of steadfastness is a separate point from any discussion of a steadfast self.

Rocknak notes that Hume says, " 'Tis impossible for the mind to fix itself steadily upon one idea of any considerable amount of time (T 2.1.4.2; SBN 283)" (133). This passage must be put in contrast with Hume's discussion of a man "strongly occupy'd with one thought" (T 1.2.3.7; SBN 35). Thus, it must be possible to have a single idea while some succession is occuring. It just is not possible for it to happen while a succession of considerable duration occurs. Confirmation is at T 1.4.2.33 (SBN 203) where Hume says, "When we fix our thought on any object, and suppose it to continue the same for some time, 'tis evident we suppose the change to lie only in the time, and never exert ourselves to produce any new image or idea of the object. The faculties of the mind repose themselves in a manner, and take no more exercise, than what is necessary to continue that idea, of which we were formerly possest, and which subsists without variation or interruption." Thus, there are steadfast ideas.

Rocknak hopes to undermine my account of Hume on time and identity by criticizing my interpretation of Hume on steadfast objects. However, her criticisms seem based on misunderstanding of what steadfastness is meant to be, and of the passages she cites. To my admittedly not-unbiased eye, most of the arguments in support of her ambitious account of Hume on body suffer similarly.

NOTES

1 Rocknak, *Imagined Causes.*

2 References to the *Treatise* are to Hume, *A Treatise of Human Nature*, ed. Norton and Norton, hereafter cited in the text as "T" followed by Book, part, section, and paragraph number, and to Hume, *A Treatise of Human Nature*, ed. Selby-Bigge, rev. by Nidditch, cited in the text as "SBN" followed by the page number.

3 Baxter, "Identity, Continued Existence, and the External World."

4 Baxter, *Hume's Difficulty*, chs. 4, 6.

5 Bradley, *Appearance and Reality*, 19, 21.

6 Baxter, *Hume's Difficulty*, ch. 3.

WORKS CITED

Baxter, Donald L. M. *Hume's Difficulty: Time and Identity in the* Treatise. New York: Routledge, 2008.

Baxter, Donald L. M. "Identity, Continued Existence, and the External World." In *The Blackwell Guide to Hume's* Treatise, edited by Saul Traiger, 114–32. Oxford: Blackwell Publishing, 2006.

Bradley, F. H. *Appearance and Reality*, 2nd. ed. Oxford: Clarendon Press, 1897.

Hume, David. *A Treatise of Human Nature*. Edited by David Fate Norton and Mary J. Norton. Oxford: Clarendon Press, 2007.

Hume, David. *A Treatise of Human Nature*. Edited by L. A. Selby-Bigge, revised by P. H. Nidditch. Oxford: Clarendon Press, 1978.

Rocknak, Stephanie. *Imagined Causes: Hume's Conception of Objects*. Dordrecht: Springer, 2013.

Hume Studies
Volume 45, Number 1–2, 2019, pp. 59–68

What, in the World, Was Hume Thinking? Comments on Rocknak's *Imagined Causes*

DON GARRETT

Stefanie Rocknak's stimulating, challenging, and highly original new book, *Imagined Causes: Hume's Conception of Objects*, is helpfully summarized on its back cover as follows:

> This book provides the first comprehensive account of Hume's conception of objects in Book I of *A Treatise of Human Nature*. What, according to Hume, are objects? Ideas? Impressions? Mind-independent objects? All three? None of the above? Through a close textual analysis, Rocknak shows that Hume thought that objects are imagined ideas. But, she argues, he struggled with two accounts of how and when we imagine such ideas. On the one hand, Hume believes that we always and universally imagine that objects are the causes of our perceptions. On the other hand, he thought that we only imagine such causes when we reach a "philosophical" level of thought.

I will examine these two theses about Hume in turn: first, that he held that "objects are imagined ideas"; and second, that he "struggled with two accounts of how and when we imagine such ideas." In order to focus on these two theses, I will be forced to pass over without consideration a wealth of material on related topics that amply repays careful attention. My excuse is that, as Rocknak recognizes and as the back-cover summary goes on to proclaim, accepting even just these two central theses would involve fundamental alterations in our understanding of Hume's philosophy. I will argue that the truth of the two theses would carry major costs to the consistency of Hume's philosophy. I will also argue, however, that these are costs that we, and Hume, can avoid paying.

Don Garrett is Silver Professor of Philosophy, New York University, New York, NY 10003.
Email: don.garrett@nyu.edu

I. The First Thesis: Objects as Imagined Ideas

Rocknak's first thesis, that "objects are imagined ideas" for Hume, has three main terms: "objects," "ideas," and "imagine." In order to understand the thesis, therefore, we must first understand how she uses each of these terms.

Objects. Rocknak holds that Hume employs the term "objects" in (by my count) at least five senses in the *Treatise*, but the sense she employs in the first thesis is what she regards as Hume's dominant sense of the term.[1] This sense includes within its scope what he calls "bodies" (29, 75n) and carries the entailment that objects are the causes of our sense impressions (what Hume calls "impressions of sensation"). At the same time, however, this sense of the term does *not* carry any essential implication that objects have *mind-independent existence*—since on her view, Hume asserts that there are real bodies but does not "think that objects are mind-independent things; he is not a realist" (xiv).

Ideas. Rocknak grants that Hume uses the term "ideas" to designate mental particulars (xiv) that are either "copied" from impressions or composed of simpler ideas that are each "copied" from impressions (4, 10). She denies, however, that Hume holds "the replication theory" that, she reports, James Beattie, Lorne Falkenstein, and I attribute to him. This "replication theory," as she defines it, is the doctrine that "impressions and ideas must share the exact same [intrinsic] qualities (in differing degrees of vivacity)" (25). Thus, according to Rocknak, Humean ideas that are copied from visual impressions—unlike the visual impressions themselves—do not literally have such qualities as color (23, 65).

Imagine. To "imagine" something, in Hume's typical usage, is to form a non-memory idea *of* that thing,[2] often by combining simpler ideas. To "imagine an idea," in this sense, would thus be to form *an idea of an idea*—that is, to form a second-order idea of the kind that Hume mentions in the *Treatise*[3] (T 1.3.8.16; SBN 106) as making our thought *about* ideas possible. When Rocknak writes that objects are "imagined ideas," however, she does not mean that objects are ideas *of* ideas, but rather that objects simply *are* ideas constructed by a process of imagination—specifically, of what she calls the "transcendental imagination" (84). They are also imagined *as* being the causes of sense impressions.

Hence, in saying that "objects are imagined ideas" for Hume, Rocknak is interpreting him as claiming that bodies are in fact mental particulars—specifically, ideas that are composed of simpler ideas copied from impressions but lacking some or all of the intrinsic qualities of those impressions—and that these bodies are produced by an exercise of the faculty of imagination. The costs of this interpretation to the consistency of Hume's philosophy are high, in at least four different respects. First, largely because many of Hume's uses of the term "object" clearly cannot be understood in the stipulated preferred sense, Rocknak requires that he equivocate among multiple different and largely incompatible senses of the term, switching among them seemingly without warning. Second, if we combine Rocknak's interpretive claim that *all objects are ideas* with her further interpretive claim that *all objects are causes of sense impressions*, it seems we can infer that, for Hume, *all objects are ideas that cause sense impressions.* Yet as Hume defines his terms, any impressions that are (immediately) caused by ideas will not be impressions of sensation at all but rather "impressions of reflection" (T 1.1.2.1; SBN 7–8). Third, in denying that Hume accepts "the replication theory," Rocknak requires that Hume reject his own explicit statement that "impressions and ideas differ only in their strength and vivacity" (T 1.1.7.5; SBN 19)[4] and also that he undermine his own explanation of sympathy as transforming an idea into an impression simply by increasing its degree of vivacity (T 2.1.11.7–8; SBN 319–20). Finally, in holding that bodies are ideas *produced by the imagination* for Hume, she makes Humean bodies *causally dependent* on the mind for their existence, thus contradicting his own definition of "bodies" as things having not only [i] a "continu'd existence . . . even when they are not present to the senses" but also [ii] an existence "distinct from the mind and perception" that requires both [ii(a)] "*external* position as well as [ii(b)] the [causal] *independence* of their existence and operation" (T 1.4.2.2; SBN 188, emphasis in original).

Fortunately, I think, it is not necessary to pay these costs. First, as I read Hume, he does not use the term "object" in fundamentally different senses at all. Rather, he consistently uses it in the sense that the *Oxford English Dictionary* describes as "philosophical," traces back to 1651 (citing Hobbes), and defines as follows: "a thing [considered as] perceived, thought of, known, etc." Impressions, ideas, minds, and mind-independent (that is, "continu'd and distinct") bodies are *all* such "objects" for Hume, on my reading, although the context often limits what specific kinds of objects (for example "external objects") are under discussion in a particular passage. In accordance with this meaning, "the object of" a representational perception, whether that perception is an idea or an impression, is simply and consistently what that perception represents.[5] When Hume writes that the vulgar do not "distinguish betwixt the objects and perceptions of the senses" (T 1.4.2.31; SBN 202), he means that they do not draw a distinction between sense impressions themselves and the (mind-independent) things that the sense impressions represent and thereby allow us to perceive.

Second, it is not necessary to interpret Hume as holding, contrary to his definition of "impression of sensation," that *objects are ideas that cause sense impressions*. As just explained, he certainly holds that *some objects are ideas*, and also that *some ideas have bodies as their objects* (as is evident from the fact that we think about bodies). He also agrees that bodies are objects that cause sense impressions. It does not follow, however, and Hume nowhere implies, that any *bodies are themselves ideas*, or that any *ideas cause sense impressions*.

Third, it is not necessary to interpret Hume as rejecting the "replication theory." Rocknak postulates that Hume *must* reject it because the theory has two absurd entailments: (i) that a thought about an impression (such as one of *orange* or *sweet*) would either *be* that impression, or would *cause* that impression (26); and (ii) that merely thinking about a bodily event (such as *getting a sunburn* or *jumping off the Empire State Building*) would produce that bodily event and all of its consequences (such as *having a sunburn*, or *being dead in the morgue*), but "in a less vivacious way" (15). In fact, however, neither of these is an entailment of the replication theory at all, at least in the form in which I have attributed it to Hume.

Concerning the first proposed entailment—(i) above—Rocknak writes that "the most compromising passage for the replication theory" from the *Treatise* is this: "To give a child an idea of scarlet or orange, of sweet or bitter, I present the objects, or in other words, convey to him these impressions; but proceed not so absurdly, as to endeavor to produce the impressions by exciting the ideas" (T 1.1.1.8; SBN 5). She continues, "Thinking *about* an impression neither is, nor causes us to have an impression. Thus, ideas are qualitatively different from impressions" (26). But this is a *non sequitur*; there is no reason why an idea need bring with it the additional vivacity required to make it into an impression. One might equally well argue that, since having an impression *does* often "cause us to have" an idea of the impression, ideas are *not* qualitatively different from impressions. It is true that, for Hume, *thinking* with ideas is not, and generally does not lead to, the kind of *feeling* that characterizes the having of impressions. But this fact in no way violates the replication theory, since Hume explains this difference between thinking and feeling precisely as a difference of vivacity (liveliness), not as a difference in some other intrinsic quality.

Concerning the second proposed entailment—(ii) above—it is entirely compatible with the replication theory that ideas be used to represent things as having qualities (such as *being one mile long, being sunburnt,* or *falling from a building*) that the impression-resembling ideas themselves do not have. Furthermore, although having an idea of a bodily event may or may not lead to an idea of the bodily consequences of that event, the idea need not and—unless it happens to incite suitable passions and volitions—generally will not produce those bodily consequences themselves in any form.

Finally, it is not necessary to interpret Hume as holding that bodies are ideas or are produced by the imagination, in violation of his definition of bodies as having an existence that is causally independent of the mind. In defense of treating Humean bodies as ideas, Rocknak cites Hume's well-known paragraph of the *Treatise* distinguishing "two systems [of] reality": "the first . . . the object of the memory and senses; the second of the judgment" (T 1.3.9.3; SBN 107–108). As I interpret her, she treats the paragraph as providing a license to systematically *conflate* ideas of bodies with the bodies that are their objects (53–58). Such a reading might be plausible if we understood the paragraph as offering a reductive definition (in the style of Berkeley) of the "reality" of bodies themselves to the "reality" of the ideas *of* them, with the latter "reality" understood in turn as the ideas' having a certain vivacity and coherence with other ideas. In fact, however, the passage is not best read as a *metaphysically reductive definition* of the "reality" of bodies to features of ideas of them. Instead, it provides a *psychological explanation* of how the mind manages to attribute (either correctly or incorrectly) real existence *to* the distinct objects that certain ideas represent, which it is said to do as a result of certain features of the ideas *with which* we represent those objects. The reductive reading greatly exceeds, while the psychological reading perfectly suits, the modest needs of the context of the paragraph, which calls only for an explanation of why the associative relations of contiguity and resemblance do not lead to inference in the way that the associative relation of cause and effect does.[6]

II. The Second Thesis: Incompatible Accounts of Objects as Causes of Impressions

Rocknak's second thesis is that Hume's *Treatise* provides two different and incompatible accounts of how we first come to distinguish "objects"—in her primary sense of the term, which encompasses bodies within its scope—as the *causes* of our sense impressions. Unsurprisingly, one of these is simply Hume's familiar and often-discussed account, in the later paragraphs of the section "Of scepticism with regard to the senses," of the origin of the "philosophical system" of "double existence" as a reflective replacement for the earlier and more natural "vulgar" system that attributes "continu'd and distinct existence" to our impressions of sensation themselves (T 1.4.2.44–56; SBN 210–18). On this account, finding by means of a few simple experiments (such as pressing one's eyeball) that our sense impressions lack this kind of existence, yet unable to give up the previous belief that there *are* "continu'd and distinct existences," we come to conceive of—and believe in—a second set of objects as continued and distinct causes of these impressions.

The distinctive and surprising element of Rocknak's thesis is her claim that Hume provides *another* account of how we come "always and universally" to conceive of bodies as continued and distinct causes of our sense impressions that is prior to, and independent of, the mental operations that give rise first to the vulgar system and then (as a replacement) to the philosophical system of bodies. On this other Humean account, Rocknak asserts, the mind "always and universally" employs "transcendental imagination" to conceive, and "transcendental probable reasoning" to believe in, a "secret" and "transcendental" cause for a set of sense impressions and memories, a cause having a "perfect identity" that cannot be possessed by any mere impressions themselves. Rocknak finds this account to be expressed in three different places in the *Treatise*—first near the beginning of the section "Of probability; and of the idea of cause and effect" (T 1.3.2) and then twice in succession in relatively early portions of "Of scepticism with regard to the senses" (T 1.4.2). According to Rocknak, Hume regards philosophers' acceptance of the philosophical system as "mistaken" (181), but he regards the belief that results from the universal and transcendental process, which is not dependent on the vulgar system, as "justified" (240).[7]

The costs of this interpretation to the consistency of Hume's philosophy are high in at least three different respects. First, as Rocknak emphasizes, it requires Hume both to affirm and to deny that it is *only after and in response to* rejecting the vulgar system that we come to conceive of bodies as continued and distinct causes of our sense impressions. Because she finds both accounts of this belief expressed within the same section of the *Treatise*, moreover, it is particularly difficult to understand how Hume could have missed the conflict.[8] Second, it requires Hume to deny that impressions can have "perfect identity" even when they *satisfy* his definition of "perfect identity" as "invariable and uninterrupt'd existence through a supposed variation of time" (T 1.4.2.30, T 1.4.6.6; SBN 201, 253). Third, it requires Hume to postulate special "transcendental" forms of probable reasoning and causation that evidently do not involve or require *constant conjunction*, contrary to his explicit accounts of probable reasoning and causation.[9]

Fortunately, it is not necessary to pay these costs either, or so I judge. For as I read the *Treatise*, none of the three passages that Rocknak identifies constitutes an account of the conception of bodies as causes of sense impressions at all. In the interests of space, I will consider in detail only the first passage, commenting somewhat more briefly on the others. The first passage reads:

> There is nothing in any objects to perswade us, that they are either always *remote* or always *contiguous*; and when from experience and observation we discover, that their relation in this particular is invariable, we always conclude there is some secret *cause*, which separates or unites them. The same reasoning extends to *identity*. We readily suppose an object may continue individually the same, tho' several times absent from and present to the senses; and ascribe to it an identity, notwithstanding the interruption of the perception, whenever we conclude, that if we had kept our eye or hand constantly upon it, it wou'd have convey'd an invariable and uninterrupted perception. But this conclusion beyond the impressions of our senses can be founded only on the connexion of *cause and effect*; nor can we otherwise have any security, that the object is not chang'd upon us, however much the new object may resemble that which was formerly present to the senses. Whenever we discover such a perfect resemblance, we consider, whether it be common in that species of objects; whether possibly or probably any cause cou'd operate in producing the change and resemblance; and according as we determine concerning these causes and effects, we form our judgment concerning the identity of the object. (T 1.3.2.2; SBN 74; emphasis in original)

On Rocknak's interpretation, this passage constitutes a different, transcendental account of the belief in bodies as causes of sense impressions that are distinct from the impressions themselves. Her defense of this interpretation depends on three crucial claims about the terminology of the passage. These may be summarized as follows:

(i) By "contiguous," Hume is referring to the unity among the parts of a single complex thing, and by "remote" he means "distinct"—that is, "causally independent of perception" (95). Moreover, the phrase "invariable and uninterrupted" is "roughly interchangeable" with "continu'd and distinct" throughout the *Treatise* (131).[10]

(ii) By "species of objects," Hume means a set of resembling sense impressions and memories.

(iii) In his references to a "secret *cause*, which separates or unites" and to "identity," Hume is proposing that the mind "always" immediately responds to resembling sense impressions and memories by postulating an unperceived cause of the sense impressions and memories that has an invariable and uninterrupted existence. Furthermore, the mind makes this inference, on Hume's view, without reliance on experience of past constant conjunctions.

As I read the passage, however, none of these three interpretive claims is accurate. In context, Hume's purpose in the passage is to explain and vindicate his claim that *only reasoning based on the relation of cause and effect* can inform us about relations of either (a) *situation in time and place* or (b) *identity* that go beyond the information provided by our senses. Here, as everywhere else up to this point in the *Treatise*—and well beyond, until "Of scepticism with regard to the senses" (T 1.4.2)—Hume takes it entirely for granted that our senses inform us about the existence and relations of (continued and distinct) bodies; the psychological and epistemological bases for this assumption are discussed only later, in "Of scepticism with regard to the senses" itself.

Accordingly, my interpretive counter-proposals for the passage are as follows:

(i) In writing of "objects"—understood univocally, in the way I have indicated in section I—as being "contiguous" or "remote," Hume means their closeness or distance in space *to each other* (that is, their relative *situation*). His point is that we can *infer* that two objects *once* observed to be contiguous or (alternatively) remote from each other will *continue* to be so, even when unobserved, *only* if we have information about *causes of motion*. These relations of contiguity and remoteness between objects in space are entirely different from the non-relational invariableness (lack of qualitative change) and uninterruptedness (lack of a temporal gap in existence) that are required for *perfect identity*—which something may have whether it is spatially located or not, and whether it is perceived or not. Furthermore, the four characteristics just considered (contiguity, remoteness, invariableness, and uninterruptedness) are all different from the continuity (continued existence *while unperceived*) and distinctness (external position to and causal independence of the mind)—both of which are relations to the mind—that make something a "body" on either the vulgar or the philosophical view of the external world.

(ii) By "species of objects," Hume means *kinds* of objects—for example, books, or snowflakes. His point is that we can infer an *identity* between an object perceived at one time and a "perfectly resembling" object perceived at another time only on the basis of *causal* information about whether there has been a "change" or substitution of object between the two times. In judging about whether such a change has occurred—for example, in judging whether the book or snowflake I previously perceived has been replaced by another—it is highly relevant to know (on the basis of causal information) whether distinct members of that same kind of object (books, snowflakes) are often ("commonly") "perfectly resembling" with others of their kind or not.

(iii) When Hume writes of "some secret *cause*, which separates or unites" objects, he means only that when two objects are found always to be close or always to be distant in *spatial situation*, we infer that this continuing correlation in their motions has some cause (for example, glue or magnetism). In contrast, when Hume writes that

> we ascribe "an identity, notwithstanding the interruption of the perception, whenever we conclude, that if we had kept our eye or hand constantly upon it, it wou'd have convey'd an invariable and uninterrupted perception," he is simply explaining what it would have been to *perceive*, rather than to *infer*, the (perfect) identity of a single object over the period of time in question. While the capacity of that object to exist unperceived naturally presupposes that it has what he will later call a "continu'd and distinct existence," he is not here discussing or explaining that presupposition.

The second passage that Rocknak cites in defense of her thesis is Hume's discussion at T 1.4.2.20–23 (SBN 195–99) of the inference that arises "from the understanding, and from custom in an indirect and oblique manner" in response to what he calls the "coherence" of our sense impressions. As I read the passage, however, this "irregular kind of reasoning" (as he later calls it in T 1.4.5.20; SBN 242) does not lead to the belief in *causes* of sense impressions that are distinguished from the perceptions themselves. Rather, as its location in the text indicates, it is simply part—and a much lesser part, in comparison with the role played by what Hume calls the "constancy" of our sense impressions—of the mechanism by which the vulgar attribute continued and distinct existence to the bodies that they do *not* distinguish from their sense impressions.

Finally, the third passage that Rocknak cites is Hume's immediately following discussion, at T 1.4.2.26–30 (SBN 200–201), of "*invariableness and uninterruptedness*" as the "principle of individuation." Rocknak writes that having "the idea of perfect identity" requires "imagining an invariable, uninterrupted cause of a series of resembling but interrupted and changing . . . impressions and/or ideas that exactly represent impressions" (149). As I read the passage, however, it makes no mention of *imagining a cause* in order to conceive of perfect identity. Rather, an impression that does not change even while other perceptions do change fully satisfies the condition of invariableness and uninterruptedness required for perfect identity. Moreover, it is precisely the mind's tendency to mistake successions of impressions exhibiting mere interrupted "constancy" (as, for example, when one blinks) *for* such invariable and uninterrupted impressions that leads the vulgar, on Hume's account, to attribute a continued and distinct existence to their sense impressions. They do so, he explains, in order to preserve the supposed perfect identity when they subsequently become aware of the interruptions in their perception.

If I am reading Hume correctly, then, we are free to interpret him as offering only a single, consistent account of the origins of the belief in bodies that cause sense impressions; as granting perfect identity to all impressions that satisfy the definition of perfect identity (as invariableness and uninterruptedness); and as treating all probable reasoning and causal relations as requiring constant conjunction, just as he had previously required, without the need to postulate a transcendental imagination operating beyond the scope of the ordinary imagination. More generally, as I read Hume he is a mitigated skeptic but no idealist, of either a Berkeleian or proto-Kantian kind. If that seems like a cost, as it may to many, I hope the dividends in consistency are still worth the price. No matter how we balance that ledger, however, we owe Stefanie Rocknak a sincere debt of gratitude for her provocative, informative, and closely argued book. It unquestionably repays the investment of careful study with ample dividends.

NOTES

1 Following Marjorie Grene, "Objects of Hume's *Treatise*," the other senses recognized by Rocknak include: (i) a "phenomenalist sense," in which "objects are impressions"; (ii) an "intentional sense," in which "objects are the objects of thought"; and (iii) a "realist sense," in which "objects are mind-independent things" (76). Rocknak also claims to find a further "traditionally overlooked sense in which he uses the word 'objects.'" In this fourth sense, objects "are either impressions or are *ideas* that 'exactly represent' impressions"; ideas of this kind are either simple ideas or memories. Objects in this fourth sense, she goes on to call "proto-objects" (75).

2 For a few typical examples, see T 1.2.5.3, 1.3.9.18, 1.4.5.27, 2.2.3.9, 2.2.9.14, and 2.3.8.12; SBN 55, 117, 245, 351, 386, and 437.

3 References to the *Treatise* are to Hume, *A Treatise of Human Nature*, ed. Norton and Norton, hereafter cited in the text as "T" followed by Book, part, section, and paragraph number, and to Hume, *A Treatise of Human Nature*, ed. Selby-Bigge, rev. by Nidditch, cited in the text as "SBN" followed by the page number.

4 I leave aside as not directly relevant to the present question Hume's subsequent admission at the conclusion of his Appendix to the *Treatise* that "two ideas of the same object" may differ *from one another* in aspects other than "degrees of force and vivacity" (T App 22; SBN 637).

5 Hume states that passions do not represent, but he grants that impressions of sensation do (see Garrett, "Hume's Naturalistic Theory of Representation"). Because passions are impressions of reflection that do not represent, he is free to define "the object" of an "indirect passion" (such as pride, humility, love, or hatred) as the person or sensible creature to whom the passion "directs our view," as distinguished from the "quality" that is the "cause" of the passion (T 2.1.2.4 and T 2.2.1.2; SBN 278 and 329). Even in this technical usage, however, an "object" remains "a thing thought of."

6 It is also possible that Rocknak is motivated by an assumption that for Hume *only* mind-dependent perceptions can exist, or even be conceived to exist, so that bodies, if they are real at all, *must* either be impressions or ideas or some kind. While some of Hume's readers do still make this assumption, it depends on misinterpretations of the text (primarily of T 1.2.6.8–9, 1.4.2.56, and 1.4.5.15; SBN 67–68, 217–18, and 239) that cannot be discussed in detail here (but see Garrett, *Hume*, 97–105). Rocknak later indicates, however, that she regards Hume as agnostic about the existence of mind-independent objects (262), and agnosticism seems to allow their possibility and conceivability.

7 Rocknak defines "transcendental" as meaning both "presupposes ordinary experience" (120) and "presupposed by ordinary experience" (122). I assume that she intends the latter.

8 Rocknak does claim that Hume later became aware of the conflict, and that this helps to explain his dissatisfaction, expressed in the Appendix, with his account of personal identity.

9 Rocknak also allows that "transcendental imagination" violates the Copy Principle (152), although I am not certain whether she is required to do so.

10 Rocknak uses the qualifier "roughly" because there are complications with invariability that she finds difficult to accommodate. However, these do not affect the current analysis.

WORKS CITED

Garrett, Don. *Hume*. London and New York: Routledge, 2015.

Garrett, Don. "Hume's Naturalistic Theory of Representation." *Synthese* 152, no. 1 (2006): 301–19. https://doi.org/10.1007/s11229-006-9007-2

Grene, Marjorie. "The Objects of Hume's *Treatise*." *Hume Studies* 20, no. 2 (1994): 163–77.

Hume, David. *Treatise of Human Nature*. Edited by David Fate Norton and Mary J. Norton. Oxford: Clarendon Press, 2007.

Hume, David. *A Treatise of Human Nature*. Edited by L. A. Selby-Bigge, revised by P. H. Nidditch. Oxford: Clarendon Press, 1978.

Rocknak, Stefanie. *Imagined Causes: Hume's Conception of Objects*. Dordrecht and New York: Springer, 2013.

HUME STUDIES
Volume 45, Number 1–2, 2019, pp. 69–75

Transcendental Inquiry and the Belief in Body: Comments on Rocknak's *Imagined Causes*

JENNIFER S. MARUŠIĆ

The title of Stefanie Rocknak's book—*Imagined Causes: Hume's Conception of Objects*—neatly and concisely captures the book's central claim: Hume holds that thinking about objects is a matter of imagining the causes of our perceptions. Rocknak argues that in giving an account of how we think about objects, Hume is engaged in a transcendental project. My comments focus fairly narrowly on this central thesis, which unfortunately means that I have set aside a great deal of interesting material in the book, including Rocknak's provocative and challenging interpretations of Hume's views about the nature of mental representation, time, and justification. I propose to focus on three related issues: First, I consider the sense in which, on Rocknak's view, Hume is engaged in a kind of transcendental project, and raise some questions about how to understand Rocknak's view about this project. Second, I want to raise some questions about how to understand the claim that conceiving of objects, for Hume, is a matter of imagining causes. Finally, I will look more closely at some of the evidence that Rocknak appeals to in support of this interpretation, and suggest that the interpretation faces two challenges. I invite Rocknak to say more about these challenges in her reply.

Part 1: Humean Transcendental Psychology

I begin with a confession: When I first received Rocknak's book and flipped through it, one of the first things I noticed was the liberal use of the word "transcendental" in the table of contents. I wondered whether this was going to be a book about Hume in which Kant is the hero. As it

Jennifer S. Marušić is Senior Lecturer at the University of Edinburgh. She can be reached at 3 Charles Street, Edinburgh, EH8 9AD, UK and by email.
Email: jennifer.marusic@ed.ac.uk

turns out, it is not. The sort of transcendental project that Hume is engaged in, in Rocknak's view, turns out to be pretty far from anything that Kant would consider to be transcendental philosophy. When one looks at what Rocknak officially counts as transcendental inquiry, it does not turn out to be transcendental in any very controversial sense.

We can start by looking at what Rocknak says about her use of the word "transcendental." She writes,

> Some might be wary of an account that characterizes Hume as a naturalist who appeals to transcendental notions, however implicitly. For, to some, transcendental inquiry must occur independently of the natural sciences; we do not do empirical research to come up with conditions of possibility for thought. Rather, transcendental inquiry is, somehow, "pure" in the respect that it operates independently of the natural sciences. However, I do not think that this is necessarily the case. Rather, generally speaking, these two modes of inquiry may be very compatible, particularly if we think of "transcendental" as merely being a way to think of those psychological tendencies that most are born with; they are literally conditions of possibility for normal human thought. (*Imagined Causes*, 74)

Rocknak here suggests that transcendental inquiry is a way of thinking about the conditions for the possibility of normal human thought. Her view seems to be that what counts as "normal human thought" is an empirical question, to be settled experimentally. But reasoning about what must be the case in order for someone to engage in normal human thought is transcendental inquiry. Thus, she continues, "In its essence, transcendental reasoning is nothing other than 'backwards reasoning.' In order for, say, X to be the case, we conclude that Z must be the case" (*Imagined Causes*, 74). She claims that this is the sense in which she uses "transcendental" in the book.

However, there is still, I think, a question about how committed Rocknak is to the *modal* character of such transcendental inquiry. She describes it as backward reasoning about what *must* be the case in order for something else to be the case or reasoning about the *conditions for the possibility* of normal human thought. In this way, transcendental inquiry still seems to be *a priori*, and its conclusions would still seem to be necessary. However, I do not think that this is actually Rocknak's view: she seems to count as transcendental inquiry anything that explains how normal human reasoning is likely to have come about, or inquiry that tries to establish by "backward reasoning" what *is* the case, rather than what *must* be the case. For example, she cites several contemporary studies as evidence of the compatibility of transcendental and empirical inquiry; she writes, "after conducting a number of behavioral tests, scientists have hypothesized that the behavior of at least some dogs is best explained if we assume that they are, to some degree, 'rational' (Kaminski et al. 2004)" (*Imagined Causes*, 74). And she asks us to "consider those scientists who hypothesize 'instincts,' or 'natural propensities,' or 'hardwired' abilities to explain both human and non-human behavior" (*Imagined Causes*, 74). Positing or hypothesizing about the causal mechanisms that underlie observable behavior counts as transcendental inquiry, in this sense. In other words, Rocknak uses "transcendental inquiry" so broadly that any kind of abduction or inference to the best explanation counts as transcendental inquiry.

Taken in this sense, it seems to me right and even uncontroversial that Hume is engaging in transcendental inquiry in developing his science of human nature. The attempts to explain how we form beliefs about the unobserved, how we acquire the belief in body, our ability to think general thoughts, our ability to sympathize, and our ability to feel the indirect passions are all transcendental in this very undemanding sense. But they are not, it seems to me, transcendental in the stronger sense that they purport to show what *must* be the case for a creature to engage in normal human thought.

This, however, is where I start to worry somewhat about Rocknak's interpretation. It seems to me that her interpretation requires that we understand "transcendental" in a stronger sense. Rocknak claims that there is a transcendental imagination, she distinguishes between transcendental probable reasoning and three other forms of probable reasoning (natural, philosophical, and indirect), she distinguishes between transcendental belief and other forms of belief, and she claims that transcendental causation is a special and mysterious kind of causation, distinct from ordinary causation. Yet it is not clear to me whether, and if so why, all these things deserve the label "transcendental." It seems that, for example, the principles of association deserve to be called transcendental, too, at least in the sense that they are appealed to in an explanation of normal human thought. Rocknak seems to be committed, as we will see, to the view that transcendental probable reasoning, transcendental belief and the transcendental imagination are all "transcendental" in a stronger sense than her official view about what counts as "transcendental" implies.

Part 2: What is Transcendental Causation?

Here we need to turn more specifically to Rocknak's claim that, according to Hume, conceiving of objects is a matter of imagining the causes of our perceptions. Rocknak calls "proto-objects" impressions and those ideas that exactly represent impressions, most importantly memories. She argues that Hume's view is that when we have a series of perfectly resembling proto-objects, "we 'always' imagine that an idea of an object with perfect identity causes this [series]," and—she claims—that "this idea of an object is imagined to represent the properties of invariability and uninterruptedness" (*Imagined Causes*, 104).

Rocknak claims that our having an idea of the cause of a series of resembling perceptions involves a special kind of causal reasoning and a special kind of causation, which she calls transcendental causal reasoning and transcendental causation, respectively.

I want to raise a few questions about this part of Rocknak's interpretation. First, I think Rocknak is clearly right that Hume does not think that ordinary causal reasoning is responsible for our believing that there are bodies with a continued and distinct existence. That is clear from *Treatise* 1.4.2.[1] However, I am not totally convinced by Rocknak's claim that there is some other kind of *causal* reasoning and some other kind of causation that explains how we come to think of their being invariable and uninterrupted causes of our perceptions. It is not entirely clear to me whether Rocknak really needs to claim that this is both a special kind of causal reasoning and a special kind of causation. Coming to think that there is an invariable and uninterrupted cause of a series of resembling perceptions involves a kind of inference that goes beyond observed regularities; this is why Hume denies in *Treatise* 1.4.2 that (ordinary) causal reasoning explains the belief in bodies with continued existence. So, if this is a case of causal reasoning at all, then it does seem to be a distinct type of causal reasoning. But if I believe that there is an invariable and uninterrupted *cause* of some series of resembling perceptions, why must it also be thought of as a cause in some different or special sense? This is Rocknak's official view, because she describes it as a mysterious kind of causation.

The trouble is I am not sure what kind of causation it is supposed to be: why do I not just imagine a regular-old cause of my resembling perceptions? And if this really is supposed to be a special and mysterious kind of causation, I am not sure why it should be the case that what I am imagining is a *cause* of my perceptions and not something else. In short, if transcendental probable reasoning is a distinct kind of reasoning about a distinct kind of relation, transcendental causation, why should we think of it as causation or probable reasoning at all?

Part 3: The Priority of Transcendental Causal Reasoning and Belief

Rocknak claims that this special kind of reasoning is transcendental because she claims that Hume holds that it always occurs and because experience presupposes it. In this way, she argues that transcendental probable reasoning is prior to ordinary forms of probable reasoning. Moreover, transcendental belief seems to be prior to ordinary causal beliefs. And this is because ordinary causal reasoning depends on experience but experience presupposes transcendental causal reasoning. Rocknak claims, "this special 'kind of reasoning of causation' (T 1.4.2.19; SBN 195) appears to occur prior to the reasoning from causation that is based on 'common experience' (T 1.4.2.20; SBN 196)" (*Imagined Causes*, 115).

My worry about this, however, is that this argument for the priority of transcendental causal reasoning seems to equivocate on the word "experience." It seems clear that this mysterious kind of reasoning is distinct from ordinary causal reasoning, and it seems clear that the ability to think of bodies with a continued and distinct existence is a central and important part of ordinary human thought. So, this kind of reasoning is transcendental in Rocknak's official, undemanding sense. But one could equally claim that forming beliefs about the unobserved and beliefs about causal relations is a central and important part of ordinary human thought, and our ability to engage in ordinary causal reasoning, then, is transcendental in exactly the same sense. When Rocknak claims that ordinary causal reasoning depends upon experience (and so does not seem to be transcendental), "experience" here is used much more narrowly: ordinary causal reasoning depends on our having perceptions and these perceptions' exhibiting certain patterns, that is, certain types of perceptions are constantly conjoined. But what Rocknak calls transcendental causal reasoning equally depends on experience in this sense, since it depends on our having perceptions and these perceptions' exhibiting certain patterns, though in this case their being series of exactly resembling perceptions. So, both transcendental and ordinary causal reasoning depend on experience in this sense, and both are important to explaining ordinary human thought.

I think this is significant because it bears on Rocknak's claim that the transcendental causal reasoning that is responsible for our coming to imagine causes of our perceptions is distinct from the imaginative processes by which the vulgar come to believe in bodies, and also distinct from the reasoning that leads philosophers to believe in bodies that cause our perceptions. This is central to Rocknak's view, because she argues forcefully that the transcendental account she attributes to Hume is distinct from both the vulgar view and the philosophical view about bodies in *Treatise* 1.4.2. (Strictly speaking, Rocknak argues that there are two vulgar views, and both are distinct from the transcendental view, but I will set this aside for simplicity.)

Thus, Rocknak holds that the transcendental reasoning that leads us to imagine the causes of our perceptions is prior to ordinary causal reasoning, but also prior to the imaginative processes that give rise to the vulgar belief in body. And as a result, it is prior to (and distinct from) the philosophical belief in body, since the philosophical belief in body presupposes the vulgar belief. That the transcendental account is prior to and distinct from the vulgar and philosophical accounts is one of the central features of her interpretation.

I want to raise two problems facing this claim. One of them she recognizes and discusses at length in the book; the other she does not. The first problem, which she recognizes, is that Hume seems to hold that philosophers' coming to believe in bodies that cause perceptions depends on rejecting the vulgar view, but according to Rocknak's interpretation we always (transcendentally) conceive of bodies as the causes of our perceptions, prior to experience. Rocknak thinks that this is a serious problem for Hume and marks a serious rift in his thought. However, I worry that she underestimates the extent to which it is a serious problem for her interpretation. She argues that this is the problem that Hume has in mind when he has his second thoughts about personal identity. But it seems to me that the problem that she thinks Hume faces just would not arise without her interpretative claim that there is a transcendental account of our belief in body that is prior to, and distinct from, both the vulgar and philosophical views.

Moreover, it seems that the textual evidence for this distinct, transcendental account does not support the claim that this account is prior to the vulgar belief in body. One of the key pieces of textual evidence Rocknak cites in support of her view is *Treatise* 1.3.2.2. Here is the part of the passage that most strongly supports her view:

> 'Tis only causation, which produces such a connexion, as to give us assurance from the existence or action of one object, that 'twas follow'd or preceded by any other existence or action. . . . There is nothing in any objects to perswade us, that they are either always *remote* or always *contiguous*; and when from experience and observation we discover, that their relation in this particular is invariable, we always conclude there is some secret *cause*, which separates or unites them. The same reasoning extends to *identity*. We readily suppose an object may continue

> individually the same, tho' several times absent from and present to the senses; and ascribe to it an identity, notwithstanding the interruption of the perception, whenever we conclude, that if we had kept our eye or hand constantly upon it, it wou'd have convey'd an invariable and uninterrupted perception. But this conclusion beyond the impression of our senses can be founded only on the connexion of *cause and effect*. (T 1.3.2.2; SBN 74)

It does seem that Hume here claims that *causal reasoning* is responsible for our believing in the continued existence of an object despite interruptions in our perception. And it looks like this is in clear conflict with his claim in *Treatise* 1.4.2 that causal reasoning cannot explain how we come to believe in bodies with a continued and distinct existence. One way of avoiding the conflict would be to claim that the kind of belief that Hume is attempting to explain in this passage is distinct from the various kinds of belief in body that Hume attempts to explain at *Treatise* 1.4.2. Indeed, this is exactly what Rocknak argues, and she argues that the belief explained here is the transcendental belief in body that is prior to the vulgar and philosophical belief. However, I want to suggest that this gets things the wrong way around—Hume seems here to be describing a kind of causal reasoning that depends on our already having a belief in body, rather than explaining how we come to think of bodies in the first place. Thus, when Hume claims that "we conclude, that if we had kept our eye or hand constantly upon it, it wou'd have convey'd an invariable and uninterrupted perception," it seems that the belief that we acquire by causal reasoning presupposes that we already think of the object we are sensing as having a continued and distinct existence: this is the referent of "it." Indeed, Hume also seems to presuppose that we think of the object as distinct from our perception of it. The passage does not seem to me to support the priority claim.

The second problem for the claim that the transcendental belief in body is prior to the vulgar belief in body is one that Rocknak does not discuss. If Hume indeed held that we always imagine invariable and uninterrupted causes of our perceptions, and that this is prior to the vulgar belief in body, why would we need the vulgar belief? If there is this basic, transcendental belief in bodies, what is left for the vulgar account to explain? Moreover, if the transcendental belief involves imagining the causes of our perceptions, it seems that the transcendental belief requires that we distinguish between our perceptions and their causes. But this suggests that we ordinarily distinguish between bodies and our perceptions. It seems odd to me to think that we first distinguish between perceptions and their causes, and then when we come to have the vulgar belief in body we begin to conflate perceptions and bodies. Yet I think that Rocknak's interpretation commits Hume to exactly this. I want to conclude by asking Rocknak to say something more about why there should be a vulgar belief in body, assuming that there is a prior transcendental belief in body.

NOTES

1 References to the *Treatise* are to Hume, *A Treatise of Human Nature*, ed. Norton and Norton, hereafter cited in the text as "T" followed by Book, part, section, and paragraph number, and to Hume, *A Treatise of Human Nature*, ed. Selby-Bigge, rev. by Nidditch, cited in the text as "SBN" followed by the page number.

WORKS CITED

Hume, David. *A Treatise of Human Nature,* ed. L. A. Selby-Bigge and P. H. Nidditch, 2nd edn. Oxford: Clarendon Press, 1978.

Hume, David. *A Treatise of Human Nature,* ed. David Fate Norton and Mary J. Norton. Oxford: Oxford University Press, 2000.

Rocknak, Stefanie. *Imagined Causes: Hume's Conception of Objects*. New York: Springer, 2013.

HUME STUDIES
Volume 45, Number 1–2, 2019, pp. 77–93

Reply to My Critics

STEFANIE ROCKNAK

§1 Response to Baxter

First, let me note that I agree with one of Donald Baxter's opening claims, namely, that Hume often uses the word "object" to include perceptions. Indeed, my entire book is devoted to showing as much. In particular, I show that we must distinguish between three distinct ways in which Hume explains the psychological process whereby we conceptualize an object, or a body. In all three processes, it turns out that objects, or bodies, are perceptions. In particular, they are imagined ideas, and so, in no case, are they mind-independent things. These three processes are: the vulgar process, the philosophical process, and the Humean process.

Very briefly, we may distinguish these processes as follows: 1) The vulgar *imagine* that objects are identical to impressions. 2) The philosophers, in virtue of making a reasoned rejection of the vulgar position, *imagine* that objects are mind independent and are the causes of our perceptions. However, they are unaware that they are imagining objects. Instead, they think that reason, and reason alone, shows that objects exist as mind-independent entities. 3) Hume thinks that we always *imagine* that objects are the "invariable and uninterrupted" causes of our perceptions; this is a condition of possibility for almost all thought, including our ability to reason. In this very general respect, we may refer to this as a transcendental conception of objects.

However, unfortunately, in the course of his remarks, Baxter does not explicitly acknowledge these distinctions (that is, 1–3 above), both in regard to my reading of Hume, as well as in regard to his own interpretation. Doing so highlights a very significant disagreement between the two of us—in addition to our disagreement about "steadfast objects."

Steff Rocknak is Chair and Professor of Philosophy at Hartwick College, Oneonta, NY.
Email: rocknaks@hartwick.edu

For instance, on the second page of his remarks, after sketching my position regarding the Humean transcendental position on objects, Baxter writes: "I myself do not see how the vulgar could feel the pull of this question . . . in my view the idea that bodies cause impressions is much further downstream when the philosophers get into the picture" (Baxter, "Comments").[1] However, as noted above, I address at length in my book how the transcendental position is related to (and distinct from) both the vulgar and philosophical position. In particular, as far as the vulgar are concerned, they never consciously "feel the pull of this question." According to my reading, it would make sense to say that *none* of us, including the vulgar, "feel the pull" of this question—rather, almost unconsciously, imagining ideas of objects is something that we must all do, almost immediately it seems, in order to function at all. More specifically, to even think that impressions are identical to "objects" (as the vulgar do), we must first have some idea of what an "object" is such that we mistakenly identify "it" with impressions; in other words, we need what Bennett would call an "objectivity concept."[2]

With these general remarks in mind, let me now address some of the more specific claims that Baxter makes, beginning with Hume's notion of "reality."

§1.1 Reality

Baxter writes: "Rocknak takes [Hume's] first system of realities to consist of impressions and memories of impressions and takes the second system of realities to consist of transcendentally imagined causes of the first system" (Baxter, "Comments"). However, this is not quite what is going on in my book. Although I show that transcendentally imagined causes could not belong to the first system of reality, and so, must belong to the second system, my explanation of Hume's two systems of realities is meant to illustrate Hume's notion of *justification*. In particular, actual impressions, and memories of impressions are "real" and so, in Hume's sense of the word, are "justified." In this respect, everything in the first system of reality is justified.

Moreover, I point out at length in my book, that according to Hume, in the second system of reality, we do not necessarily use transcendental causal reasoning. Rather, we also seem to use what I call "indirect causal reasoning" as well as ordinary causation to conclude for example, that Rome exists (Rocknak, *Imagined Causes*, 57). In the former case, we can justify the "reality" of something that we have not had an impression of (for example, Rome) via the experience of a trustworthy source. As a result of understanding Hume's notion of justification, we can, ultimately, understand why some imagined causes are justified, and others are not, that is, why some are "real" and others are not. In particular, those imagined causes (that is, ideas that we imagine are invariable and uninterrupted objects) that are also imagined to cause a series of resembling impressions that we have actually had (or maybe that a trustworthy source has had) are *justified*. Meanwhile, other imagined causes are *not* justified, for instance, unicorns, substances, or primary qualities.

§1.2 *Treatise Passage 1.3.2.2*

Baxter, Garrett, and Marusic all make specific remarks about my reading of T 1.3.2.2 (SBN 73). For the sake of organization, I will address all of their objections in this section, and after doing so, return to addressing Baxter's remarks.

First, let us consider Baxter's objections. In regard to T 1.3.2.2 (SBN 73), Baxter suggests, contrary to my reading, that:

> [Hume] is in the process of arguing that only ordinary causation enables us to infer the existence of objects we are not currently sensing. When we have observed that things of one type are always accompanied by things of another type, and we have an impression something of the first type, we infer the existence of the second type that we are not currently sensing. (Baxter, "Comments")

However, I explicitly address this aspect of ordinary causation[3] and the possibility of applying this notion of causation to T 1.3.2.2 (SBN 73) at some length in my book (see for instance [Q5] in chapter 5 and also see chapter 2). Accordingly, I summarize some of my thoughts regarding ordinary causation and T 1.3.2.2 (SBN 73) below.

But before I do so, we must realize that in my book, I note that T 1.3.2.2 (SBN 73) is not the paradigmatic case for imagining what I call transcendental causes. Rather, I write: "The reader should note that this chapter merely serves as an introduction to Hume's theory of imagined causes and perfect identity, while chapters 6,7, and 8 provide us with more fully developed version" (Rocknak, *Imagined Causes*, 91).

With these caveats in mind let us now consider T 1.3.2.2 (SBN 73) in its entirety:

> All kinds of reasoning consist in nothing but a comparison, and a discovery of those relations, either constant or inconstant, which two or more objects bear to each other. This comparison we may make, either when both the objects are present to the senses, or when neither of them is present, or when only one. When both the objects are present to the senses along with the relation, we call this perception rather than reasoning; nor is there in this case any exercise of the thought, or any action, properly speaking, but a mere passive admission of the impressions through the organs of sensation. According to this way of thinking, we ought not to receive as reasoning any of the observations we may make concerning identity, and the relations of time and place; since in none of them the mind can go beyond what is immediately present to the senses, either to discover the real existence or the relations of objects. It is only causation, which produces such a connexion, as to give us assurance from the existence or action of one object, that it was followed or preceded by any other existence or action; nor can the other two relations be ever made use of in reasoning, except so far as they either affect or are affected by it. There is nothing in any objects to perswade us, that they are either always remote or always contiguous; and when from experience and observation we discover, that

> their relation in this particular is invariable, we, always conclude there is some secret cause, which separates or unites them. The same reasoning extends to identity. We readily suppose an object may continue individually the same, though several times absent from and present to the senses; and ascribe to it an identity, notwithstanding the interruption of the perception, whenever we conclude, that if we had kept our eye or hand constantly upon it, it would have conveyed an invariable and uninterrupted perception. But this conclusion beyond the impressions of our senses can be founded only on the connexion of cause and effect; nor can we otherwise have any security, that the object is not changed upon us, however much the new object may resemble that which was formerly present to the senses. Whenever we discover such a perfect resemblance, we consider, whether it be common in that species of objects; whether possibly or probably any cause cou'd operate in producing the change and resemblance; and according as we determine concerning these causes and effects, we form our judgment concerning the identity of the object. (T 1.3.2.2; SBN 73)

In particular, here Hume writes: "There is nothing in any objects to perswade us that they are always remote or contiguous" (T 1.3.2.2; SBN 73). Note that in my book, there is a typo in my citation of this passage that affected my reading. I mistakenly wrote "object" rather than "objects." Once I caught this typo (after the book went to press), I realized that it makes more sense to conclude that Hume is talking about at least *two* objects here, where they are remote and contiguous from *each other*. This is opposed to the interpretation I offer in my book, where I argue that an object is contiguous with itself (and thus, admits of a certain kind of unity) and is distinct from (remote from) our perception.

However, in no way does this amendment affect the deeper implications of my interpretation. For, Hume explains here, we must conclude that there is a "secret cause" that is responsible for any contiguity and remoteness that might hold between objects. Immediately afterwards, he writes: "*The same reasoning* extends to identity" (emphasis added). That is, and crucial to note, Hume is setting up an *analogy* here: Just as a "secret cause" is responsible for either the "remoteness" or "contiguity" between at least two objects, when we observe a "perfect resemblance" that obtains of "a species of objects" (let us refer to that species as "B"), we conclude that some unobserved (and thus, "secret") object (let us refer to this "object" as "A") caused that resemblance. This phenomenon—where we speculate that an unobserved object (A) causes, or is responsible for the resemblance that obtains between certain sets of resembling perceptions (B)—captures, I claim, the spirit of Hume's notion of identity.

However, if we interpret this passage as Baxter suggests, then the idea is that we may, using ordinary causal reasoning, infer the identity of an unobserved "object" (Y) from the existence of an observed "object" (X); that is, the existence of (X) causes us to believe in the existence/identity of (Y), primarily because we have *experienced* (X) and (Y) constantly conjoined. However, as I explain in my book, this could not be what Hume has in mind in T 1.3.2.2 (SBN 73) regarding identity (Rocknak, *Imagined Causes*, 101). For Hume explicitly tells us in T 1.3.2.2 (SBN 73) that we imagine a cause that we have *never* sensed (nor does it resemble anything we have ever sensed). In particular, it is "secret," and so it constitutes a conclusion that "lies beyond the impressions of our senses." In particular, we think that this analogous "secret cause" has the properties of invariability and uninterruptedness, properties that we know are *imagined* (thanks to all of T 1.4.2, but particularly T 1.4.2.24, 1.4.2.29–30, 1.4.6.6; SBN 199, 200–201, 253–55).

And thus, quite simply, we could never have had an impression of such a cause such that we have observed it constantly conjoined with anything else; again, this is precisely why it is "secret."

With this in mind, let me now respond to one of Jennifer Marusic's comments regarding my interpretation of T 1.3.2.2 (SBN 73). In particular, similar to Baxter, she asks why this passage does not pertain to a "regular old cause" (Marusic, "Comments"), as opposed to what I identify as a transcendental cause. But this question was answered just above: this passage does not pertain to a "regular old cause" because we never have an impression of the "secret cause" discussed in T 1.3.2.2 (SBN 73); nor do we have impressions of a similar kind of secret cause discussed in T 1.4.2.15–24, 1.4.2.25–30, 1.4.6 (SBN 194–99, 199–201, 251–63). I explain how and why this is the case in chapters 5, 6, 7 and 10 in my book.

Marusic also writes: "Hume seems here to be describing a kind of causal reasoning that depends on *our already having a belief in body*, rather than explaining how we come to think of bodies in the first place" (Marusic, "Comments", emphasis added). She cites the following line from T 1.3.2.2 (SBN 73) as evidence: "we conclude, that if we had kept our eye or hand constantly upon it, it wou'd have convey'd an invariable and uninterrupted perception."

However, I do not think that this is the case. In the immediately following sentence, Hume writes that we determine a "conclusion beyond the impressions of our senses." Moreover, it is a conclusion that "can be founded only on the connexion of cause and effect." That is, our notion of identity (that is, this "conclusion") which "lies beyond the senses," is a *product*, or a *result* that comes about *thanks* to this peculiar kind of causal reasoning. Thus, this causal reasoning could not presuppose our notion of identity. Rather, it *produces* our notion of identity such that we imagine that an object is invariable and uninterrupted. Moreover, if T 1.3.2.2 (SBN 73) presupposed our understanding of identity, we would have to wonder why Hume would present it as explanation *of* identity.

With this in mind, let us now consider Don Garrett's thoughts on T 1.3.2.2 (SBN 73). First, I need to stress that I do not think that Garrett is correct to underline what he takes to be the *difference* between contiguity and remoteness vs. uninterruptedness and invariability such that (as I read his interpretation) there is no analogy that holds between these pairs of properties regarding the role of "secret causes." And thus, when Garrett claims that a "secret cause" only pertains to spatial relations, that is, to contiguity and remoteness, I think that he is overlooking Hume's claim that "*the same reasoning extends to identity*;" that is, Garrett is overlooking the clear analogy that Hume is setting up here.

Garrett also offers a competing interpretation of what Hume means by "species of objects" in T 1.3.2.2 (SBN 73). In particular, Garrett explains that each resembling member of the species would belong to a "kind." For example, a snowflake would be a kind of object that manifested itself in resembling particulars. Accordingly, Garrett's reasoning seems to be, if I perceive a snowflake at time T1, and then another similar snowflake (or the same snowflake again)[4] at time T2, then I know that they both belong to the same kind.

However, it seems to me that this presupposes that we already know that particular things, for instance, snowflakes, are things, that is, have an identity, such that they belong to a "kind." Moreover, it seems fairly clear that Hume is attempting to explain how we come to understand the identity of *particular* things in this passage, not general things, that is, "kinds." Note, however, that in my book, I argue that Hume's account of particular things is related to his account of general things (that is, abstract ideas). For when we (justifiably) imagine a cause, we select a member of the species of resembling objects, and imagine that is the invariable and uninterrupted cause of the set. In virtue of doing so, a particular member effectively "calls to mind" the rest of the set (or most of it) (see Rocknak, *Imagined Causes*, 148–49, 227–28).

Relatedly, Garrett claims in regard to T 1.3.2.2 (SBN 73) that "here as everywhere else up to this point in the *Treatise* (until 1.4.2) Hume takes it for granted that our senses inform us about the existence and relations of (continued and distinct) bodies" (Garrett, "Comments"). However, I would need to see the textual evidence that is necessary to substantiate this interpretation. Also, I find it odd that Hume would assume that the senses legitimately provide us with a concept of objects/identity and then completely overturn this account in T 1.4.2.4–11 (SBN 191–92) where he writes: "We may therefore, conclude with certainty, that the opinion of a continu'd and of a distinct existence *never* arises from the senses" (T 1.4.2.11; SBN 192 emphasis added). And of course, Hume also rejects the notion that the senses provide us with a concept of identity/objects when discussing the vulgar (T 1.4.2.31–43; SBN 201–209). Thus, if Garrett is correct that T 1.3.2.2 (SBN 73) presupposes that our notion of an object/identity is provided by the senses, then Hume must be contradicting himself in T 1.4.2.11 (SBN 192) and in T 1.4.2.31–43 (SBN 201–209). Or, somehow, Hume just changed his mind in these later passages. Either way, this shift in Hume's thought would have to be accounted for by Garrett.

Finally, Garrett asserts in regard to my interpretation of T 1.3.2.2 (SBN 73) that continuity and distinctness are relations to the mind, while invariableness and uninterruptedness are non-relational features that may be possessed by either perceptions or bodies (Garrett, "Comments"). However, I think that this claim is problematic in three respects: a.) There is at least one other instance (in addition to, I claim, T 1.3.2.2 (SBN 73)) where Hume uses these pairs of terms somewhat interchangeably, that is, T 1.4.2.33–36 (SBN 203–205). B.) Garrett seems to suggest that impressions can be invariable and uninterrupted, that is, "steadfast" in the Baxterian sense (which I disagree with; see below). C.) Garrett suggests that according to Hume, there are invariable and uninterrupted mind-independent bodies. Garrett seems to believe that Hume was a realist in regard to bodies. Indeed, b.) and c.) might constitute the most important points of disagreement between myself and Garrett.

§ 1.3 Constancy and Coherence

Let us now return to Baxter's comments, particularly, his comments on the relations of constancy and coherence. First however, it will be helpful to sketch the basic structure of T 1.4.2.

In the opening passages—T 1.4.2.1–14 (SBN 187–93)—Hume explains why neither the senses nor reason "produces the opinion" (T 1.4.2.2; SBN 187–88) of continued and distinct existences. Rather "that opinion must be entirely owed to the imagination" (T 1.4.2.14; SBN 193). Immediately following, that is, in T 1.4.2.15–24 (SBN 194–99), he discusses how this is possible—this is the "constancy and coherence" section. Immediately following this, to better explain the role that constancy plays (and how it invokes the vulgar position), Hume launches into his four-part system. Part 1 consists of a discussion of his *principium individuationis* (T 1.4.2.26–30; SBN 200–201). In Part 2, he dismisses what, I argue comprises Version I of the vulgar position (T 1.4.2.31–36; SBN 201–205), while Part 3 consists of an explanation of Version II of the vulgar position (T 1.4.2.36–40; SBN 205–208).[5] Meanwhile, Part 4 consists of a discussion of why we might believe in Version II of the vulgar position (T 1.4.2.41–42; SBN 208–209). Immediately following this, he discusses the philosophical position (T 1.4.2.43–57; SBN 208–209), where we come up with ideas thanks to the imagination AND reason; he also makes some skeptical remarks here.

However, as noted in my opening remarks, I do not think that Baxter effectively distinguishes the vulgar position from Hume's position. In particular, I argue that in the initial passages of his discussion of constancy and coherence, Hume seems to mistakenly suggest that we can imagine impressions. I say "mistakenly" because Hume makes it fairly clear in T 1.1.3 that we do not imagine impressions—we only imagine ideas. Indeed, if we *could* imagine impressions, Hume's distinction between memory and imagination would be significantly compromised. For recall that according to Hume, anything we remember must retain the order in which it was perceived, while this is not the case with the imagination. Moreover, imagined ideas, for the most part, are less vivid than ideas that are based on impressions.

However, if we could imagine impressions and then remember them, it seems we could not, on this account, effectively distinguish between the memory and the imagination. For instance, I could *imagine* an impression of a unicorn dancing on my lawn, and then remember that impression. Because this remembered idea is, technically, based on an (imagined) impression, it would seem to be as vivid as most ideas based on impressions, and thus, it would be as credible, or as "real" as most ideas based on impressions. This would clearly have a significant effect on Hume's conception of reality. And thus, it just makes more sense to conclude that Hume is being rather careless on T 1.4.2.15–16 (SBN 194).

However, to suggest otherwise, and to support his case that Hume *does* think we can imagine impressions, Baxter cites T 1.4.2.37ff (SBN 205–206). However, in this passage, Hume is pretending to speak as the vulgar would—in other words, he is clearly articulating the vulgar position, not his own. And thus, we would be hard pressed to say that this passage can be used to support any passage where Hume is *not* speaking from a vulgar point of view—as he is in the constancy and coherence section of 1.4.2. Moreover, even when in a vulgar frame of mind, we do *not*, according to Hume, imagine impressions. Rather, we imagine ideas; I explain why this the case at length in my book in chapter 8.

§ 1.4 Steadfast Objects

According to Baxter, a "steadfast object" is "a single thing coexisting with a succession of things" (Baxter, "Comments"). In brief, this amounts to claiming that according to Hume, we may perceive invariable and uninterrupted impressions. In response to my criticism of his interpretation (Rocknak, *Imagined Causes*, 125–38), Baxter begins by claiming that I use the Humean terms "'constant,' 'uninterrupted,' invariable,' 'continued,' and 'steadfast' interchangeably" (Baxter, "Comments"). Relatedly, he argues that a.) I am mistaken to identify "constant" with "invariable." Rather, "constant" means "the exact resemblance of impressions in an uninterrupted succession" (Baxter, "Comments"). B.) However, Baxter explains, such a succession cannot be identified with a Baxterian "steadfast object" because on T 1.2.3.8, Hume explains that the former can produce an idea of time while the latter cannot.

In response to a.), realize that I claim that only in *some* cases may the term "constant" be used interchangeably with the term "invariable." Indeed, I explain that in some cases, "constant" means just what Baxter thinks it means. Note: "Level 1 perceptions are, indeed, 'constant' in the respect that they occur in a succession where each perception in the succession exactly *resembles* each other. As such, these perceptions do *not* appear to change, although they are interrupted" (Rocknak, *Imagined Causes*, 134).

However, in other cases, contrary to Baxter's reading, I do argue that "constant" seems to mean invariable. In some cases, this pertains to the way that we perceive, that is, constantly perceiving seems to mean invariably perceiving (as is the case, I argue, in T 1.3.2.2 (SBN 73); note: "if we had kept our eye constantly upon it, it would have conveyed an invariable and uninterrupted perception"), and in other cases, it pertains to the perception itself, that is, a constant perception seems to be an invariable perception (see T 1.1.5.2, 1.4.2.22–23; SBN 14, 198–99; and Rocknak, *Imagined Causes*, 134, and chapters 5 and 6).

Thus, Baxter should have addressed my interpretation of *these* passages to effectively make his case that "constant" never means "invariable." However, recall Baxter's objection b.) above. He claims that something that is "constant"—what he interprets to always be a succession of exactly resembling ideas—cannot be identified with a "steadfast" object. This is the case because according to T 1.2.3.8 (SBN 35–36), the former can produce an idea of time, while the latter cannot. Note however, that on page 137 of my book, I explicitly address T 1.2.3.8 (SBN 35–36), and in *agreement* with Baxter, I explain that the term "unchangeable" (which I argue, also seems to mean "steadfast") could not pertain to a succession of resembling impressions here, that is, something that is "constant." In still other words, in *agreement* with Baxter, I argue that "steadfast" or "unchangeable" could not mean "constant" here. Rather, "unchangeable" (that is, "steadfast") seems to pertain to what I call an imagined cause. In particular, I write:

> However, there is at least one instance where, in regard to "steadfast" or unchangeable objects, Hume does not seem to be making a distinction between successions of changeable perceptions v. successions of unchangeable perceptions (the latter being what I believe is a correct interpretation of "steadfast objects"). He writes: "Now as time is compos'd of parts, that are not co-existent; an unchangeable object, since it produces none but co-existent impressions, produces none that can give us the idea of time" (T 1.2.3.8; SBN 35–36). Given what we have seen thus far in this book, we know that if Hume is speaking of an invariable and uninterrupted object that seems to "produce" certain impressions here, he must have an imagined idea of an object in mind. Thus, here, he seems to be speaking of an imagined cause of our perceptions, which, as such, may seem to cause or "produce" co-existent impressions. For instance, if I imagine that an invariable and uninterrupted chair is causing my impressions of a chair, these impressions would seem to occur simultaneously, as I look at what at what I perceive to be the object "the chair." However, such a set of perceptions cannot, Hume tells us, inspire the idea of time; they do not change. Our imagined idea of the invariable and uninterrupted chair does not seem to change, and thus, the impressions that are allegedly caused by it do not seem to change either. As a result, Hume concludes: "consequently [the idea of time] must be deri'vd from a succession of changeable objects." (Rocknak, *Imagined Causes*, 138)

Thus, Baxter should have noted that I do address T 1.2.3.8 (SBN 35–36), and then explained why my interpretation of "unchangeable" (that is, "steadfast") is incorrect here.

Baxter then objects that contrary to my reading Hume, the term "steadfast" is also not interchangeable with the term "continued." Baxter's argument is, as I understand it: "continued" means that an object continues to exist even we are not perceiving it. In other words, continuity applies to those times we are *not* perceiving an object. However, Baxter claims, an object can be "steadfast" when we *are* perceiving it, and yet *not* continue when we are not perceiving it.

However, to make his case, Baxter once again cites Hume's explanation of the *vulgar* conception of objects, and so, I think, confuses matters. Moreover, as noted above, I explain at length in my book that even in the vulgar case, our perceptions are ultimately interrupted, despite how "steadfast" or invariable they may initially seem. In brief, this is the case regardless if we (while in a vulgar state of mind) "fix our gaze," that is, stare in one direction for a prolonged period of time. For in this case, although, our perceptions might *seem* to be invariable, ultimately, they are not. Or, as I explain in my book:

> In particular, according to Hume, when in a vulgar state of mind, we may grasp perfect identity only as the ultimate result of trying to uninterruptedly observe what we take to be an object. This occurs when "we fix our thought on any object" (T 1.4.2.33; SBN 203). For instance, we might just stare at a violet for some length of time without looking away. As a result, our impression of the violet, is, it seems, virtually invariable and uninterrupted. But just "fixing our thought" does

> not quite give us an idea of perfect identity. For although it would seem to follow that any impression or corresponding idea that we have of the violet while we are "fix[ing] our thought on it," is invariable and uninterrupted, this is not the case (at least initially). Rather, Hume claims, simply due to the successive nature of all our impressions (despite how much we fix our thought), a certain discreteness obtains of the impression we "fix our thought" on and the idea have of it. This occurs as we proceed from "one moment to another" (T 1.4.2.33; SBN 203), although this procession (succession) is "scarce felt" (T 1.4.2.33; SBN 203). . . . Or, as Hume puts it immediately after the passage cited above: "The faculties of the mind repose themselves in a manner, and take no more exercise, than what is necessary to continue that idea, of which we were formerly possest, and which [as such, thanks to these faculties] subsists without variation or interruption" (T 1.4.2.33; SBN 203; emphasis added). This means that the "faculties" of the mind, i.e., the imagination processing the idea at hand, 14 "continue[s]" that idea, e.g., the violet. Thus, contrary to Baxter (2008, p. 32), we (particularly, the vulgar) do not have an uninterrupted impression, and thus, this passage does not support Baxter's notion of a "steadfast" object. (Rocknak, *Imagined Causes*, 165–67)

Thus, to effectively make his case, Baxter should have, I think, addressed this passage from my book.

In regard to T 1.4.6.2 (SBN 251–52), Baxter objects that Hume is not claiming that we do not have perceptions that are both invariable and uninterrupted; rather, he is claiming that we do not have an impression of the self that "continue[s] invariably the same, thro' the course of our lives; since self is uppose'd to exist after that manner" (T 1.4.6.2; SBN 251–52). Moreover, Baxter continues, when Hume claims here that "They are the successive perceptions only that constitute the mind" (T 1.4.6.4; SBN 252–53), this is not inconsistent with his notion of steadfast objects. Rather, an invariable and uninterrupted object that is not a succession may be a *part* of a succession: "Being steadfast is being a single thing coexisting with a succession. It is certainly not being a single thing that exists for all eternity in a succession" (Baxter, "Comments").

I do not think though, that this is what is going on in T 1.4.6.2 (SBN 251–52), and I explicitly anticipate and address part of this objection on page 132 of my book. Here, Hume is claiming that *all* perceptions are interrupted and variable. As a result, we could not, in principle, ever have an impression of the self that is uninterrupted and invariable, *regardless* if it is a part of a succession or not. I think that Hume makes this rather clear when he writes: "there is *no* impression constant and invariable" (T 1.4.6.2; SBN 251–52; emphasis added), Indeed, as a result of this fact, Hume claims that it cannot "be from any of these impressions, or from any other that the idea of [an invariable and uninterrupted] self is deriv'd" (T 1.4.6.4; SBN 252–53). Rather, in no uncertain terms, Hume claims that we must *imagine* the idea of the self—an idea of the self that is invariable and uninterrupted, that is, admits of a perfect identity; see at least the following passages to substantiate this reading: T 1.4.6.2, 1.4.6.5, 1.4.6.6, T 1.4.6.7, 1.4.6.8, 1.4.6.11, 1.4.6.15, 1.4.6.16, 1.4.6.18, and T 1.4.6.22 (SBN 251–63).

In short then, as explained in my book, *contra* Baxter, we do not have a sense perception (impression) of an invariable and uninterrupted self because none of our sense perceptions (impressions) are invariable and uninterrupted, even when in a vulgar state of mind.

Baxter also addresses T 2.1.4.2 (SBN 283), where Hume writes: "'Tis impossible for the mind to fix itself steadily upon one idea for any considerable amount of time." Baxter explains that this passage "must be put in contrast" with a passage from Book 1, namely, "Hume's discussion of a "man 'strongly occupy'd with one thought." (T 1.2.3.7; SBN 35). The latter passage leads Baxter to conclude that it is possible, according to Hume, to have an invariable and uninterrupted sense perception, namely, one that occurs as result of "fixing" or "occupy[ing]" ourselves with one thought. He once again cites T 1.4.2.33 (SBN 203) as evidence for this.

In response, I must say, a.) As explained above, in T 1.4.2.33 (SBN 35), Hume is discussing the *vulgar* position, not his own position on objects, and b.) even still, here Hume does *not* think that we have a sense perception of an invariable and uninterrupted object; rather it is imagined, as noted above and as explained at length in my book. Finally, c.) Baxter does not address the passages that I cite to present clear evidence that according to Hume, we never have an impression of an invariable and uninterrupted "object," regardless if that "object" is the self or not—T 1.2.3.11, 1.2.5.28–29, 1.4.2.3–11, 1.4.2.15–22, 1.4.2.27–29, 1.4.2.32–35 (SBN 37, 64–65, 188–92, 194–98, 200–201, 202–204), as well as numerous passages from T 1.4.6, cited above.

Thus, in short, I think to effectively address my position, Baxter should have 1.) shown why Hume does not distinguish between the vulgar position and his own position; 2.) shown why my explanation of the vulgar case where we seem to perceive and uninterrupted and invariable perception T 1.4.2.33; SBN 203 but do *not*, is wrong, and finally, 3.) shown why the numerous passages I have cited above do not significantly compromise the claim that according to Hume, we perceive invariable and uninterrupted impressions.

§2 Response to Garrett

Garrett divides his remarks into two sections. In the first, he sketches four "costs" that we must pay if we accept my claim that according to Hume, objects are imagined ideas. In the second section, he addresses what he takes to be an additional cost—the idea that according to my interpretation, Hume offers incompatible accounts of objects as the causes of impressions.

§2.1 The Four Costs

As Garrett sees it, if we accept my reading, we must pay the following 4 costs: [1] Hume equivocates between "five different and largely incompatible senses of the term 'object,' switching among them seemingly without warning" (Garrett, "Comments"). [2] "if we combine Rocknak's interpretive claim that *all objects are ideas* with her further interpretive claim that *all objects are causes of sense impressions*, it seems we can infer that, for Hume, *all objects are ideas that cause sense impressions*" (Garrett, "Comments"). And thus, Garrett immediately concludes: "Yet as Hume defines his terms, any impressions that are (immediately) caused by ideas will not be impressions of sensation at all but rather 'impressions of reflection.' (T 1.1.2.1; SBN 7–8)" (ibid.). [3] Hume contradicts himself about the way in which an idea may represent an impression. [4] Bodies, or objects, are causally dependent on the mind, but this contradicts what Hume says about bodies/objects on T 1.4.2.2 (SBN 187–88).

Let me address these costs in order:

[1] *Objects as Imagined Ideas*: In my book, I do, indeed, argue that Hume uses the word "object" in multiple ways, and sometimes he does switch between them without warning. For Hume, on occasion, uses the word "object" in I) what we might call a "phenomenonalist" sense, where objects are impressions; this is the way in which the vulgar attempt to think of objects. II) The intentional sense, where objects are the "objects of thought." As such, this kind of object includes impressions, ideas, and mind-independent things, because they all can be the objects of our thoughts/ perception/ knowledge.[6] III) The realist reading, where the term "object" simply means a mind-independent thing. IV) Objects are imagined causes of our perceptions. V) Objects can also be understood as what I call "proto-objects." These are the impressions and/or the ideas that exactly represent impressions (and so, are not imagined); to some degree, this characterization overlaps with the phenomenalist sense of objects.

However, although Hume does, I argue, switch between these terms, this does not mean that he has presented us with an entirely inconsistent system in the *Treatise*. Rather, it is just very complicated, and it is our job to sort through that complexity as best we can. In my book, I provide extensive evidence for each sense in which Hume uses the term "object." Thus, to reject my taxonomy, we would need to carefully consider that evidence, which Garrett does not do here.

[2] Crucial to note, I never argue in my book that according to Hume "all objects are causes of sense impressions" (Garrett, "Comments"), and nor do I claim, or infer, that according to Hume, "all objects are ideas that cause impressions" (ibid.). Rather, I take pains to explain throughout my book that we *imagine* that our ideas of *some* objects (namely, those with a perfect identity) cause sense impressions. And thus, the title of my book: *Imagined Causes*. Accordingly, at no point do I argue, or infer, that ideas *actually* and immediately cause impressions that are not impressions of reflection. I am afraid that this is simply a misreading on Garrett's part.

[3] *Representation*. In my book, I argue that in Book 1 of the *Treatise*, Hume did not think that what contemporary scholars refer to as the "Copy Principle" means that ideas are *identical* to impressions in all respects except for how "vivacious" they are. For, according to this reading, an idea of red square would literally be red, and would literally be square. Similarly, the idea of the smell of a rose, would, literally, smell. I argue that saying as much would put Hume in a rather difficult position. It would mean, for instance, that thinking about say, sitting in the sun, could literally entail getting a sunburn, although a less vivacious one. Similarly, thinking about jumping off the Empire State building would entail dying, but

somehow, in a less vivacious way. Garrett's response, as I understand it, is as follows: in these cases, I conflate the bodily *effects* of impressions (for example, a sunburn and dying) with the qualities of the impressions. Ideas, for example, the ideas of say, sitting in the sun or jumping off the Empire State Building, he argues, may or may not incur the same *effects* that impressions do, for example, respectively, sunburns and dying.

However, there may be an issue with my examples here. Rather than saying "sitting in the sun," I could have used the examples of "getting a sunburn" and "experiencing significant bodily harm." In these cases, on Garrett's account, if I remember these impressions, I should re-experience all of their qualities, but in a less vivacious way, which entails their bodily effects, since these impressions *constitute* bodily effects; they *are* the impressions of effects. Thus, I should experience a less-vivacious sunburn, and less-vivacious bodily harm (which could put me in the hospital, nevertheless). Similarly, in my book, I also use the example of the impression of getting warm, which Garrett does not mention in his remarks. For if I remember the impression of getting warm, I should, on Garrett's account, literally get warm (although in a less vivacious way). And thus, realistically, no one would freeze to death, they need only recall those times they sat by a fire, and so on.

Moreover, Garrett cites the following line from my book: "Thinking *about* an impression neither is, nor causes us to have an impression. Thus, ideas are qualitatively different from impressions" (Rocknak, *Imagined Causes*, 26). Garrett responds: "But this is a *non sequitur*; there is no reason why an idea need bring with it the additional vivacity required to make it into an impression. One might equally well argue that, since having an impression does often "cause us to have" an idea of the impression, ideas are not qualitatively different from impressions" (Garrett, "Comments").

True enough. I am not however, trying to say that in every instance, if (X) causes (Y), then (X) is not qualitatively distinct from (Y). Rather, the point is Hume's. Recall the passage that inspired this discussion: "To give a child an idea of scarlet or orange, of sweet or bitter, I present the objects, or in other words, convey him these impressions; but proceed not so absurdly, as to endeavor to produce the impressions by exiting the ideas" (T 1.1.1.8; SBN 5). In other words, according to Hume, it is "absurd" to say that an idea of say, sweetness, will "produce," that is, cause us to have a sweet sensation, or an impression of sweetness. This suggests that having an idea of sweetness is *not the same as having an impression* (an actual sensation) of sweetness, even if that is a "less-vivacious" impression/sensation. Rather, an idea *represents* an impression without *being* an impression. In other words, an idea is not an impression, less vivacious or not. Thus, it seems, generally speaking, that impressions are qualitatively distinct from ideas.

[4] Garrett claims that "Hume does indeed regularly claim that bodies cause sense impressions, but nowhere does he claim that bodies are also *ideas* or are *produced by the imagination*" (Garrett, "Comments"). Indeed, as I explain at length in my book, Hume does occasionally speak as if he is a realist, where mind-independent "bodies" seem to cause sense impressions, but in every instance where he does so, these remarks must be understood in context. As a result of doing so, we see that they do not necessarily commit Hume to a realist

position. In particular, not only do these remarks need to be understood in regard to their immediate textual context, they must be understood in juxtaposition to claims like: "[impressions of sensation] arise in the soul originally, from unknown causes" (T 1.1.3.1; SBN 8–9). That is, according to Hume, we do *not* know if impressions are caused by bodies. And "[t]he only existences, of which we are certain, are *perceptions*, which being immediately present to us by consciousness, command our strongest assent and are the first foundations of all our conclusions" (T 1.4.2.47; SBN 212, emphasis added). That is, we *don't know* if "bodies" exist; but we can be certain that our perceptions exist.

Moreover, and most importantly, as I point out at length in my book, Hume repeatedly claims that our *ideas* of bodies or objects are necessarily *imagined*, regardless if we are in a vulgar, philosophical, or what I call, a transcendental state of mind. This is evidenced, in particular, by at least the following passages: T 1.4.2.14, 1.3.2.2, 1.4.2.22, 1.4.2.29, 1.4.2.32–34, 1.4.2.36, 1.4.2.47–52, 1.4.2.40, and almost all of T 1.4.6 (SBN 193, 73, 198, 200–201, 202–204, 205, 207, 212–16).

And thus, when Garrett writes, "As far as I can judge, Rocknak is led to treat Humean bodies as ideas by a well-known paragraph about "two systems [of] reality" (Garrett, "Comments")," this is surely not the case. Rather, as explained at length in my book, I conclude that Hume thought that we imagine ideas of objects, or bodies, through careful consideration of the passages noted above, *in addition to* consideration of Hume's notion of the two systems of reality. In particular, the following chapters are devoted to these passages: 5, 6, 7, 8, 9, 10 and 11.

§2.2 Incompatible Accounts of Objects as Causes of Impressions

In this section, Garrett addresses in more detail the three portions of text in the *Treatise* that, I argue, support my interpretation for a transcendental account of objects. With this in mind, let me address Garrett's three broader concerns.

First, he objects that according to my interpretation, there is a conflict between the transcendental account and the philosophical account—for on the one hand, we always imagine causes, and on the other hand, we only do so in virtue of a reasoned rejection of the vulgar. And this conflict, according to Garrett, is a "cost."

I argue that this is, indeed, a conflict. In particular, in my book, I argue that the conflict between the transcendental conception of objects vs. the philosophical conception of objects manifests itself in T 1.4.6, where Hume discusses personal identity, that is, the imagined object, "the self." However, this should not come as a surprise. Recall that Hume explicitly acknowledges that his account of the "self" is flawed in the Appendix, and so, if it can be shown that this flaw occurs as a result of a conflict between the transcendental concept of the object the "self" vs. the philosophical account, then it is entirely plausible to conclude that this conflict pervades all of Book 1—cost or no cost.

However, there is another, very general way to look at this conflict, which makes it seem less problematic for Hume, and so, to some degree, addresses Garrett's (as well as Marusic's) suggestion that this tension is just too significant to accept: in order to conceive of objects at all (that is, generate "objectivity concepts"), we must, very early on, imagine that there are continuous and distinct (or uninterrupted and invariable) causes of our impressions. From there, we naturally proceed to (mistakenly) imagine, *qua* the vulgar position, that objects are impressions (while all the while retaining our legitimate objectivity concepts, such that we can even make this mistake). Following, we reject the vulgar position, and become "philosophers" where, using reason, we come to believe that objects are mind-independent causes. However, *all the while,* our notion of an "object" is being informed by our initial transcendental conception of objects such that we can conceptualize the fact that the vulgar have the wrong notion of an "object." And thus, there is no substantive conflict. However, I do not push for this reading in my book, although I think I could have, and perhaps should have.

Second, Garrett objects that "[my reading] requires Hume to deny that persisting impressions can have "perfect identity" even when they satisfy his definition of "perfect identity" as "invariable and uniterrupt'd existence though a supposed variation of time" (T 1.4.2.30, 1.4.6.6; SBN 201, 253–55)" (Garrett, "Comments"). Here, Garrett seems to be referring to a Baxterian "steadfast object" with an appeal to the vulgar account of objects, and the section on personal identity, to support his claim. But as noted earlier, I think that Baxter's notion of "steadfast objects" is very problematic, and so, I think that Garrett's objection is likewise problematic.

Third, Garrett claims that "[my reading] requires Hume to postulate special "transcendental" forms of probable reasoning and causation that evidently do not involve or require constant conjunction, contrary to his explicit accounts of probable reasoning and causation" (Garrett, "Comments"). Yes, this is true, and I acknowledge as much in my book. This is why this is a special kind of causation, as noted by Hume. However, although this complicates our reading of Hume, I do not think, as noted earlier, that complication necessarily warrants skepticism.

Finally, let me respond to one of Garrett's more specific remarks about the three portions of the text to which I appeal to make my case. In regard to T 1.4.2.26–30 (SBN 200–201), Garrett writes: "As I read the passage . . . it makes no mention of *imagining a cause* in order to conceive of perfect identity" (Garrett, "Comments"). However, as explained at length in my book, on T 1.4.2.29 (SBN 200–201), Hume tells us that his account of identity here is *analogous* to his conception of time (and thus, he writes, we must "have recourse to it.") And so, I write in my book:

> To get around the fact that unity and number appear to be disparate concepts, we must, Hume asserts, conclude that the idea of identity is imagined, analogous to how we think of time in terms of objects [1.4.2.29]. In this respect, an "unchangeable" object somehow "participates" (emphasis added) in "the changes of co-existent objects;" in particular, in our changing "perceptions." Thus, to properly understand this analogy, we must pause to recover Hume's thoughts on time in 1.2.5, "The same subject continu'd." (Rocknak, *Imagined Causes,* 125)

Thus, in my book, I explain at length how time may be understood as an imagined cause, where I examine, in particular, T 1.2.5.29 (SBN 65) (where Hume discusses objects observed at five o'clock and six o'clock). Here is where we see the evidence for imagined causes that Garrett claims is lacking in T 1.4.2.26–30 (SBN 200–201).

§3 Response to Marusic

In the course of responding to Baxter and to Garrett, I have addressed almost all of Marusic's major concerns, but let me end by addressing some important questions she raises about my use of "transcendental." In particular, she suggests that it might be too liberal, and so, it would seem to incorporate all of the psychological machinery that Hume employs in the *Treatise*, for example, all of our natural tendencies to associate perceptions in a certain way, including ordinary causation, and so on.

However, this is not quite the case. Rather, there seems to be a hierarchy of psychological abilities at play for Hume, that is, some abilities must be employed before others. In particular, according to Hume, as I see it, we must be able to imagine ideas of objects (that is, come up with "objectivity concepts") before we can engage in what he refers to as "common experience" (T 1.4.2.20; SBN 195–97), where "common experience" seems to involve experiencing a world of "objects." In the course of such experience, we become conditioned to causally associate certain "objects" with other "objects;" obviously we could not do so if we did not have any idea of what an "object" is. This suggests that our notion of an "object" is privileged, or in other words, "common experience" presupposes it.

However, as pointed out in my book, it is not entirely clear if Hume's notion of natural causation (which recall, is merely a habituated reflex that does not involve reflection) presupposes our notion of an "object." For the textual evidence suggests that we may become conditioned to associate perceptions without necessarily imagining that these perceptions are either distinct from ourselves, or "continue" when we are not perceiving them. Nor must we necessarily think of them as being invariable and uninterrupted (although it seems we should be able to conceive of them as being distinct from each other, but we need not tackle this difficulty here). And thus, it seems that the natural relation of causation is "transcendental" in the general respect that I have used the term in my book; perhaps Hume could have argued that we become conditioned to think in a natural "causal" way first, such that we may then have a notion of cause which we can employ in our transcendental notion of identity, that is, a "secret *cause*." However, I do not think that is necessarily problematic for my interpretation or for Hume, although I think that Marusic is correct to ask these questions.

NOTES

1 Note that Jennifer Marušić has a similar objection in her remarks, which may be addressed in the course of responding to Baxter.

2 Bennett, Locke, Berkeley and Hume, 324.

3 For our purposes, "ordinary causation" is that which is based on habituation, where we have actually experienced (X) (the "cause") and (Y) (the "effect") as constantly conjoined. In cases of *natural* ordinary causation, we will, upon experiencing (X), reflexively *imagine* (Y), but realize that we imagine (Y) based on our experience of similar (Y) impressions that we have had in the past.

4 I am not entirely sure what Garrett has in mind here, that is, if we are experiencing similar particular snowflakes, or the same snowflake multiple times.

5 See Rocknak, *Imagined Causes*, 159–78, as well as Rocknak, "The Vulgar Conception of Objects" and "Constancy and Coherence in 1.4.2 of Hume's *Treatise*."

6 To some degree, this seems to be the way in which Garrett occasionally interprets a Humean object, in light of the *Oxford English Dictionary* definition that Garrett attributes to Hume in his comments, that is, an object is "a thing [considered as] perceived, thought of, known, etc." (Garrett, "Comments").

WORKS CITED

Bennett, J. *Locke, Berkeley and Hume: Central Themes*. Oxford: Oxford University Press, 1971.

Hume, David. *A Treatise of Human Nature*. Edited by L. A. Selby-Bigge, revised by P. H. Nidditch. Oxford: Clarendon Press, 1978.

Hume, David. *A Treatise of Human Nature*. Edited by David Fate Norton and Mary J. Norton. Oxford: Oxford University Press, 2002.

Rocknak, S. "Constancy and Coherence in 1.4.2 of Hume's *Treatise*: The Root of 'Indirect' Causation and Hume's Position on Objects." *The European Legacy* 4 (2013): 444–56. https://doi.org/10.1080/10848770.2013.791462

Rocknak, S. *Imagined Causes: Hume's Conception of Objects*. Dordrecht: Springer, 2013.

Rocknak, S. "The Vulgar Conception of Objects in 'Of skepticism with regard to the senses.'" *Hume Studies* 33, no. 1 (2007): 67–90. https://doi.org/10.1353/hms.2011.0209

Hume Studies
Volume 45, Number 1–2, 2019, pp. 95–99

Précis of *Hume's True Scepticism*

DONALD C. AINSLIE

In *Hume's True Scepticism* (hereafter "HTS"), I offer a new interpretation of David Hume's epistemology and philosophy of mind as presented in *A Treatise of Human Nature*.[1] I approach this task by developing what I take to be the first comprehensive[2] investigation of Part 4 of Book 1. The arguments Hume offers there have frequently been addressed by the secondary literature in a piecemeal fashion, especially his account of personal identity and of our belief in the external world. But I argue in HTS that they should be read as a sustained investigation of the human temptation to form philosophical systems. Consider its title: "Of the sceptical and other *systems of philosophy*" (emphasis added). Hume, I suggest, is interested both in defending his own preferred approach to what he calls the "science of human nature" (T Intro.9, 1.1.1.12, 1.2.5.19, 1.3.8.2; SBN xviii, 7, 60, 98), and explaining how the mind's structures lead other philosophers to succumb to certain characteristic errors. The outcome is a "true" scepticism (T 1.4.7.14; SBN 273) in which we acknowledge that philosophical beliefs about the mind are not fundamentally different in kind from vulgar beliefs about the world: both depend on the associative tendencies built in to human nature and thus do not equip us to penetrate into how things are independently of our cognitive capacities—their "real nature and operations" (T 1.2.5.25–26; SBN 63–64). It follows that there is no "obligation" to philosophize (T 1.4.7.10; SBN 270), and it is domesticated into an activity that should be pursued only by those with an inclination for it (T 1.4.7.12; SBN 270–71).

A central theme in HTS is the role of reflection in philosophy and in everyday life. I suggest that Hume holds that, in everyday life, the "vulgar"—all of us most of the time (T 1.4.2.36; SBN 205)—are fully engaged by our reasoning and sensing. Thus we are not normally aware of the mental mechanisms that Hume details throughout the *Treatise*, nor are we even aware of the perceptions that he takes to be the vehicles for our mental lives. Rather, we typically

Donald C. Ainslie, Department of Philosophy, c/o University College, University of Toronto, 15 King's College Circle, Toronto, ON M5S 3H7, Canada.
Email: donald.ainslie@utoronto.ca

remain focused solely on that which our reasonings and sensings concern. In calculating a tip at a restaurant, for example, our thoughts concern only the bill. In going about our business in the world, we take ourselves to be moving in the same world of tables and chairs and trees as everyone else. In chapter 2, I argue that even this 'taking' is something we are not normally aware of. Instead, we carry along a mostly unarticulated and unrecognized assumption that we are in touch with the world.

I spend a fair amount of time in chapters 2 and 3 showing how Hume understands the mind to produce this assumption. I argue that a proper interpretation of the relevant material (especially T 1.2 and 1.4.2) requires that we see his empiricist theory of representation as being much more flexible than it is often taken to be, where the so-called copy principle—the requirement that every simple idea be derived from a prior simple impression—is treated dogmatically, as if Hume himself does not immediately qualify it, first, with the "missing shade of blue" (T 1.1.1.10; SBN 5–6), and shortly thereafter with his account of general ideas (T 1.1.7; SBN 17–25). In the latter, Hume argues that we are able to think of universals, despite never having impressions of them, because the imagination associates ideas of particular members of the kind in an appropriately structured manner when accompanied by a linguistic token. I take the linguistic dimension of Hume's account to be especially significant, in that it brings in a normative and social dimension (T 3.2.2.10; SBN 490) to his otherwise narrowly naturalistic and individualistic treatment of the mind. I argue that, for Hume, this set of associative and linguistic structures serves a *constitutive* role, enabling a thought to be of a *kind*, not by means of any single perception that represents it, but by the dynamics of the mind as regularized by language.

Hume characterizes fictions by saying that "[i]deas always represent the objects or impressions, from which they are deriv'd, and can never without a *fiction* represent or be apply'd to any other" (T 1.2.3.11; SBN 37; emphasis added). Insofar as a general idea represents a universal without being derived from it, it satisfies this characterization. Thus, I think we can appeal to something similar to the treatment of general ideas in understanding core fictions in Hume's account: the idea of the vacuum (T 1.2.5.1–27; SBN 53–64), of object persistence (T 1.2.5.28–29; SBN 64–65), and ultimately of external objects themselves (T 1.4.2.23–43; SBN 198–210). In particular, no sensory impression represents such an object on its own (it presents either an array of coloured and tangible points [T 1.2.3], or non-spatial imagistic content [T 1.4.5.7–16; SBN 234–40]). I take the core account in "Of scepticism with regard to the senses" (T 1.4.2; hereafter "SwS") to show that the dynamics of the imagination as regularized by language enable impressions that are constant or coherent to represent the public world of objects around us. Indeed, this public world is in part constituted by our collectively having organized our experience in that fashion.

Though I take Hume to hold that, most of time, we are fully immersed in the perceptual processes that produce our mental lives, he allows that we can also step back from and reflect on them, both in everyday life and as a vehicle for philosophy. I spend a significant chunk of Chapter 4 (especially in §4.3) investigating how Hume accounts for our capacity to observe the mind. This issue is surprisingly neglected in Hume scholarship, but I argue that he relies on the association of "secondary" ideas—ideas that are of "primary" impressions and ideas (T 1.1.1.11; SBN 6)—to produce beliefs that are analogous to those investigated in SwS, in this case the belief in the continued existence of perceptions in the mind even when we are not introspectively observing them, and the belief that they exist distinctly from our introspective observation of them (HTS 130–31). Philosophers are thus, for Hume, *vulgar with respect to the mind*, a point which plays an essential role in my interpretation of his scepticism, in that it leaves the epistemic credentials of introspective philosophical verdicts no better or worse than those of vulgar sensory verdicts.

Hume's consideration of scepticism is, as the name of the Part suggests, the dominant issue in T 1.4, and I discuss it in three chapters (chapters 1, 4, and 7). My strategy is to excavate the parallels between his scepticism with regard to reason (T 1.4.1; SBN 180–87) and with regard to the senses (T 1.4.2; SBN 187-218). In each case, we reflect on our minds, *reasoning* about the reliability of our reasoning, or introspectively *observing* the imagistic perceptions that purport to portray the world. In each case, there seems to be a sense in which we should give up on the verdicts we are examining. Hume famously says that we go on believing nonetheless (T 1.4.1.7, 1.4.2.50, 1.4.7.10; SBN 183, 214, 269). I argue that Hume emphasizes the resilience of our rational and sensory verdicts because he needs empirical evidence in favour of his model of the mind, where it is nothing but a bundle of related perceptions, without a superintending subject that decides whether to accept what our reasoning and sensing suggest. Sometimes he defends this model merely by "enter[ing] most intimately into" himself and reporting what he finds (T 1.4.6.3; SBN 252). But no doubt he knows that others claim to find something quite different when they introspect. Thus, I think that one point he is making in emphasizing our immunity to sceptical challenges is that, if we did need to make a *decision* to accept what reason and the senses tell us, we could be "total" (T 1.4.1.7; SBN 183) or "extravagant" (T 1.4.2.50, 1.4.4.6; SBN 214, 228) sceptics. Our incapacity to reach these negative conclusions is evidence that the mind is not so structured. We are not as such *required* to decide what to believe.

Nonetheless, we *can* reflect. We can ask whether we calculated the tip correctly, or whether the puddle that seems to be on the highway is an illusion. Normally we resolve these questions by reconsidering the evidence—recalculating or looking again. The sceptical challenges depend on maintaining the reflective posture, either by iterating our recalculations or persisting in our introspective observation of the mind. Why would we do this? I suggest that Hume's answer is that it is *philosophy* that pushes us into this special kind of reflection, one that is not satisfied until it can show that the verdict we are tempted by is how things *really* are (HTS §§1.4, 4.6, 7.5). There is nothing wrong with this endeavour. It is just that nothing requires it of us either. Some of us pursue it nonetheless because it "mixes itself with some propensity" (T 1.4.7.11; SBN 270) we happen to have. We find these kinds of abstruse investigations a "point of pleasure;" "this is the origin of . . . philosophy" (T 1.4.7.12; SBN 271).

The problem is that, as we persist in these reflections, we start to lose the very things we were investigating. I call this the problem of *reflective interference* (HTS 37–38, 146–47, 240). Because reason and introspection depend on the same principles of association as those the sceptical challenges use to attack reason and the senses, these principles start to break down. Both the challenges and the faculties they attack are undermined, leaving us merely with massive confusion of the kind exemplified in the climax of the "Conclusion of this book": "Where am I, or what? . . . I . . . begin to fancy myself in the most deplorable condition imaginable, inviron'd with the deepest darkness, and utterly depriv'd of the use of every member and faculty" (T 1.4.7.8; SBN 269). We are thus to learn that philosophy cannot accomplish some of the tasks it sets itself because of its tendency to get in the way of itself. In escaping from the sceptical crisis by playing backgammon or dining with friends (T 1.4.7.9; SBN 269), Hume shows, however, that philosophy's incapacity to answer some of its most fundamental questions is a problem *for philosophy*, not for everyday life. Because we do not *need* a verdict on the ultimate warrant for our reasoning or sensing, we can go on reasoning and sensing as well as we ever did (or even better, thanks to Hume's excavation of rules for causal reasoning in T 1.3.15).

In chapters 5 and 6, I discuss Hume's "examination [of] some general systems both ancient and modern, which have been propos'd" of the "external and internal world" (T 1.4.2.57; SBN 218) in Sections 3 through 6 of Book 1, Part 4 of the *Treatise*. These systems count as forms of what he calls "false" philosophy (T 1.4.3.9; see also 1.3.14.27, 1.4.7.13; SBN 223, 168, 272). The ancient philosophers search for a deep foundation for our beliefs, one that would ground them in something radically mind-independent, such as fundamental *substances* that would underlie the world (T 1.4.3; SBN 219–25) or the mind (T 1.4.5; SBN 232–51). It might seem that Hume here ascribes to them a task that, on his own view, should not even be *thinkable*. Not having impressions of a deep foundation for sensible qualities or perceptions, we should not be able to have an idea of such a thing. But I argue that his brief invocation of our capacity to use "relative" ideas to conceive of something "specifically different" from our human ways of thinking (T 1.2.6.9; SBN 68; HTS §3.3.2) allows him to characterize what the ancients seek. He and they can *negatively* recognize that there are human limits to cognition through a denial of all that human nature contributes to our conception of the world. The problem is that the ancients also want to give a *positive* characterization of what they take to be the deep structure of things. Hume, I argue, thinks that any such attempt must end in failure if it tries to say more than that the world absolutely independently of our perspective is how it would appear if *per impossibile* we removed our ways of thinking from our conception of it. The ancients go wrong by trying to describe how things are from the outside of the human perspective, while—inevitably—staying within it.

The modern philosophers make a different mistake. I have noted that, for Hume, philosophers are vulgar with respect to the mind. Just as the vulgar take themselves to get the world right without giving our perceptual access to it any mind, the moderns take themselves to get the mind right without giving our introspective access to it any mind. Thus, they think that our beliefs about the external world are problematic, in need of a categorization in terms of those sensations that are accurate (those of primary qualities) and those that give us mere appearances (those of secondary qualities) (T 1.4.4; SBN 225–31). They also think that we have a special intimate knowledge of our minds that guarantees our grasp of its simplicity and identity (T 1.4.6.1; SBN 251). In fact, our beliefs about our minds are no better or worse than the vulgar's beliefs about the world.[3]

NOTES

1 References to the *Treatise* are to Hume, *A Treatise of Human Nature,* ed. Norton and Norton, hereafter cited in the text as "T" followed by Book, part, section, and paragraph number, and to *Hume, A Treatise of Human Nature*, ed. Selby-Bigge and Nidditch, cited in the text as "SBN" followed by the page number.

2 Robert Fogelin's *Hume's Skeptical Crisis* focuses on the same texts, but does not aim to present a fully detailed analysis (see HTS ix–x, 8).

3 The final chapter of HTS addresses Hume's second thoughts about personal identity in the "Appendix" to the *Treatise,* where I argue that his initial treatment in "Of personal identity" (T 1.4.6) cannot account for the belief in the unity of the reflecting mind with the mind being reflected upon. He originally explained the belief in the simplicity and identity of the mind on the basis of the association of secondary ideas of introspectively observed primary perceptions (T 1.4.6.14, App. 20; SBN 258, 635). There is not a problem so long as the secondary ideas remain invisible to the one having them—as is normally the case for philosophers who, being vulgar with respect to the mind, are not normally thinking of the secondary ideas that afford them their introspective beliefs. But, as a true sceptic who understands his irremediable vulgarity in his philosophy and in everyday life, Hume comes to believe that there are *unobserved* secondary ideas being associated in the mind without any explanation of why we believe *them* to be in the same mind as those perceptions they represent.

WORKS CITED

Ainslie, Donald C. *Hume's True Scepticism.* New York: Oxford University Press, 2015.

Fogelin, Robert. *Hume's Skeptical Crisis: A Textual Study.* New York: Oxford University Press, 2009.

Hume, David. *A Treatise of Human Nature.* Edited by L. A. Selby-Bigge and P. H. Nidditch. Oxford: Clarendon Press, 1978.

Hume, David. *A Treatise of Human Nature.* Edited by David Fate Norton and Mary J. Norton. Oxford: Clarendon Press, 2000.

Hume Studies
Volume 45, Number 1–2, 2019, pp. 101–108

Comments on Ainslie's *Hume's True Scepticism*

ANNEMARIE BUTLER

Donald C. Ainslie's Hume's True Scepticism (hereafter "HTS") is a wonderful book—clearly written and forcefully argued—and was deservedly honored with Journal of the History of Philosophy's Book Prize for 2016. The focus of the book is part four of the first Book of Hume's Treatise, "Of the sceptical and other systems of philosophy." Ainslie develops an interpretation that takes seriously Hume's psychological claims, using them to solve puzzles in Hume scholarship, including the extent of Hume's scepticism, the nature of his sceptical crisis, and the basis for his second thoughts on personal identity.

I would encourage Ainslie to go further in tracing Hume's psychological explanations. In what follows, I will discuss three areas: the role of language in the formation of the "vulgar" (or non-philosophical) belief in body; Hume's analysis of continued existence; and the nature of secondary ideas.

1. The Role of Language in the Vulgar Belief

Hume explicitly credits the "great philosopher" Berkeley (T 1.1.7.1n4; SBN 17n1) for his rejection of abstract general ideas and his theory of general ideas. "[A]ll general ideas are nothing but particular ones, annex'd to a certain term, which gives them a more extensive signification, and makes them recal upon occasion other individuals, which are similar to them" (T 1.1.7.1; SBN 17).[1] Ainslie describes Hume's account of general ideas as "a model for the later fictions Hume develops" (HTS 67), particularly noting the use of a word or term to facilitate thought.

Ainslie reconstructs Hume's explanation of the "vulgar" belief in objects in Treatise 1.4.2. The "vulgar" includes anyone who is not engaged in philosophical reflection (T 1.4.2.38, 53;

Annemarie Butler is Associate Professor of Philosophy at Iowa State University. 437 Catt, 2224 Osborn Dr., Ames IA 50011-4009.
Email: butlera@iastate.edu

SBN 206, 216), including non-human animals. (Hume describes animal causal inferences about objects in Treatise 1.3.16.) According to Hume, the "vulgar" do not distinguish between objects and perceptions; we think the hat or stone is the very thing we sense (T 1.4.2.31; SBN 202).

Ainslie holds that there is a "linguistic element" that scholars overlook in Hume's account of the vulgar belief in objects. According to Ainslie, language serves a normative role, distinguishing between good and bad judgments about whether something is the same object or not. Ainslie offers a developmental story (HTS 94–97), in which one develops beliefs in object-identity and linguistic skills together. The associations that a child or adult makes are modified in response to linguistic prompts from other people in his or her social group. Not only would it take more argument to establish that language can perform the task Ainslie thinks Hume assigns to it, the interpretation is textually underdetermined. As Ainslie admits, there is not much evidence in Treatise 1.4.2 to support this interpretation (HTS 92, 96–97); instead, he points to Treatise 1.4.3 ("Of the antient philosophy") and Treatise 1.4.6 ("Of personal identity"). In Treatise 1.4.2, I would argue, Hume is more interested in the fundamental questions of how we can conceive and believe in continued and distinct existence at all. That is, given the starting point of impressions and ideas, how can I conceive (and believe) that one and the same object that I believe to exist now also existed and operated at earlier times when I did not observe it? On my interpretation, this automatic, vulgar belief in objects is common both to humans and non-human animals, and is therefore pre-linguistic.

2. Continued Existence

In Treatise 1.4.2, Hume aims to explain the causes of belief in body (T 1.4.2.1; SBN 187); to this end, he searches for the experiential origins of the idea of externality. He distinguishes two features of external existence: continued existence and distinct existence (T 1.4.2.2; SBN 188). According to Hume, continued existence involves belief that the same objects exist "even when they are not present to the senses" (ibid.). Distinct existence includes existence and operation independent of the perceiving mind. Hume adds, "Under this last head I comprehend their situation as well as relations, their external position as well as the independence of their existence and operation" (ibid.). According to Hume (and for reasons he does not explain well) continued existence entails distinct existence and vice versa (ibid.), and belief in continued existence produces belief in distinct existence and vice versa (T 1.4.2.23, 44; SBN 199, 210).

After arguing that continued and distinct existence are not given features of sensory impressions (T 1.4.2.3–13; SBN 188–93) and are not the conclusions of reasoning (T 1.4.2.14; SBN 193), Hume concludes that belief in continued and distinct existence is produced by imaginative processes (T 1.4.2.15; SBN 194). His explanation begins from the initial situation of the mind: the only things I am directly aware of are impressions and ideas, and they last only as long as they are perceived. Hume offers two psychological accounts of how non-philosophers come to attribute continued existence to the very things they perceive: an inference from constancy (qualitatively indistinguishable perceptions repeated at different times, T 1.4.2.18–19,

23–43; SBN 194–95, 198–210) and an inference from coherence (T 1.4.2.19–23, 42; SBN 195–99, 208–209). Hume devotes more space to explaining the inference from constancy.

Hume divides his explanation into four parts. The first part is Hume's principle of individuation (T 1.4.2.26; SBN 200).[2] An identical thing is "invariable" and "uninterrupted" "thro' a suppos'd variation of time" (T 1.4.2.30; SBN 201). Two perceptions are "invariable" if and only if their qualities are "perfectly resembling" (T 1.4.2.42: 208; cf. T 1.4.2.18, 24; SBN 194–95, 199). Two constant perceptions are "interrupted" if and only if there is one or more moment between them when there is not a related perception—in the case of the belief produced by constancy, the relevant relation is perfect resemblance. The second and third parts explain the psychological processes by which the imagination identifies perfectly resembling, but interrupted, perceptions, and then invents and attributes continued existence to the resembling perceptions in order to maintain the identity ascription in the face of interrupted experience. In the fourth part, Hume applies his account of belief to explain how the fictive idea of continued existence is enlivened.

My criticism here applies mainly to Ainslie's interpretations of parts two and three. Like the interpretation offered by Stefanie Rocknak, Ainslie thinks that, in the second and third parts, Hume describes two different (stable) beliefs.[3] Let's consider an illustration. Suppose that, over a long period of time, I have had many perfectly resembling mountain-impressions, with other impressions and ideas mixed in between (books, fires, mail, and so on). In this sequence of impressions, the many mountain-impressions (not just today, but over many observations) exhibit what Hume calls "constancy," because they are "invariable" or perfectly resembling. The current mountain-impression is automatically associated with memories of other mountain-impressions, on account of their perfect resemblance. Attending only to mountain-impressions and mountain-memories, my imagination feels an "easy transition" from thinking of one perception to the next (T 1.4.2.34, 35; SBN 204). This "uninterrupted progress of the imagination" feels just like thinking of a single perception (T 1.4.2.34; SBN 204). This second resemblance in feelings of the mind leads the imagination to "confound" the selected collection of constant perceptions with a single perception (ibid.). If this process stopped here—as Rocknak and Ainslie's interpretations allow that it could—this would result in my believing that I continuously sense the mountain. (Notice that the supposition of one continuous occurrent perception achieved in the second part is not Hume's explanandum [viz. the idea of continued existence even when unperceived], which does not arise until the third part.[4]) This belief in continuance and identity would be false, because the mountain-impressions were experienced as interrupted (T 1.4.2.36; SBN 205).[5] In the third and fourth parts, Hume explains that this tension (between the imagination's ascription of identity and the senses' experience of interruption) prompts the vulgar mind to invent continued existence, by supposing that the mountain continues to exist even when it is not perceived. This supposition reconciles the tension by admitting (with the senses) that there are times at which the mountain is not perceived, but accepting (from the imagination) that the different impressions are appearances of numerically the same mountain (ibid., cf. T 1.4.2.43; SBN

209). Thus, interruption is a crucial component of Hume's explanation of the experiential origin of the idea of continued existence.

Ainslie analyzes the relevant concepts[6] (HTS 52, 70): continued existence (C), distinct existence (D), and in addition, he offers an identity version of continued existence (I):

(Cn) The belief of an object (say, a table) that has been sensed but is not currently being sensed, that it (the table) exists;

(Dn) The belief, of an object (the table) that is currently being sensed, that it (the table) exists;

(In) The belief, of an object (the table now) currently being sensed and of an object (the table then) that was previously sensed, that it (the table) is one continuing object.

On Ainslie's interpretation, In is the belief formed in the second part of Hume's explanation of the vulgar belief in continued existence formed from constant impressions (including memories of impressions). According to Ainslie, this is "the belief of an object, such as the bed, seen before and after our blinking, that it is one bed" (HTS 75). In parts three and four, Ainslie claims, Hume describes a new belief, Cn, on which "even when we are not perceiving it, we believe that the bed continues to exist" (ibid.).

I agree that there is a difference between In and Cn, but I disagree with Ainslie's analysis. In the second part, Hume is clear that he is not considering only brief interruptions, such as blinking. Hume writes, "I now proceed to explain the second part of my system, and show why the constancy of our perceptions makes us ascribe to them a perfect numerical identity, tho' there be very long intervals betwixt their appearance, and they have only one of the essential qualities of identity, viz. invariableness" (T 1.4.2.31; SBN 201–202; second emphasis added). In the above example, when I identify the different mountain-impressions, I do so because the "interrupting" impressions of non-mountains are not included in the association by resemblance. But to believe that this sequence of mountain-impressions is actually one and the same mountain over time requires including all times between the first impression and the current impression. This requires conceiving of many distinct times when there were no mountain-impressions. When these "interrupting" impressions are included, the supposed identity is destroyed. The only way to save the supposition of identity is by distinguishing existence and being perceived; that is, by attributing existence to the mountain at times when I happened not to perceive it. This is Cn (as I interpret it).

Thus, the psychological processes involved in the second part will never alone yield a belief in an object's existence when it is not perceived. They yield supposition of the continuance and identical existence of an uninterrupted thing—that is, the supposition of a thing uninterruptedly perceived. Notice that the continuance involved in the supposition of identity in the second part is not Hume's technical sense of "continued existence," which is a component of the concept of external existence (T 1.4.2.2; SBN 188). Mere continuance does not entail distinct existence—Hume acknowledges "stedfast" or "unchangeable" perceptions.[7] To explain the experiential origin of the idea of continued existence, interruption is required.[8] This experienced interruption contradicts the imagination's supposition of continuance and identity, and the supposed identity cannot be sustained. The supposition of the object's continuing to exist when not perceived resolves this psychological tension.

Ainslie claims that In is a version of Cn, because Hume "often cashes out the belief in continued existence as a belief in the identity of an object across interrupted perceptions" (HTS 49). On Ainslie's own analysis, Cn is not a more general account of belief in continued existence, because Ainslie requires for Cn that the object "is not currently being sensed," but in In beliefs, the object is "currently being sensed." However, for Hume, In is incorporated into Cn (in part 3), and only with Cn do we get the supposition of something's existence when it is not perceived.

I agree with Ainslie that Hume thinks that we believe in continued existence both in cases in which we currently perceive the object and when we do not currently perceive the object. I disagree with Ainslie that the inference from constancy ever operates in cases in which the supposedly continuing object is not currently perceived; on my interpretation, that belief is produced by the inference from coherence. Nevertheless, I think we can modify Ainslie's analysis of the belief in continued existence so that it encompasses both inferences. The correction I would offer to the analysis is:

> (Cn*) The belief of an object (say, a table) that is currently being thought about and of an object that was previously thought about, that it (the table) is one continuing object.

"Being thought about" includes cases in which the object is currently being sensed and that the object was previously sensed, which accommodates the inference from constancy and some of the inferences from coherence (for example, fire). But Hume gives other examples of the inference from coherence in which the external object is not currently observed: for example, he believes that his unobserved staircase exists now, which is inferred from the porter's arrival in his chamber, which is not on the ground floor. This inferred staircase is believed to be one and the same as the previously observed staircase. But Hume also gives examples in which the external object may never have been observed: for example, "a letter, which upon opening I perceive by the hand-writing and subscription to have come from a friend, who says he is two hundred leagues distant" (T 1.4.2.20; SBN 196). It may be that Hume has never been to the land from where his friend writes, but he may identify it as one and the same place attested to by maps or other testimony.

Hume adds that once we have developed an idea of continued existence and have applied it to a variety of constant and coherent experiences, we can apply continued existence "to objects, which are perfectly new to us, and of whose constancy and coherence we have no experience." Hume explains, "'tis because the manner, in which they present themselves to our senses, resembles that of constant and coherent objects; and this resemblance is a source of reasoning and analogy, and leads us to attribute the same qualities to the similar objects" (T 1.4.2.42; SBN 209).

3. Secondary Ideas

Hume famously distinguishes between impressions and ideas. Hume writes, "Every one of himself will readily perceive the difference betwixt feeling and thinking" (T 1.1.1.1; SBN 1–2). He articulates and defends the general proposition (with "singular" exceptions, T 1.1.1.10; SBN 6), "that all our simple ideas in their first appearance are deriv'd from simple impressions, which are correspondent to them, and which they exactly represent" (T 1.1.1.7; SBN 4). Hume appeals to experience to confirm that impressions precede ideas: to give a child the new idea of orange or bitter requires presenting an orange or bitter object to the child; we cannot "produce the impressions by exciting the ideas" (T 1.1.1.8; SBN 5). Similarly, if one never uses a sensory organ, he or she will never acquire the corresponding sensory impressions or ideas (T 1.1.1.9; SBN 5).

Hume extends this claim about the priority of impressions to ideas to a class of perceptions he calls "secondary ideas":

> But besides this exception, it may not be amiss to remark on this head, that the principle of the priority of impressions to ideas must be understood with another limitation, viz. that as our ideas are images of our impressions, so we can form secondary ideas, which are images of the primary; as appears from this very reasoning concerning them. This is not, properly speaking, an exception to the rule so much as an explanation of it. Ideas produce the images of themselves in new ideas; but as the first ideas are suppos'd to be deriv'd from impressions, it still remains true, that all our simple ideas proceed, either mediately or immediately, from their correspondent impressions. (T 1.1.1.11; SBN 6–7)

As I interpret this passage, secondary ideas are copies of those ideas derived immediately from impressions. For ease of exposition, let's call the immediately derived ideas "primary ideas." On my reading, Hume is claiming that secondary ideas are not a counterexample to his maxim that impressions precede ideas; secondary ideas are mediately derived from impressions, through the intermediary primary ideas.

Ainslie interprets this passage as allowing that secondary ideas may be copies of primary ideas or of impressions. Ainslie distinguishes between primary and secondary ideas in terms of the content of what is copied (HTS 121–34, 211–12). In primary ideas, only the content of the impression is copied. I have an idea of the apple (HTS 123; cf. HTS 212). In contrast, in secondary ideas, not only is the content copied, so is the "action of the mind" (T 1.3.8.16, 3.3.1.2; SBN 106, 456) or "awareness" (HTS 212). I have an idea of seeing the apple (in the case of a secondary idea of an impression) or of thinking about the apple (in the case of a secondary idea of an idea).

This strikes me as a not-very-economical psychological process. For each impression, not only would the memory have to copy the content of the impression in a primary idea, but the memory would also have to copy the action of the mind in a secondary idea. On the alternative explanation, only one copy is made for each impression, copying both the content and the action of the mind in one and the same primary idea. Against this complaint, I suspect Ainslie would point to Hume's descriptions of the difficulties (and the philosophical errors induced) in trying to keep straight which perception one attends to when introspecting.

Still, I have a couple of questions for Ainslie's interpretation.

1) Ainslie acknowledges that secondary ideas copy both the image-content and the awareness of the primary perception (impression or idea) it copies (HTS 123, 212). However, the mind can focus on the awareness to the exclusion of the image-content (HTS 124). Ainslie uses this psychological ability to explain how I can come to infer an unremembered impression as the cause of my idea. However, if one acknowledges this psychological ability, can't the alternative interpretation use it to explain how I can use primary ideas (as copies of impression) to either focus on the awareness (the sensing) or the image-content (the papaya)?

2) Hume repeats that the act of the mind (sensing or thinking) is not a distinct perception over and above the image-content. He describes force, liveliness, and vivacity as the manner of the perception. Ainslie's interpretation has the problem that a primary idea can copy the image-content of an impression without copying its manner. That is, it separates features of an idea which seem not to be separable. (Compare with HTS 212.) Hume allows that we can form ideas of inseparable aspects using distinctions of reason. For example, I can think of color without thinking of shape (T 1.1.7.18; SBN 25). This will be achieved by calling to mind particular ideas of colored shapes and focusing on the color to the exclusion of the shapes. It stands to reason that ideas of apples or papayas will focus on the remembered apple-content or papaya-content to the exclusion of the remembered sensation. (Compare to Ainslie's use of "stop focusing," HTS 127)

Ainslie convincingly argues that secondary ideas are required for introspective awareness of one's perceptions. Thus, secondary ideas are an ineliminable component of any interpretation of Hume's account of our belief in personal identity. This is one of the lasting and very important contributions of Ainslie's work on part four of the first Book of Hume's Treatise.

NOTES

1 References to the *Treatise* are to Hume, *A Treatise of Human Nature*, ed. Norton and Norton, hereafter cited in the text as "T" followed by Book, part, section, and paragraph number, and to Hume, *A Treatise of Human Nature*, ed. Selby-Bigge, rev. by Nidditch, cited in the text as "SBN" followed by the page number.

2 Because Hume offers conceptual analysis, it is awkward to describe this as a "stage" of "a four-stage explanation of how this constancy in experience produces Cn" (HTS 75 and *inter alia*). (Price

also uses "stage," *Hume's Theory of the External World*, 38 and *inter alia*].) Hume himself calls them "four things requisite" "to justify this [vulgar] system" (T 1.4.2.25; SBN 199; cf. "part" in T 1.4.2.31, 36, 43; SBN 201, 205, 209–10; "member of this system" in T 1.4.2.41; SBN 208). Elsewhere, Ainslie describes it as a "four-step argument for the belief in continued existence of sensory objects" (HTS 90; cf. Hume's use of "argument" in T 1.4.2.35n39; SBN 205n).

3 Rocknak, *Imagined Causes*, 160–70. Ainslie explains that his interpretation differs from Rocknak's in holding that In is a belief about "re-encounter[ed]" objects, whereas Cn is about objects not currently being sensed (HTS 90n30).

4 Thanks to David Owen, Donald Ainslie, Nick Stang, and Richard Fry for pressing me to clarify the difference between the supposed continuance in the second part, and supposed continued existence in the third part.

5 This point holds even for Ainslie's example in which the interruptions are blinks. I would not come to believe that the bed is an external object (as In as a species of Cn would imply), only a continuous perception.

6 The subscript "n" denotes the naïve point of view about perceptions that we hold in non-philosophical moments. This is to be distinguished from interpretations that attribute "sophisticated" views (subscript "s") about the nature of perceptions to the vulgar—views which Ainslie persuasively rejects (HTS 49ff.).

7 Hume discusses "stedfast" and "unchangeable" objects at T 1.2.3.11, 1.2.5.29, 1.4.2.29; SBN 37, 65, 200–201. See Baxter, *Hume's Difficulty*, 30–47; and Ainslie, HTS 83–89.

8 To be sure, Hume does describe examples in which the psychological processes described in the inference from constancy are triggered by an uninterrupted sequence of qualitatively different impressions (T 1.4.2.34–35, 1.4.3.3, 1.4.6.6; SBN 203–204, 220, 254). These examples are not showcased in Hume's explanation in *Treatise* 1.4.2, because they could not serve as the origin of the idea or belief in continued existence (that is, existence even when not perceived.)

WORKS CITED

Ainslie, Donald C. *Hume's True Scepticism*. New York: Oxford University Press, 2015.

Baxter, Donald L. M. *Hume's Difficulty*. London: Routledge, 2008.

Hume, David. *A Treatise of Human Nature*. Edited by David Fate Norton and Mary J. Norton Oxford: Oxford University Press, 2007.

Hume, David. *A Treatise of Human Nature*, 2nd ed. Edited by L. A. Selbwy-Bigge, revised by P. H. Nidditch. Oxford: Clarendon Press, 1978.

Price, H. H. *Hume's Theory of the External World*. Oxford: Clarendon, 1940.

Hume Studies
Volume 45, Number 1–2, 2019, pp. 109–119

Perceptions, Minds, and Hume's Self-doubts: Comments on Ainslie's *Hume's True Scepticism*

JONATHAN COTTRELL

In *Hume's True Scepticism*, Donald C. Ainslie offers a highly original, systematic interpretation of *Treatise* Book 1, part 4, and of much else in the *Treatise* besides. Along the way, he provides new solutions to two of the main outstanding problems of Hume scholarship: what is the relationship between Hume's skepticism and his commitment to pursuing a naturalistic science of man? And what "very considerable mistake" about personal identity does Hume mean to report in the Appendix? These are fantastic achievements. I congratulate Ainslie on the book, and on the JHP Book Prize, which I am happy to learn he has won.

To keep things interesting, these comments will focus on three related topics where I am not yet convinced by what Ainslie has to say: 1) the nature of perceptions; 2) Hume's views about minds in the *Treatise* section "Of personal identity"; and 3) Hume's second thoughts about this section in the Appendix.

1. Perceptions

Hume argues that a mind is a "bundle" or (as he says later) a "system" of causally integrated perceptions, or impressions and ideas (T 1.4.6.4, 1.4.6.19; SBN 252, 261).[1] But what is a perception? According to a standard interpretation, an impression is *what we are aware of*, when having a sensation or feeling a passion or sentiment; and an idea is what we are aware of when thinking. For Hume, impressions of sensation would then be particular instances of sensible qualities and particular bodily sensations, for these are what we are aware of, when we have

Jonathan Cottrell is a Lecturer in History of Philosophy, University of Edinburgh, Dugald Stewart Building, 3 Charles Street, Edinburgh, EH8 9AD.
Email: j.cottrell@ed.ac.uk.

sensations (T 1.1.2.1, 1.1.6.1; SBN 7–8, 16). Impressions of reflection would presumably be instances of the qualities that we experience when feeling passions or sentiments. Ideas would be quality-instances that are fainter than, but otherwise exactly similar to, the impressions from which they are copied.

Ainslie gives several arguments against this standard interpretation. One goes like this: if perceptions were *what we are aware of*, when having a sensation, passion, sentiment, or thought—as the standard interpretation says—then a mind would have to be a bundle of perceptions *plus our "awarenesses" of those perceptions*; but a Humean mind is merely a bundle of perceptions; so, the standard interpretation is incorrect (HTS 53–54, 211).[2]

I find this argument unpersuasive. In the *Treatise* section "Of scepticism with regard to the senses," Hume addresses what it is for a mind to "perceive," or be aware of, its perceptions (T 1.4.2.40; SBN 207–208). This passage provides an answer to Ainslie on behalf of the standard interpretation. To see this, we first need some background. Hume claims that we ordinarily "take [our] perceptions to be [our] only objects, and suppose, that the very being, which is intimately present to the mind, is the real body or material existence" (T 1.4.2.38; SBN 206). In doing so, we attribute continued existence to something that is, in fact, a perception: "this very perception or object is suppos'd to have a continu'd uninterrupted being, and neither to be annihilated by our absence, nor to be brought into existence by our presence" (T 1.4.2.38; SBN 207). To say that perceptions have continued existence or "continu'd uninterrupted being" is to say that they "continue to exist, even when they are not perceiv'd" (T 1.4.2.2; SBN 188). When we attribute continued existence to something that is, in fact, a perception, we suppose that it is sometimes perceived, sometimes unperceived: "When we are absent from it, we say it still exists, but that we do not feel, we do not see it. When we are present, we say we feel, or see it" (T 1.4.2.38; SBN 207). After explaining this, Hume raises several questions, including the one that now concerns us: "what [do] we mean by this *seeing*, and *feeling*, and *perceiving*?" (T 1.4.2.38; SBN 207).

Hume answers this question two paragraphs later. In doing so, he uses the terms "external object," "sensible object" and "perception" interchangeably, because he is still discussing the beliefs of those (the "vulgar") who attribute continued, unperceived existence to things that are, in fact, perceptions:

> External objects are seen, and felt, and become present to the mind; that is, they acquire such a relation to a connected heap of perceptions, as to influence them very considerably in augmenting their number by present reflections and passions, and in storing the memory with ideas. The same continu'd and uninterrupted being may, therefore, be sometimes present to the mind, and sometimes absent from it, without any real or essential change in the being itself. An interrupted appearance to the senses implies not necessarily an interruption in the existence. The supposition of the continu'd existence of sensible objects or perceptions involves no contradiction. (T 1.4.2.40; SBN 207–208)

As I read it, this passage explains what it is for an impression of sensation to be perceived, or to be an object of awareness: *being perceived* consists in *being causally related to other perceptions in a distinctive way* (namely, so as to cause certain kinds of reflections, passions and memory-ideas among them). Presumably, Hume would give similar accounts of what it is for impressions of reflection and ideas to be objects of perception or awareness.

Based on this passage, a proponent of the standard interpretation can answer Ainslie's argument as follows. To say *that a mind or bundle is aware of its perceptions* is just to say *that the causal relations among bundle-members include the distinctive kinds of causal relations that Hume describes in T 1.4.2.40* (SBN 207–08*)*. This does not imply that the mind or bundle contains anything in addition to causally related perceptions. So, contrary to Ainslie's argument, Hume can accept that perceptions are objects of awareness, without committing himself to the view that a mind is a bundle of perceptions plus "awarenesses" of those perceptions.

In place of the standard interpretation, Ainslie proposes that "sensory perceptions"—that is, impressions of sensation and ideas derived from them—have "two inseparable aspects" (HTS 212): an *image-content* and an *act of awareness*.[3] A perception's image-content is *what we are aware of*, in having that perception. "Most primitively," image-contents are "unextended colored or tangible points, or non-spatial smells, tastes, and the like" (HTS 211–12). The other aspect of a perception is the "action of the mind" whereby we are aware of the image-content (HTS 212). These two aspects of a perception are inseparable: an image-content's *esse* is *percipi* (HTS 212n29), so there cannot be an image-content without an act of awareness of it; conversely, there cannot be an act of sensory awareness "without it being the awareness of image-content" (HTS 212). In Ainslie's view, a perception's degree of force and liveliness is a feature of its act-aspect, not of its image-content (HTS 213).

With passions, things are different. Hume notoriously argues that passions are non-representational (T 2.3.3.5; SBN 415). Ainslie infers that passions do not have image-content (HTS 212, 213–14); instead, they are "nothing but different 'flavors' of vivacity" (HTS 213). I am unsure what Ainslie thinks of ideas copied from passions. He distinguishes two different kinds of copying-relation, which produce two different kinds of ideas (HTS 123, 127). The first kind of copying-relation produces a "primary idea," which repeats the image-content of the impression from which it derives (HTS 123). The second kind of copying-relation produces a "secondary idea," whose "content" is the "primary perception," that is, the impression or primary idea, from which it derives (HTS 123). An idea cannot stand in the first kind of copying-relation to a passion, because a passion has no image-content. So, ideas copied from passions must stand to their originals in the second kind of copying-relation: that is, they must be secondary ideas, whose contents are the passions—the "flavors of vivacity"—from which they are copied. Ainslie describes secondary ideas as having "image-contents": the image-content of a secondary idea is the primary perception from which it is copied (HTS 131–32). I infer that an idea copied from a passion has that passion as its image-content.[4]

I see two main problems with this account of Humean perceptions. First, Hume aims to *naturalize* the intentionality (the directedness upon an object) involved in perceiving: that is, he aims to explain it in terms of properties and relations that are found throughout the natural world (not just in minds) and that are not, individually, peculiar to intentional mental entities.[5] We can see this in T 1.4.2.40 (SBN 207–08), quoted above, where Hume claims that an impression's *being perceived* consists in its *being causally related to other perceptions in a distinctive way* (so as "to influence them very considerably," and so on). Causal relations are found throughout the natural world; they are not peculiar to intentional mental entities. So, in this passage, Hume is trying to naturalize the intentionality involved in perceiving. But the view that Ainslie attributes to Hume conflicts with this goal. On this view, every sensory perception—hence, every simple sensory perception—has an aspect that is an act of perceiving or awareness. Hume does not try to explain the intrinsic nature of simple perceptions in other, more basic terms: they are the fundamental entities in his theory of mind. So, if he accepted the view that Ainslie attributes to him, Hume would have to allow that simple sensory perceptions involve an explanatorily basic kind of intentionality: the directedness of an act of awareness upon an image-content. And if Hume allowed this, then he could not consistently aim to naturalize the intentionality involved in perceiving. Because I think he has this aim, I do not think he accepts the view that Ainslie attributes to him.

The second problem concerns sympathy. Hume says that, when we sympathize with someone, we start with an idea that represents a certain passion. This idea receives an influx of vivacity, which turns it into an impression—a passion resembling the one that it initially represented (T 2.1.11.3–8; SBN 317–20). We have seen evidence that, for Ainslie, an idea of a passion has an image-content: namely, the passion (the "flavor of vivacity") from which it is copied. But a passion itself has no image-content. So, Ainslie will have to say that, when we sympathize, a perception that initially has an image-content (when it is an idea) *ceases* to have an image-content (when it becomes a passion), simply by receiving vivacity. But how can this be? For Ainslie, a perception's degree of vivacity is a feature of its act-aspect, not of its image-content. How can modifying one aspect of a perception (its act-aspect/vivacity) *destroy* its other aspect (its image-content)? I found this upshot of Ainslie's interpretation quite mysterious.[6]

I am therefore skeptical about Ainslie's account of Humean perceptions. However, this account has several virtues that I have not been able to consider here (see, especially, HTS 211–17). I am unsure whether any rival account shares all these virtues. So, even if the problems I have raised here are genuine, it may be that Ainslie's account makes better sense of the texts than any other.

2. Minds

Let us now turn to the *Treatise* section "Of personal identity." According to Ainslie, this section's opening paragraphs attack a metaphysical view held by certain philosophers: the view that a mind has a "real unity," that is, perfect simplicity and perfect identity (HTS 205). Against this view, Hume claims to make "the introspective discovery that the mind is merely a bundle of perceptions," which "means that it has no real unity" (HTS 205). Ainslie then writes: "Accordingly, Hume's explanandum is not the *real* unity of the bundle of perceptions:

there is none. Instead, his explanandum is our [that is, introspecting philosophers'] tendency to *believe* that the mind is unified when it is under observation" (HTS 206). This suggests that, following its opening paragraphs, "Of personal identity" makes no further metaphysical claims about minds, and instead focuses entirely on what I will call the Psychological Question: how do introspecting philosophers come to believe in the unity of their minds? It also suggests that, having discovered that a mind is "merely a bundle of perceptions," Hume does not owe us answers to any further metaphysical questions about minds. If this is what Ainslie thinks, then I believe he is wrong on both counts.

As I read "Of personal identity," its later paragraphs offer a further metaphysical claim about what a mind is. Hume argues that a mind is a system of causally integrated perceptions (T 1.4.6.19; SBN 261). As such, a mind is a composite thing: at any given time, it has diverse "co-existent parts" (T 1.4.6.22; SBN 263); over time, it is a "succession of perceptions," that is, something that has diverse temporal parts (T 1.4.2.20; SBN 261).[7] More specifically, a mind is a composite thing whose parts are all its perceptions. Hume makes this especially clear in his "Abstract" of the *Treatise*, where he says that our "several particular perceptions . . . *compose* the mind" (T Abs 28; SBN 658, italics in original); and in the Appendix, where he says "'Tis the composition of these [perceptions], therefore, which forms the self" (T App 15; SBN 634). So, if Ainslie thinks that "Of personal identity" makes no further metaphysical claims about minds, following its opening paragraphs, then I believe he is wrong about this. (Hume sometimes qualifies his metaphysical claims about the mind with phrases like "as far as we can conceive it," or "have [a] notion of it": for example, see T Abs 28 (SBN 657) and T App 19 (SBN 635). For ease of exposition, I will suppress these qualifications, as Hume himself often does.)

Because of his claim that minds are systems composed of perceptions, Hume owes us an answer to a further metaphysical question about minds. To see this, consider my perceptions, that is, the ones in the system that is my mind. Call these perceptions "the *x*s." For Hume, the *x*s compose a mind. Now consider, in contrast, one half of my perceptions (say, the ones that make up the first temporal half of my mental life) and one half of yours (say, the perceptions that make up the second temporal half of your mental life). Call all these perceptions, taken together, "the *y*s." For Hume, the *y*s do not compose a mind: there is no mind or system that includes both the first half of my perceptions and the second half of yours. We can therefore ask: when several perceptions compose a mind, in virtue of what do they do so? For example, in virtue of what do the *x*s compose a mind, the *y*s not? Let us call this the Composition Question. Hume owes us at least a qualified answer to this question: an answer of the form "as far as we can conceive it, the *x*s compose a mind in virtue of. . . ." So, if Ainslie thinks that, having discovered that a mind is a bundle of perceptions, Hume does not owe us answers to any further metaphysical questions about minds, then I believe he is wrong about this.

Later in his book, Ainslie may mean to argue that Hume does not owe us an answer to the Composition Question. He claims that, for Hume, "the bundling of perceptions into minds" is "a brute fact," that is, one with no explanation (HTS 264n42). By "the bundling of perceptions into minds," Ainslie may mean *the composition of a mind by its perceptions*. If so, then he is saying that, when several perceptions compose a mind, this fact about them is "brute" or inexplicable. In other words, there is nothing *in virtue of which* they compose a mind—they just do, and that's all there is to say.[8] If this were Hume's view, then he would not owe us an answer to the Composition Question: by his lights, this question would have no answer.

However, I do not think Hume can consistently accept that this fact about composition is brute. Composition is a *relation* between the parts and the whole. If it were a brute fact that several perceptions compose a mind, then composition would have to be a basic or fundamental kind of relation, that is, one that is not explained in terms of any further relations. (If composition *were* explained in terms of some further relations—for example, in terms of the parts' being causally integrated—then the fact that several perceptions compose a mind *would not* be brute: it would be explained in terms of the fact that these further relations obtain among the perceptions.) But composition does not appear on Hume's list of the seven basic kinds of "philosophical relations": resemblance, identity, spatiotemporal relations, quantitative relations, qualitative relations, contrariety, and causation (T 1.1.5; SBN 13–15). So, Hume cannot consistently regard the fact that several perceptions compose a mind as brute.[9]

I therefore believe Ainslie is wrong, if he means to say that Hume regards facts about the composition of a mind by perceptions as brute. But I cannot find any other reason, in *Hume's True Scepticism*, to deny that Hume owes us an answer to the Composition Question. And so, I think Ainslie is too quick to conclude that Hume does not owe us answers to any further metaphysical questions about minds, beyond those addressed in the opening paragraphs of the section "Of personal identity."

This opens the possibility that Hume's second thoughts about "Of personal identity" concern his inability to answer the Composition Question satisfactorily—not, as Ainslie claims, his inability to answer the Psychological Question satisfactorily.

3. Hume's Self-Doubts

In the Appendix, Hume claims to see a problem with his account of "the principle of connexion, which binds [all our particular perceptions] together, and makes us attribute to them a real simplicity and identity," or "the principles, that unite our successive perceptions in our thought or consciousness" (T App 20; SBN 635–36). As Barry Stroud observes in *Hume* (135), these descriptions are ambiguous. Hume might mean that he cannot satisfactorily explain "what actually unites our successive perceptions into one mind or one consciousness—what actually ties them together to make up one mind." In other words, he might mean that he cannot satisfactorily answer the Composition Question. Alternatively, Hume might mean "that he has no hope of explaining what features of our perceptions and what principles of the mind combine to produce in us the thought or belief that we are individual minds." In other words, he might mean that he cannot satisfactorily answer the Psychological Question.

In keeping with his view that "Of personal identity" focuses on the Psychological Question, Ainslie argues for the latter option. He claims that Hume's second thoughts do not touch his metaphysics of minds (HTS 257). Instead, they concern his answer to the Psychological Question. In Ainslie's view, "Of personal identity" argues that associations among our *ideas of our perceptions*, or *secondary ideas*, cause us (introspecting philosophers) to attribute unity to the primary perceptions we observe by means of those secondary ideas. The problem is that Hume's approach does not allow him to explain why we believe that our secondary ideas are unified with our primary perceptions. Of course, Hume could posit *tertiary* ideas, that is, ideas of secondary ideas, to explain why we believe that our secondary ideas are unified with our primary perceptions. But this would not solve the problem: it would not explain why we believe that *all* our perceptions are unified together, because it would not explain why we believe that our *tertiary* ideas are so unified.

When Ainslie first presented this interpretation, in his "Hume's Reflections on the Identity and Simplicity of Mind," he met with the following objection:[10] Hume can easily solve the problem that Ainslie raises, by giving up the claim (if he ever made it) that anyone has a belief about *all* his or her perceptions. Hume can say that reflecting on one's primary perceptions by means of secondary ideas leads one to believe that all one's primary perceptions are unified. If one then reflects on one's secondary ideas, by means of tertiary ideas, this will induce the further belief that one's secondary ideas are unified with one's primary perceptions. And so forth. Hume need not say that anyone ever has a belief about *all* his or her perceptions.

Ainslie now makes clear that this objection is off target. Hume *must* say that at least one person has a belief about all his perceptions: namely, *Hume himself*, when he states his own view in "Of personal identity." In giving his answer to the Psychological Question, Hume himself "knows that his mind includes both observed and unobserved perceptions"—that is, both primary perceptions and the secondary ideas that Hume's theory posits—"both of which he takes to be present in the *same mind*" (HTS 255, italics in original). So, Hume now has what Ainslie calls a "new belief in mental unity—not the belief that the observed perceptions are unified, but the belief that the secondary ideas are unified along with the observed perceptions" (HTS 255). The problem is that Hume cannot explain this "new belief in mental unity." He cannot explain why *he himself* believes his secondary (and tertiary, quaternary, and so on) ideas to be unified together with his primary perceptions.

I think this interpretation is unsatisfactory as it stands. In the section "Of personal identity," Hume appeals to associations among secondary ideas in order to explain the belief that our minds have *perfect identity* and *perfect simplicity* (T 1.4.6.6, 1.4.6.22; SBN 253–55, 263). Hume himself does not share this belief. On the contrary, he rejects it. By his lights, it involves an "improper" and "inexact" use of ideas. The ideas of perfect identity and perfect simplicity cannot be derived from a variable, interrupted and composite thing, such as a mind. For Hume, if an idea cannot be derived from an object, then "it can never in any propriety or exactness be apply'd to it" (T 1.2.3.11; SBN 37).[11] So, when we apply the ideas of perfect identity and perfect simplicity to our minds, in order to form the belief that our minds have perfect identity and perfect simplicity, we are using these ideas improperly and inexactly. As Hume puts it, "we attribute identity, *in an improper sense*, to variable or interrupted objects" (T 1.4.6.7; SBN 255, italics added; note how this echoes the language of T 1.2.3.11; SBN 37).

Hume's own beliefs about the mind do not involve applying the ideas of perfect identity and perfect simplicity to it. For him, "the true idea of the human mind" represents a system of causally integrated perceptions that *lacks* perfect identity and perfect simplicity (T 1.4.6.19, 1.4.6.22; SBN 261, 263). So, Hume does not have the kind of belief in mental unity that he explains in terms of the associations among secondary ideas described in "Of personal identity." So, I see no reason to think that he would wish to explain his own beliefs about the mind in terms of these associations. And so, even if Ainslie is right that Hume could not satisfactorily explain his own beliefs about the mind in terms of these associations, I see no reason to think that Hume would regard this as a problem.

If this argument is correct, it shows that there is a lacuna in Ainslie's interpretation, as presented in *Hume's True Scepticism*. Ainslie owes us a reason to think that Hume would wish to explain his own beliefs about the mind in terms of the associations described in "Of personal identity," even though these beliefs do not involve the "improper" and "inexact" applications of ideas that he explains in terms of these associations.

Whether or not Hume's answer to the Psychological Question is problematic in the way Ainslie says, I do not think this can be the only problem that Hume means to raise in the Appendix. In paragraph 10 of the Appendix, Hume announces that he will "present the arguments on both sides," starting with those that led him "to deny the strict and proper identity and simplicity of a self or thinking being" (T App 10; SBN 633). That is, he will start with arguments for a metaphysical claim: the claim that a mind lacks strict and proper (or *perfect*) identity and simplicity. The next nine paragraphs, 11–19, then present arguments in favor of this metaphysical claim. It is left to paragraphs 20 and 21—those that contain Hume's second thoughts—to present the promised other "side." So, these two paragraphs must contain an argument *against* Hume's metaphysical claim that a mind lacks strict and proper identity and simplicity. If they presented a purely psychological argument, with no implications for Hume's metaphysics of mind, then they would not constitute another "side" to the nine metaphysically-focused paragraphs that precede them.[12]

I therefore believe that Hume's second thoughts arose because he cannot satisfactorily answer the Composition Question. Ainslie would classify this proposal as a "bundling interpretation" (HTS 262–65). He rejects such interpretations on the grounds that "Hume seems to treat it as a brute fact that when we reflect, we observe a limited set of perceptions" (HTS 264). I find this puzzling: as an objection to the kind of interpretation I favor, it seems to be a non-sequitur. The "brute fact" that Ainslie mentions here concerns *introspection* (or "reflection"), not *composition*. Even if Ainslie is right that Hume considers this fact about introspection "brute," I cannot see why this is a problem for the view that Hume's second thoughts concern his inability to answer the Composition Question. In a note added to the same paragraph on page 264, Ainslie says that Hume "take[s] the bundling of perceptions into minds as a brute fact" (HTS 264n42). As discussed in section 2, this claim might mean that Hume regards *the composition of a mind by its perceptions* as a brute fact. If so, then he would think the Composition Question needs no answer. But I have argued that Hume cannot consistently regard this fact about composition as brute (section 2). So, if this is Ainslie's objection to my preferred kind of interpretation, then I think it fails.

However, I am not sure that Ainslie has this kind of interpretation clearly in view. His category of "bundling interpretations" seems to include both what we might call *introspection interpretations*, on which Hume's second thoughts concern his inability to explain the fact that each mind's introspective view is limited to its own perceptions; and what we might call *composition interpretations*, on which Hume's second thoughts concern his inability to explain the composition of a mind by its perceptions. Perhaps Ainslie has refuted introspection interpretations, but—for the reasons given above—I do not think he has refuted composition interpretations.

In any case, I do not think Ainslie need be hostile to composition interpretations as such. My own composition interpretation of the Appendix is indebted to Ainslie's interpretation for its structure.[13] Briefly, I have argued that Hume's problem is a conflict between his metaphysics of mind and his view of the part-whole relation. According to Hume, a mind is a composite thing: it is a whole, whose parts are all its perceptions. But composition is ideal, not real: our minds provide the glue that binds parts into a whole; and, in order for a mind to do this, it must contain a further perception (or perceptions) of the parts that are to be bound. Consequently, a mind cannot bind *all* its perceptions into a whole, as Hume's metaphysics of mind requires: in order to do so, it must, *per impossibile*, contain a further perception (or perceptions) of them. This interpretation has the same structure as Ainslie's: according to both him and me, Hume fails to explain a feature of *all* a mind's perceptions because—in order to explain this feature—his account posits a further perception, or perceptions, to which that account does not extend. So, perhaps Ainslie and I can agree that Hume's second thoughts concern *both* the psychology *and* the metaphysics presented in "Of personal identity."

NOTES

1 References to "T" are to Hume, *A Treatise of Human Nature*, ed. Norton and Norton, followed by Book, part, section and, where appropriate, paragraph number (references to paragraphs of the Appendix to the *Treatise* and of Hume's "Abstract of a Book Lately Published" are preceded by "App" and "Abs," respectively). Each of these citations is followed by the corresponding page numbers in Hume, *A Treatise of Human Nature*, ed. Selby-Bigge, rev. by Nidditch, set off by "SBN."

2 References to "HTS" are to Ainslie, *Hume's True Scepticism*, followed by page number.

3 Adapted versions of this paragraph and the one following it appear in my forthcoming work, "Representation and Copying in Hume's *Treatise* and Later Works." I thank the editors of *Hume Studies* for their permission to re-use this material there.

4 Once, Ainslie seems to deny this: he says that ideas copied from passions "are not imagistic" (HTS 59n25). (I thank Hsueh Qu for pointing this out to me.) But I do not think Ainslie means to deny that these ideas "portray" passions and in this sense have "image-content" (HTS 132). When he says that these ideas "are not imagistic," I presume he means that they are not images in some

stronger, more demanding sense of "image": for example, that they are not *sensory* (visual, tactile, gustatory, and so on) images.

5 For fuller and more nuanced discussions of what "naturalism" can mean in philosophy, and of Hume's naturalism, see Garrett, "Hume's Naturalistic Theory of Representation."

6 I develop the argument of this paragraph more fully in Cottrell, "Representation and Copying in Hume's *Treatise* and Later Works."

7 For helpful discussion of Hume's concept of a "succession," see Baxter, *Hume's Difficulty*, ch. 2 and 3.

8 I am unsure whether Ainslie means that Hume regards the composition of a mind by its perceptions as "brute" or inexplicable. Ainslie seems to treat the following claims as equivalent: 1) it is a brute fact that perceptions are bundled into minds (HTS 246n42); and 2) it is a brute fact that, when we reflect, we observe a limited set of perceptions (HTS 246). Claim (2) is about *introspection* (or "reflection"), not about *composition*. So, claim (2) does not seem to mean that the composition of a mind by its perceptions is brute. If (1) is equivalent to (2), then presumably (1) does not mean that the composition of a mind by its perceptions is brute, either.

9 Some scholars may deny that Hume regards composition as a relation between parts and whole. For Hume, they may say, talking of "a system" is not a way of talking about one whole composed by many perceptions; instead, it is just a convenient way of talking about the many perceptions (for example, see Baxter, 25–26). But there would still be a further metaphysical question to which Hume owes us an answer. Consider my perceptions again. Even if these perceptions do not compose a whole, they are nonetheless related to each other in a distinctive way; let us say they are *co-mental*. In contrast, none of my perceptions is related to any of your perceptions in this distinctive way: none of my perceptions is co-mental with any of yours. Hume therefore owes us an answer to the Co-Mentality Question: When several perceptions are co-mental, in virtue of what are they so? Hume cannot consistently say that facts about co-mentality are "brute" or inexplicable, because *co-mentality* does not appear on his list of the seven basic kinds of relation. So, facts about co-mentality must be explained by facts about further relations. And so, such facts cannot be brute. Readers who deny that Hume regards composition as a relation can substitute the Co-Mentality Question for the Composition Question throughout my discussion.

10 One often encounters this objection in conversation. For published versions, see Ellis, "The Contents of Hume's Appendix and the Source of His Despair," 212–13; and Penelhum, "Hume, Identity, and Selfhood," in *Themes in Hume: The Self, the Will, Religion*, 117–19 and 125.

11 In what sense is it "improper" or "inexact" to apply an idea to an object from which it cannot be derived? It is hard to determine Hume's answer to this question. (For discussion, see Cottrell, "A Puzzle about Fictions in the *Treatise*.") I try to avoid taking a stand on this issue by saying that Hume *rejects* the belief that one's mind has perfect identity and simplicity. Perhaps he rejects it because he regards it as *false*; but perhaps he rejects it because he regards it as *unjustified* or *incoherent*, or in some other way defective.

12 For a fuller presentation of this argument, see Cottrell, "Minds, Composition, and Hume's Skepticism in the Appendix," 535–43.

13 Cottrell, "Minds, Composition, and Hume's Skepticism in the Appendix."

WORKS CITED

Ainslie, Donald C. "Hume's Reflections on the Identity and Simplicity of Mind." *Philosophy and Phenomenological Research* 62 (2001): 557–78. https://doi.org/10.1111/j.1933-1592.2001.tb00074.x

Ainslie, Donald C. *Hume's True Scepticism*. New York: Oxford University Press, 2015.

Baxter, Donald L. M. *Hume's Difficulty: Time and Identity in the "Treatise."* New York: Routledge, 2008.

Cottrell, Jonathan. "Minds, Composition, and Hume's Skepticism in the Appendix." *The Philosophical Review* 124, no. 4 (2015): 533–69. https://doi.org/10.1215/00318108-3147021

Cottrell, Jonathan. "A Puzzle about Fictions in the *Treatise*." *Journal of the History of Philosophy* 54, no. 1 (2016): 47–73. https://doi.org/10.1353/hph.2016.0023

Cottrell, Jonathan. "Representation and Copying in Hume's *Treatise* and Later Works." *Ergo*, forthcoming.

Ellis, Jonathan. "The Contents of Hume's Appendix and the Source of His Despair." *Hume Studies* 32, no. 2 (2006): 195–232.

Garrett, Don. "Hume's Naturalistic Theory of Representation." *Synthese* 152, no. 3 (2006): 301–19. https://doi.org/10.1007/s11229-006-9007-2

Hume, David. *A Treatise of Human Nature*. Edited by L. A. Selby-Bigge and P. H. Nidditch. Oxford: Clarendon Press, 1978.

Hume, David. *A Treatise of Human Nature*. Vol. 1, *Texts*. Edited by David Fate Norton and Mary J. Norton. Oxford: Clarendon Press, 2007.

Penelhum, Terence. "Hume, Identity, and Selfhood." In *Themes in Hume: The Self, the Will, Religion*, 99–126. New York: Oxford University Press, 2000.

Stroud, Barry. *Hume*. London: Routledge and Kegan Paul, 1977.

Hume Studies
Volume 45, Number 1–2, 2019, pp. 121–127

Comments on Ainslie's *Hume's True Scepticism*

BARRY STROUD

I understand the title of this book, *Hume's True Scepticism,*[1] not as a promise to identify some thesis, or doctrine, that is a statement of Hume's scepticism and is true, but rather to *explain* what Hume's scepticism really amounts to, what it truly is—the real thing. That is what I too would like to discuss. And I applaud Ainslie's concentration on the concluding section of Book 1 of the *Treatise* as the best place to look for an expression of that Humean scepticism. I have long regarded that section, with the corresponding parts of the first *Enquiry*, as essential to the proper understanding of Hume as a philosopher.

Hume set out to investigate empirically the general character of all human experience, thought, understanding, knowledge, feeling, and action; he sought a "science of human nature." But in reviewing his progress at the end Book 1 of his *Treatise*, he laments at great length, and in dramatic, personal terms, the completely hopeless position he finds himself in. This presents us with these questions. What exactly is that "hopeless position"? What makes Hume think it is "hopeless"? If it really is "hopeless," how could Hume get out of it? *Does* he get out of it? And if he doesn't get out of it, how can he carry on his further philosophical studies in Books 2 and 3 of the *Treatise*, not to mention the two *Enquiries*?

These last questions are what Ainslie draws most attention to. I will try to say something about this.

Hume's laments about the position he finds himself in are all expressed in the first person, and they are personal laments. It is David Hume who complains that "After the most accurate and exact of my reasonings, I can give no reason why I should assent to it; and feel nothing but a strong propensity to consider objects *strongly* in that view, under which they appear to me" (T 1.4.7.3; SBN 265).[2] That is because he has found in his researches that certain "principles

The late Barry Stroud was Willis S. and Marion Slusser Professor of Philosophy at the University of California, Berkeley.

of the imagination" are responsible for human beings believing and feeling and doing all the things we do. It is only because "the mind enlivens some ideas beyond others" that we "assent to any argument, [or] carry our view beyond those few objects that are present to our senses" (T 1.4.7. 3; SBN 265). And which ideas happen to get "enlivened" in the mind depends only on the operation of the "principles of the imagination." Experience and habit, "conspiring to operate on the imagination, make me form certain ideas in a more intense and lively manner" (T 1.4.7.3; SBN 265).

Hume describes those principles of the imagination as "so trivial, and so little founded on reason" (T 1.4.7.3; SBN 265). He does not mean they are trivial in their effects; we think and feel and believe as we do only because those principles are in operation. But they operate independently of whether the beliefs they thereby produce are true or false, or even reasonable. It is no wonder, then, as Hume puts it, that a principle, "so inconstant and fallacious, shou'd lead us into errors, when implicitly follow'd (as it must be) in all its variations" (T 1.4.7.4; SBN 265–66). If we yield to every effect of the imagination, "we must at last become asham'd of our credulity" (T 1.4.7.6; SBN 267). But to adhere only to the understanding would be fatal, since "the understanding, when it acts alone, . . . entirely subverts itself, and leaves not the lowest degree of evidence in any proposition, either in philosophy or common life" (T 1.4.7.7; SBN 267–68).

In speaking of "philosophy" here, Hume means the very enterprise he is engaged in in the *Treatise*. His study of human nature has apparently revealed to him that human beings in common life have no reasons for believing any of the things they do. But Hume is a human being, so he too has no reasons for believing anything, even the very conclusions he takes himself to have arrived at in his study of human nature, that is, in "philosophy." He really is in despair.

> The intense view of these manifold contradictions and imperfections in human reason has so wrought upon me, and heated my brain, that I am ready to reject all belief and reasoning, and can look upon no opinion even as more probable or likely than another. (T 1.4.7.8; SBN 268–69)

But even this resolution "to reject all belief and reasoning" provides no escape. When he tries to carry it out, Hume finds he simply cannot do it. Not because there is reason against it; that would not help even if it were true. But because even having reached his gloomy verdict on human reasoning he simply finds himself "absolutely and necessarily determin'd to live, and talk, and act like other people in the common affairs of life. . . . I must yield to the current of nature, in submitting to my senses and understanding" (T 1.4.7.10; SBN 269).

Ainslie makes what I think is a very important point about this. Hume's investigations and his responses to the challenge of scepticism show that, as Ainslie puts it: "We are fully engaged by our mental processes, naturally believing the conclusions of our reasoning and the verdicts of our senses rather than standing over and superintending them" (219). We can reflect on the conclusions we have been led to accept, and perhaps we have second thoughts about them, or even change our mind, but in all this, as Ainslie puts it, "we continue to be engaged in our reasoning and sensing" (219), not to stand above it, or beside it, or to assess it from some other standpoint. This is important, for Hume and for the rest of us; *there is* no other standpoint from which to engage in sensing and reasoning about whatever it might be.

But Ainslie suggests that despite this inevitable engagement:

> Philosophy . . . wants something more—a vindication of our cognitive capacities as enabling us to get things right. It turns out that philosophy is impotent when it takes on this task. . . . But . . . this was a problem only *for philosophy*, and leaves us, in common life, continuing to believe our reasonings and sensings without trouble. (219)

This is the basis of Ainslie's idea that the disappointment Hume expresses in the final Section of Book 1 of the *Treatise* is disappointment with *philosophy*: that philosophical reflection interferes with, and undermines, our tendencies to believe and reflect (219). Ainslie sees Hume's chief concern in his confrontation with scepticism as a matter of understanding and explaining the place of philosophy in Hume's conception of the mind or human nature (219).

I have doubts about this as an account of what Hume is really up to in that final Section of Book 1. For one thing, philosophy, as Hume understands it, is precisely the empirical, explanatory enterprise he is engaged in throughout the *Treatise*. A "philosophy" that seeks a "vindication" of our cognitive capacities as a source of truth would seem to be something "standing over" our human capacities in some way, trying to assess their adequacy, or "superintending" them. But in that final section of Book 1, Hume is not "standing over" his efforts and asking what the philosophy he is engaged in can legitimately do, or what kinds of claims it can make on us. He is a human being directly engaged in trying to understand human nature as it is. And he reports that his efforts leave him as a scientist of human nature "disappointed" (T 1.4.7.5; SBN 266), with "no reason" why he should assent to whatever he assents to (T 1.4.7.3; SBN 265), with no "hope of ever attaining satisfaction" (T 1.4.7.5; SBN 267), and "asham'd of our credulity" (T 1.4.7.6; SBN 267): "When we trace up the human understanding to its first principles, we find it to lead us into such sentiments, as seem to turn into ridicule all our past pains and industry, and discourage us from further enquiries" (T 1.4.7.5; SBN 266).

These are Hume's despairing responses "from within" philosophy, or the study of human nature. They are responses Hume thinks any engaged human student of human nature will find himself with. Ainslie suggests that overcoming or avoiding a disappointingly "impotent" philosophy, or regarding philosophy as an "optional" activity to be engaged in or not at our will, would leave us free to perceive, believe, and reason about the things we do in everyday life without difficulty. Of course, there is a sense in which that is right. Philosophy is in that sense "optional," in Ainslie's word. We can take it or leave it. But that is no help to Hume in the position he finds himself in. Even Hume does not engage in philosophy every hour of the day and night; most of the time he is like the rest of us. The problem for Hume is that when he does investigate human nature in general, he cannot get an understanding of it that he himself can find satisfactory. And he thinks anyone else who investigates human nature empirically and dispassionately will be led to the same outcome.

For Ainslie this raises a difficult problem of interpretation. If Hume fully "endorsed" the reflections that led him to his sceptical plight (226), if he is "committed to the negative verdicts about his beliefs" that he had reached at that stage (228), how could he or we explain his continuing his philosophical studies beyond the end of Book 1 of the *Treatise*? "Once we have learned that our cognitive capacities are fundamentally unsound," Ainslie says, "there is no longer any *reason* for our continued attraction" to such studies. Without having left those sceptical reflections behind, he says, "we would still *believe* the negative verdicts" (229). But "if we really believed that we are as cognitively disordered as the sceptical interpretation of Hume suggests, it is hard to see how we would ever continue to philosophize" (230).

I think there is an answer, or at least the beginnings of an answer, to this interpretative question in Hume. It lies in what his scepticism, or what he calls his "scepticism," really amounts to. The answer depends on what is unsatisfactory about the state Hume first finds himself in, and then on how he gets out of that state. He escapes the position he finds hopeless not by abandoning all belief and reasoning, which he simply cannot do, but by yielding to "the current of nature" and so, finding himself "absolutely and necessarily determin'd to live and talk, and act like other people in the common affairs of life" (T 1.4.7.10; SBN 269). He finds that he cannot accept what his study of human nature has revealed to him: that he has no reasons for believing anything. He cannot accept that and act in the light of it. And in yielding to the current of nature, and living and talking and acting like other people in the common affairs of life, as he finds he must, Hume says "I shew most perfectly my sceptical disposition and principles" (T 1.4.7.10; SBN 269).

What Hume here calls his "sceptical disposition and principles" is akin to the attitudes attributed to sceptics in antiquity who were said to pursue a trouble-free way of life by following their natural inclinations and "going along with appearances." Hume thought we cannot live and act without beliefs, but he aligns himself with the sceptical tradition in his acquiescence in beliefs that are fully "natural" to human beings and so unavoidable. Hume found the beliefs of common life unavoidable even in the face of his despair about finding reasons to believe anything. The forces of nature alone are what free him from that sceptical plight: "Most fortunately it happens, that since reason is incapable of dispelling these clouds, nature herself suffices to that purpose, and cures me of this philosophical melancholy and delirium" (T 1.4.7.9; SBN 269). "'Tis happy," Hume says, "that nature breaks the force of all sceptical arguments in time" (T 1.4.2.13; SBN 187).

The general forces of nature—human nature—free Hume from the paralyzing position he would otherwise have found himself in. And more specific forces of nature—David Hume's nature—lead him to continue his philosophical enquiries into the questions that concern him. He is "naturally inclin'd" to carry his view into all those subjects (T 1.4.7.12; SBN 270); he "cannot forbear having a curiosity" about them (T 1.4.7.12; SBN 270); he is "uneasy to think" that he approves of one thing and disapproves of another "without knowing upon what principles" he proceeds (T 1.4.7.12; SBN 271). "These sentiments spring up naturally" in him, and he "*feels* he shou'd be a loser in point of pleasure" if he were to avoid them (T 1.4.7.12; SBN 271). The feelings are not even exclusively self-interested. As he explains, with all due humility: "Human nature is the only science of man; and yet has been hitherto the most neglected. 'Twill be sufficient for me, if I can bring it a little more into fashion" (T 1.4.7.14; SBN 273).

In yielding to these natural inclinations, and proposing to continue his philosophical investigations, Hume describes himself as proceeding "upon sceptical principles" (T 1.4.7.11; SBN 270): "A true sceptic will be diffident of his philosophical doubts, as well as of his philosophical conviction; and will never refuse any innocent satisfaction, which offers itself, upon account of either of them" (T 1.4.7.14; SBN 273). This description in the *Treatise* of the attitudes of a "true sceptic" comes close to expressing what Hume in the last section of *An Enquiry Concerning the Human Understanding* comes to call "mitigated scepticism." That condition is "the natural result" of "Pyrrhonism, or *excessive* scepticism, when its undistinguished doubts are, in some measure, corrected by common sense and reflection" (EHU 12.24; SBN 161).[3] The "innocent satisfaction" Hume seeks and expects from his continued philosophical investigations are not to be foregone simply because of the "excessive" doubts and melancholy that temporarily overwhelmed him.

This "sceptical disposition" with which Hume proposes to continue in philosophy—what he later calls "mitigated scepticism"—promises a way of thinking and reflecting that combines acknowledgement both of the profound "excessive" doubts of "Pyrrhonism" that overcame him at first, and of the "natural instincts" that he found to free him, and so, protect him from those "excessive" doubts: "To bring us to so salutary a determination, nothing can be more serviceable, than to be once thoroughly convinced of the force of the Pyrrhonian doubt, and of the impossibility that anything but the strong power of natural instinct can free us from it" (EHU 12.25; SBN 162). Hume here stresses the equal importance of both ingredients in the combination. We must see and appreciate *both* the impossibility of a satisfactory answer to the "excessive" doubts of "Pyrrhonism," *and* the impossibility—the human impossibility—of accepting that scepticism, and living as if it is true. The "mitigated scepticism" within which Hume continues to philosophize is attainable *only* by our being once "thoroughly convinced" of the force of the Pyrrhonian doubt, and *then* finding that in fact, the forces of nature have freed us from the inactivity that the doubts seem to imply. At the very end of Book 1 of the *Treatise*, I think Hume acknowledges the presence of both those ingredients in the truly "sceptical" way of life he finds himself in. And it is in that more "diffident" spirit that he ventures to "launch out into the immense depths of philosophy which lie before" him.

Hume thinks such a durable combination of attitudes is likely to lead to greater "modesty and reserve." "The greater part of mankind," he says, "are naturally apt to be affirmative and dogmatical in their opinions," and "a small tincture of Pyrrhonism might abate their pride" and encourage in them "that degree of doubt, and caution, and modesty, which . . . ought forever to accompany a just reasoner" (EHU 12.24; SBN 161–62). "Another . . . natural result of the Pyrrhonian doubts and scruples, is the limitation of our enquiries to such subjects as are best adapted to the narrow capacity of human understanding . . . avoiding "all distant and high enquiries" (EHU 12.25; SBN 162).

> While we cannot give a satisfactory reason, why we believe, after a thousand experiments, that a stone will fall, or fire burn; can we ever satisfy ourselves concerning any determination, which we may form, with regard to the origin of worlds, and the situation of nature, from, and to eternity? (EHU 12.25; SBN 162)

What Hume thinks the "excessive" and unanswerable force of Pyrrhonian doubt brings home to us what he calls:

> the whimsical condition of mankind, who must act and reason and believe; though they are not able, by their most diligent enquiry, to satisfy themselves concerning the foundation of these operations, or to remove the objections, which may be raised against them. (EHU 12.23; SBN 160)

Hume himself was certainly unable to satisfy himself concerning the "foundation" of his acting, reasoning, and believing as he does. His despair at that point seemed far from "whimsical." And he saw his own dissatisfaction with the foundations of those operations as the fate of all of us. There is no satisfactory vindication of our cognitive capacities in general that meets the Pyrrhonist's standards. Not because philosophy, in standing over our reasonings and assessing their validity, is impotent to show that those standards have been met. And not because superintending philosophical reflection interferes with, or undermines, our natural inclinations to reflect and believe. The Pyrrhonian conclusion cannot be accepted simply because the lively endorsement required for believing and acting as we do comes from fully natural forces or instincts. And those forces operate even in the face of what we recognize, and even feel, to be a paralysis of reason.

Our being naturally unable to resist believing things does not provide a "naturalist vindication" of the beliefs we naturally arrive at, or of the processes which generate them. It is simply an undeniable fact about human thinkers and believers and agents as we find ourselves in the world. That is what frees Hume from "excessive" scepticism and leads him to his "mitigated scepticism." There are questions Hume does not answer about this apparently more liberated "sceptical" condition within which he resolves to continue his philosophical reflections. Exactly what attitude does he hold towards those things he cannot help believing, while being unable to satisfy himself about their "foundation," or to remove objections that can be raised against them? Does he fully endorse them, or not? How "diffident" can he consistently be towards these questions about reasons while continuing to accept what he believes? These and other questions would need to be answered before Ainslie's challenge to this "sceptical" understanding of Hume could be fully met.

But there seems little doubt that Hume himself understood the position he found himself in in some such way. Given his questions, and his natural curiosity, about human nature, he cannot refrain from investigating more closely the details of human life, despite being unable to satisfy himself concerning the foundation of the very operations he recognizes to be the only ways of finding out anything about the world. And in carrying on as he does, he shows "most perfectly" his "sceptical disposition and principles."

NOTES

1 Numbers alone in parentheses in the text refer to the pages of this book.

2 References are to Hume, *A Treatise of Human Nature*, ed. Norton and Norton, hereafter cited in the text as "T" followed by Book, part, section, and paragraph number, and to Hume, *A Treatise of Human Nature*, ed. Selby-Bigge, rev. by Nidditch, cited in the text as "SBN" followed by the page number.

3 References are to Hume, *An Enquiry concerning Human Understanding*, ed. Beauchamp, hereafter cited in the text as "EHU" followed by section and paragraph number, and to Hume, *An Enquiry Concerning Human Understanding*, ed. Selby-Bigge, rev. by Nidditch, hereafter cited in the text as "SBN" followed by page numbers.

WORKS CITED

Ainslie, Donald C. *Hume's True Scepticism*. New York: Oxford University Press, 2015.

Hume, David. *A Treatise of Human Nature*. Edited by David Fate Norton and Mary J. Norton. Oxford: Oxford University Press, 2007.

Hume, David. *A Treatise of Human Nature*. Edited by L. A. Selby-Bigge, revised by P. Nidditch. Oxford: Clarendon Press, 1978.

Hume, David. *An Enquiry Concerning Human Understanding*. Edited by Tom L. Beauchamp. New York: Oxford University Press, 1999.

Hume, David. *Enquiries Concerning the Human Understanding and Concerning the Principles of Morals*. Edited by L. A. Selby-Bigge. Oxford: Clarendon Press, 1978.

HUME STUDIES
Volume 45, Number 1–2, 2019, pp. 129–141

Reply to My Critics

DONALD C. AINSLIE

I owe thanks to Annemarie Butler, Jonathan Cottrell, and Barry Stroud for their thoughtful criticism of my interpretation in *Hume's True Scepticism* (hereafter "HTS") of David Hume's epistemology and philosophy of mind as presented in *A Treatise of Human Nature* (especially Part 4 of Book 1).[1] Butler focuses on my account of the mental mechanisms Hume provides for our everyday beliefs about external objects. She also challenges my appeal to what Hume calls "secondary" ideas (T 1.1.1.11; SBN 6) in my explanation of Humean introspection. Cottrell raises questions about my interpretation of perceptions generally, both introspective and non-introspective, as well as my understanding of Hume's conflicted statements about the mind as a "bundle" of related perceptions. Stroud's main concern is my interpretation of Hume's scepticism. I will address these criticisms more-or-less following the order in which they appear in the book, which in turn mostly follows the order of exposition in *Treatise* 1.4. I finish with a response to Cottrell's discussion of Hume's second thoughts about personal identity in the "Appendix" to the *Treatise*.

I. Vulgar Beliefs

Butler worries that I over-emphasize the role of language in Hume's account of the vulgar belief in external objects (HTS 73–74, 91–97), in that I analyze fictions, including those of such objects, through the lens of his treatment of general ideas, where linguistic terms trigger the associative tendencies involved in these thoughts (T 1.1.7.7; SBN 20–21). She is right that he does not thematize language in "Of scepticism with regard to the senses" (hereafter "SwS"), though it does not go unmentioned, as in his concern with what we "say" about absent objects (T 1.4.2.38; SBN 207) and what the "propriety of speech" (T 1.4.2.29; SBN 201)

Donald C. Ainslie, Department of Philosophy, c/o University College, University of Toronto, 15 King's College Circle, Toronto, ON M5S 3H7, Canada.
Email: donald.ainslie@utoronto.ca

requires in our identity claims; it is also striking how much he treats identity claims as "verbal" or "grammatical" in "Of personal identity," both as they apply to persons and to other kinds of entities (T 1.4.6.21; see also T 1.4.6.7, 1.4.6.13; SBN 262, 255, 258). Nonetheless, Hume repeatedly stresses our continuity with non-linguistic animals throughout the *Treatise* (for example, T 1.3.16, 2.1.12, 2.2.12; 2.3.9.32, SBN 176–79, 324–28, 397–98, 448), and I do not disagree with Butler that my claiming that vulgar beliefs about the world have a linguistic structure is in some tension with Hume's claims about non-human animals, which surely also have similar beliefs.

In my defence, recall that Hume compares linguistic conventions to those that define property, where a person's actions "have a reference to those of . . . other[s]" (T 3.2.2.10; SBN 490); similarly, when someone believes that, say, the desk in the office is the same as the one that was there when she was last in the room, her beliefs have an implicit reference to our shared expectations for how desks behave—they tend not to move about on their own—and how we all respond to constant and coherent experiences. And she ought to defer should someone in a position to know explain to her that the desk had actually been switched for the one from next door. Animal belief will not have this structure, even if it has some of the same associative bases as the human analogues. The difference is the kind of normativity. While the woman and those in her community hold her to their shared standards for desk-persistence, an animal's errors will emerge only by its failed practical interactions with the object in question. When its associations lead it to believe, say, that the poison it encounters is the same object as the tasty snack that was there earlier, it will end up dead. Our linguistic practices allow us to navigate the world collectively, rather than simply waiting for it to surprise us when it does not conform to our expectations. The analogy between property and language as both being convention-dependent is telling, for Hume acknowledges that animals are "incapable of right and property" (T 2.1.12.5; SBN 326); I think it follows that they are incapable of interacting with external objects with the kind of right that follows from the "propriety of language" (T 1.4.6.13; SBN 158).[2]

Butler also worries that, in my explanation of the four-part mechanism at the heart of Hume's explanation of our beliefs about objects (T 1.4.2.24–43; SBN 199–210), I have unduly separated the first two parts—those yielding a belief in an object's being the same despite our interrupted awareness of it—from the latter two—those yielding a belief in the existence of an unperceived object. On the one hand, I think there is both textual and phenomenological evidence for this separation. Hume says, after explaining the first two parts, that "[t]he persons, who entertain this *opinion* concerning the identity of our resembling perceptions, are in general all the unthinking and unphilosophical part of mankind" (T 1.4.2.36; SBN 205, emphasis added). And indeed, when I, say, return to my office, I typically take the desk to be the same as the one that was there previously, giving literally no thought to what the desk was up to between my sensings of it. On the other hand, Butler is right that Hume attributes an instability to this belief that is resolved by a conception of the desk as existing between the times I was perceiving it (T 1.4.2.36–40; SBN 205–208). I think our interpretations ultimately put different emphases on a common point: when I encounter a desk, I take it to be a temporally extended object that lasts beyond my momentary sensing of it (see HTS §3.3) in part because of my tendency, emphasized in the third and fourth parts of Hume's explanation, to take the desk to continue existing identically when I happen to think of it during those times I am not sensing it.

II. Secondary Ideas

Butler raises several challenges to my account of Humean introspection in terms of secondary ideas (as does Cottrell, whose criticisms I discuss in the next section of my reply). First, she worries that Hume will end up over-populating the mind, with every impression being copied into both primary and secondary ideas.[3] I think rather that, while every sensory impression is copied into an idea (T 1.1.1.5; SBN 3), we do not usually form secondary ideas of our perceptions. Sometimes they will occur spontaneously, as when we find ourselves thinking not of *things* we have experienced but of our *experiences* (T 1.3.8.16; SBN 106). Philosophers use this capacity in a more disciplined fashion by "entering most intimately" into themselves in order to "observe" the mind (T 1.4.6.3; SBN 252) and, in this case, secondary ideas serve as the vehicles for their observations.

Second, Butler also wonders whether it is legitimate to appeal to secondary ideas to account for Humean introspection and, third, if so, whether he actually needs to appeal to them. Both problems arise because of my claim that Humean perceptions are properly understood as mental events—perceivings—rather than as mental objects (HTS §6.6). Briefly, I worry that the standard object-interpretation must appeal to some kind of mental activity that would make us aware of the perceptions (as if we were, say, "conscious" of perceptions,[4] or have "experiences" of them[5]), landing it in conflict with Hume's claim that the mind is nothing but a bundle of related perceptions (T 1.4.6.4; SBN 252). I argue that, instead, a perception is an *episode* of awareness that, in the case of sensations, includes both imagistic content and the mental "action" (T 1.2.5.21, 1.3.8.16, 1.4.2.35n39, 3.3.1.2; SBN 61, 106, 204–205) by which we are aware of that content. These two aspects of sensations are inseparable, though by a "distinction of reason" (T 1.1.7.17–18; SBN 24–25) we can think of each.

Butler questions the legitimacy of my appeal to secondary ideas when she notes that, because "a primary idea can copy the image-content of an impression without copying its manner, . . . it separates features of an idea which seem not to be separable" (her question [2]). I do not think there is a problem here, in that the primary idea copies a sensory impression, not by *separating out* the impression's image-content, but by making a qualitatively identical *copy* of it, accompanied now by a different, inseparable mental action, a thinking, as opposed to a sensing. Consider the analogous case of a white globe, where the globe's shape and colour are, for Hume, inseparable though distinct by reason (T 1.1.7.18; SBN 25). A black copy of the globe could be made that had a qualitatively identical shape though now with a different colour. The inseparability of neither the original globe's colour and shape, nor of copy's colour and shape, is threatened.[6]

Butler's third worry is that secondary ideas are not really needed: Because a primary idea copies the image-content of a primary impression, she suggests that it can just as easily be used to copy the mental-activity aspect of the impression. As I understand it, her point is that since, by a distinction of reason, we can think of either the content or the mental action involved in a primary perception, this distinguishing is sufficient for both introspective and everyday mental activity. I think this proposal will not work. Consider again Hume's example of a white globe; we must already have it in view prior to distinguishing its (inseparable) aspects. In the case of introspective thought, then, we would already need to have the perception in view before we could separate out either its image content or its being an episode of awareness. And this is where I take Hume to appeal to secondary ideas: they allow us to have our perceptions in view. Perhaps Butler has something else in mind, but I do not see how distinctions of reason could enable Hume to avoid positing what I take to be his replacements for Locke's ideas of reflection (see HTS §4.3.1).

III. Perceptions

Cottrell raises concerns, not just about my treatment of secondary ideas, but also about my interpretation of perceptions more broadly. I discuss this topic primarily in chapter 6 when examining how Hume responds to "modern" systems of the "internal world" (T 1.4.2.57; SBN 218). He attributes a view to "some philosophers"—I suggest in HTS that Locke comes closest to his target (HTS §6.2)—whereby we have a special, intimate grasp of the simplicity and identity of mind (T 1.4.6.1; SBN 251), and rejects it after entering "most intimately" into himself and observing "nothing but a bundle or collection of different perceptions, which succeed each other with an inconceivable rapidity, and are in a perpetual flux and movement" (T 1.4.6.3–4; SBN 252). As I noted above, I take the perceptions that compose the mind to be best understood as *perceivings*—episodes of awareness—and Cottrell takes issue with this claim. He raises two main concerns. First, I have left Hume with an unreduced notion of awareness that Cottrell takes to be in violation of Hume's naturalistic scruples. Second, I am not able to adequately account for impressions of reflection—passions and emotions—and the ideas that copy them, especially as they play a role in his account of sympathy.

Taking the second objection first, Cottrell worries that my interpretation seems to leave all ideas that copy passions as secondary ideas. Because my focus in the book is Part 4 of Book 1 of the *Treatise*, I mostly neglect impressions of reflection, which Hume primarily considers in Books 2 and 3 (though of course the impression of necessity is a crucial such impression that appears in Book 1; see T 1.3.14.22; SBN 165–66). I do briefly suggest, however, that, whereas sensations for Hume have imagistic content and thus should be understood as awarenesses-of-image-content, impressions of reflections lack such content (T 2.3.3.5; SBN 415) and thus should be understood as modifications of *how* we are aware of whatever objects we are thinking of. They are mere "flavours" of vivacity that thereby serve to "colour . . . our outlooks on the world" (HTS 213–14).

Cottrell suggests that this understanding of impressions of reflection will prove inadequate for Hume's analysis of sympathy, where we come to feel what another person is feeling, first, by a causal inference's leading us to form an idea of her or his passion, and then by this idea's being converted into the passion itself by an infusion of vivacity from the "idea, or rather impression of ourselves" that is "always intimately present with us" (T 2.1.11.4; SBN 317). This analysis, no matter how you understand Humean perceptions, is far from trouble-free,[7] but Cottrell worries in particular that I will need to treat the idea of the other's passion as a secondary idea; it will thus have something analogous to image-content that would allow for it to serve as a belief in the existence of a mental state (HTS 131–32). How then would an injection of vivacity convert this perception into the passion, where passions lack such content (T 2.3.3.5; SBN 415)?

I think this problem can be avoided if Hume can be found to have two different ways that an idea can copy a passion, just as he has two different ways that an idea can copy a sensory impression (HTS 127). In both cases, it is possible for the idea to copy the prior perception so that it becomes *of* that perception-as-a-mental-state; the idea, in this case, would be a secondary idea that is a form of introspective thought. In addition, for sensory impressions, a (primary) idea can copy the impression by copying its image-content, though it is now entertained with less vivacity; thus, we can think of what we have previously sensed. I think that something analogous can also happen with passions, though of course, lacking image-content, all that the primary idea can copy will be the "flavour" or "outlook" the passion in question involves, though with less vivacity. An idea of, say, the desire for chocolate would be a perception of chocolate (a separate perception with imagistic content) accompanied by a flavouring of that awareness by the addition or superimposition of a desiderative manner of conceiving. We would be thinking of the chocolate *in a wanting manner*, though not to the extent that we actually want it. A secondary idea of the desire, in contrast, would be a thought of the *wanting*. If Hume can appeal to this kind of idea in his sympathy mechanism—and there is no direct textual evidence for or against—he avoids the problem that Cottrell points to.

Cottrell's primary—and more significant—challenge to my interpretation of Humean perceptions is a defense of the more standard view that takes perceptions to be mental objects. He argues that perceptions can be understood as the sensible qualities or feelings we are *aware of* when, say, seeing an object or in the grip of a passion. He notes that I challenge interpretations of this kind in part by questioning how they can understand the *awareness* they invoke, given that Hume identifies the mind with a bundle of related perceptions, not a bundle plus a set of awarenesses of them. Cottrell responds to this concern by pointing to Hume's claim in the middle portion of SwS that "*seeing*, *feeling*, and *perceiving*" (T 1.4.2.38; SBN 207) are nothing but perceptions' acquiring "such a relation to a connected heap of perceptions, as to influence them very considerably in augmenting their number by present reflections and passions, and in storing the memory with ideas" (T 1.4.2.40; SBN 208). Being aware of a perception is thus nothing but its being in the bundle, casually linked to other perceptions in the right way. Moreover, Cottrell suggests, this analysis of perceptions allows

Hume to naturalize intentionality by explaining it in terms of relations "found throughout the natural world (not just in minds)."

I am not persuaded by Cottrell's proposal. Hume, I think, in "glean[ing] up [his] experiments . . . from a cautious observation of human life" (T Intro. 10; SBN xix), is trying to explain, *inter alia*, our everyday awareness[8] of things when we sense and think, and our feelings and reactions to what we experience. Where does this awareness fit into Cottrell's model? A child's seeing of an orange (T 1.1.1.8; SBN 4) is, for him, the entrance of the relevant perception—the complex impression that is an orange sphere—into the child's mind-bundle (where it causes the thought of the orange, a desire for the taste, a memory of a trip to Florida, and so on; and note that the awareness that is part of our normal conception of thinking, desiring, and remembering cannot be assumed by Cottrell). It seems then either that the impression when in the bundle just is the *seeing-of-the-orange* that my interpretation posits, or that Cottrell's Hume is an eliminativist, where the everyday notion of awareness is explained away, with the impression remaining simply an orange sphere whether in or out of the mind. I take it that Cottrell must take the latter option, for he holds that the perception remains the same whether it is inside or outside of the bundle—and indeed such a conclusion follows from Hume's view that causal relations, which for Cottrell constitute the perceptions as a bundle, do not involve changes in the relata, but rather simply their conjunction in the right sort of way (T 1.3.14.31; SBN 170).

I think, however, that there is good textual evidence that Hume is not an eliminativist of this type. He emphasizes at various points, for example, that thoughts of objects include an "action of the mind in the meditation"—"that certain *je-ne-scai-quoi*, of which 'tis impossible to give any definition or description, but which every one sufficiently understands" (T 1.3.8.16; SBN 106)—and that we can represent this action through a memory of a *thought* (as opposed to a memory of its object). Ideas can thus be associated not just because of relations between their objects but because of resemblances in the relevant mental actions, a point that Hume describes as being "of great consequence" when he first introduces it (T 1.2.5.21; SBN 61), and that makes a crucial appearance in the four-part explanation of our vulgar beliefs about objects in SwS (T 1.4.2.35n39; SBN 204–205).

Another problem for Cottrell's view is his assumption that perceptions must enter into causal relations with *other* perceptions for them to be fully mental items. Hume, however, allows that: "We can conceive a thinking being to have either many or few perceptions. Suppose the mind to be reduc'd even below the life of an oyster. Suppose it to have only one perception, as of thirst or hunger" (T App.16; SBN 634). Presumably the sub-oyster's thirst or hunger counts as a primitive mode of awareness, even though it is the sole perception in the relevant bundle. Thus, when Hume emphasizes the separability of a perception from our mind-bundle (for example, T 1.4.5.5, 1.4.6.3, App.12; SBN 233, 252, 634), I take him merely to be indicating that it lacks an intrinsic connection with the others in the bundle and could conceivably be found on its own, a lonely perception like the mind of the sub-oyster.

Finally, the textual evidence that Cottrell relies on (T 1.4.2.38–40; SBN 206–208) is less than clear. Hume is here considering a possible Berkeleyan objection to the third part of his four-part explanation of the belief in the continued existence of objects that display constancy in our sensing of them: How can I even *think* of an object's existing when unperceived? He puts his response in terms of his analysis of the mind as a bundle of related perceptions, each of which could exist apart from the mind. This is a difficult portion of an already difficult stretch of text, and I offer my analysis of it at HTS 102–103. The main challenge as I see it is that Hume is struggling with how to characterize the vulgar belief in (what philosophers understand as [HTS 99]) external objects. The content of the vulgar belief is not found in the content of any perception taken singly, but rather is the result of the dynamics of the imagination. How then to characterize the content of this belief when explaining it philosophically? Hume settles on the less-than-helpful move of treating 'perception' and 'object' interchangeably, because the vulgar believe that what they sense exists, and the philosophers hold that what they sense is the content of a perception (T 1.4.2.31; SBN 202; he returns to his more standard use of "perception" at T 1.4.2.46; SBN 211). Ultimately, like other of Hume's interpreters,[9] I suggest he uses 'perception' ambiguously, sometimes to indicate an *object* we are aware of, and sometimes the *episode* of awareness, though for the reasons I offer in the book (HTS §6.6), I think the latter usage must be his official position on the issue.

Cottrell's most programmatic concern with my interpretation of Humean perceptions is that, by taking them to be mental episodes or states of awareness—perceivings—I violate what he takes to be Hume's naturalistic commitments. I worry, however, that Cottrell understands these commitments in a way that is too close to the "modern philosophy," of which Hume says "many objections might be made" (T 1.4.4.6; see HTS §§6.1–4). Like the moderns, Cottrell wants to separate the mentalistic (or secondary) qualities from the primary—those features of the world that figure in the natural sciences broadly. I do not think that Hume is committed to naturalism in this sense. Consider especially his discussion of the will, where he emphasizes that bodily states can cause mental ones and vice versa, where of course the perceptions here, like all causes and effects, are distinct from their correlative effects and causes (T 2.3.1, SBN 399–407; see also T 1.4.5.29–30; SBN 246–48). He does not seem bothered that the science of human nature includes mental states such as sensations that "arise in the soul originally, from unknown causes" (T 1.1.2.1, SBN 7–8; see also T 1.3.5.2; SBN 84).

IV. Scepticism

Stroud objects to my "philosophical" reading of Hume's scepticism that takes its core concern to be how philosophy fits into everyday life—that we have no "obligation" to pursue it, and that only those with an inclination should bother with it, using of course the method of a "true sceptic" (T 1.4.7.10, 1.4.7.12, 1.4.7.14; SBN 270, 270–71, 273). Stroud argues instead for a more traditional, sceptical reading, where the "desponding reflections" (T 1.4.7.1; SBN 264) of the "Conclusion of this book" (T 1.4.7; SBN 263–74, hereafter "CtB") that call into question the verdicts of reason and the senses are never resolved but rather simply ignored, as nature causes us to believe, despite our negative verdict on our human faculties. My concern with such readings is that they suffer from what Phillip Cummins has called the "integration" problem:[10] how can we understand Hume's willingness to continue on with his scientific project in Books 2 and 3, if he has so fully undermined the capacities we need for that science in CtB (see HTS 227)? Stroud's response is that Hume's nature inclines him to philosophy and that this fact suffices to explain his forging onwards with the rest of the *Treatise*. I think, however, that an appeal to inclination of this sort could be at best a causal explanation and would not yet show any positive reason for Hume to go on; but, he says that he hopes to "contribute a little to the advancement of *knowledge*, by giving in some particulars a different turn to the speculations of philosophers, and pointing out to them more distinctly those subjects, where alone they can expect *assurance* and *conviction*" (T 1.4.7.14; SBN 273, emphases added). In fact, if Hume thought that the sceptical attacks on reason and the senses remained intact, he himself admits that he would immediately give up on further inquiry (T Intro.9, 2.3.3.7; SBN xviii, 416–17). I do not think Stroud has avoided the integration problem.

The root of Stroud's and my disagreement concerns how to read CtB. Where he sees no discontinuity between the narrative voice in that Section and in the rest of the Book 1 ("it is David Hume who complains. . . ."), I see it as an account of the transition from "false" philosophy to "true philosophy" (T 1.4.3.9, SBN 222–23), namely "true" scepticism (T 1.4.7.14, SBN 273). My approach thus has some similarity with what I call the "dialectical" interpretations of Annette Baier, Edward Morris, and others (see HTS §7.4).[11] And I think there is good textual evidence for seeing Hume as starting CtB with a different attitude towards his endeavour from what he had previously displayed. Consider especially his seeming upset over the discovery that he lacks insight into the intrinsic connections between causes and effects (T 1.4.7.5; SBN 266–67)—a discovery that caused no distress in T 1.3—and the embrace of the conflict between reason and our imagination-generated belief in body (T 1.4.7.4; SBN 266) that he had previously seen as merely the expression of the "modern philosophy" (T 1.4.4.15; SBN 231; see HTS 200–204). I differ from the other dialectical interpreters, however, in that, where they hold that Hume starts CtB by impersonating "rationalist" opponents, I take him rather to be exemplifying a temptation that afflicts all forms of reflection, his own included. Because, when we reflect, we remain focused on only the mind we observe, and not the vehicles of that reflection (secondary ideas), it is easy to start thinking that a reflective attitude towards the mind comes for free, as if we were *always* superintending the mind, having to make decisions about what to believe. As he moves through the denouement of CtB, he comes to acknowledge that reflection depends on the same principles of association as our everyday forms of awareness, and thus that attacks on the latter also undermine the former (what I call "reflective interference"). When Hume then narrates the return to philosophy at T 1.4.7.11–13 (SBN 270–72), he can view the sceptical challenges, not as undermining reason and the senses, but as posing questions that philosophy turns out to be unable to answer positively or negatively (T 1.4.7.14; SBN 272–73); we can continue to reason and sense even while, as "true sceptics," recognizing that we lack a philosophical foundation for our capacities.

It is notable that Stroud must turn to the analogous section of the first *Enquiry*[12] when trying to make sense of Hume's attitude towards sceptical arguments. I take this later work, in recasting Book 1's arguments about the structure of the mind in epistemological terms, to be more amenable to a sceptical interpretation. Most famously, in the *Enquiry*, Hume uses sceptical tropes to present his argument about causation, while in the analogous Part 3 of Book 1 of the *Treatise*, the word 'sceptic' (and its cognates) appears precisely once (T 1.3.13.12; SBN 150). Hume does later say that he changed only the "manner," and not the "matter," of his philosophy when writing the *Enquiry*, and that the "Principles are the same in both" works.[13] How best to understand the differences between them remains an open question,[14] but, as I argue in the "Introduction" to HTS (16–17), I think it is worthwhile to consider how the *Treatise* reads on its own terms, not through the retrospective lens of the *Enquiry*. I remain convinced that the "true" scepticism in the former work is a scepticism about philosophy, what it can accomplish, and its place in life.

V. Personal Identity

Hume's second thoughts about personal identity in the "Appendix" to the *Treatise* have probably sparked more interpretations than almost any other topic in his philosophy; certainly, as Hsueh M. Qu has pointed out, the ratio of the secondary literature to the paragraphs of source text is extremely high.[15] Cottrell and I have both contributed our fair share already, but his criticisms of the interpretation I present in HTS helps to highlight a previously neglected issue: the difference between Hume's accounts of the *bundle of perceptions* and of the *mind* as consisting of related perceptions.

Cottrell takes my interpretation of Hume's position—that he is unable to explain our belief in the unity of observed perceptions with the secondary ideas that enable this observation—to be wholly psychological, concerned only with our *beliefs* about mental unity, and he goes on to argue for his preferred metaphysical interpretation.[16] He is not wrong that I emphasize Hume's account of our beliefs, but I take it also to have metaphysical import (it might thus best be characterized as *psychology-first* interpretation, rather than as a psychological one). Though the mind as a bundle does not have "perfect" or intrinsic unity, it does have what Hume calls "imperfect" unity that it exemplifies by causing our belief in its unity: "[T]he uninterrupted progress of the thought . . . constitutes the imperfect identity" (T 1.4.6.9; SBN 256; see HTS 90, 93, 206ff., 249, 258, 261) and, analogously, simplicity (T 1.4.6.22; SBN 263) of the mind.[17]

Cottrell, in contrast, thinks that Hume's concern is more fully metaphysical, particularly focusing on how perceptions come to "compose" a mind (T 1.4.6.16, App. 15, 20; SBN 256, 634, 635). He suggests that, for Hume, such composition is "ideal" depending on our forming secondary ideas that, by association or active relating, bring together the perceptions being composed.[18] Cottrell's and my interpretations are closely related but importantly different, in that they see Hume as addressing different questions. For Cottrell, Hume wants to analyze how perceptions come to form the "system" that is the mind (T 1.4.6.19; SBN 261); it is thus what I call a "bundling" interpretation (HTS §8.3.3). This approach is related to Cottrell's view of perceptions that I discussed above, in that he takes them to be able to enter and depart the mind depending on whether they have the relevant causal relations with the other perceptions in the system; Hume's explanatory starting point, for Cottrell, seems to be a universe of free-floating perceptions with their being 'bundled' only when they develop the relevant relations that enable them to compose a mind. Note, however, that, because perceptions are in the mind only when they are related to other perceptions in the right way, it follows that there can be no such thing as a *chaotic* bundle with random, disconnected perceptions. But surely such a bundle is conceivable (and thus possible [T 1.2.2.8, SBN 32; see HTS §5.4]); indeed, Hume seems open to such a possibility at T 1.4.6.17 (SBN 260), where he sets out to see whether resemblance and causal relations actually do obtain between perceptions.

My interpretation, in contrast, focuses on how the mind has "imperfect" identity and simplicity—that is, how, when we observe perceptions within us that have no intrinsic connections between them, we nonetheless believe that they are unified with one another. Should they not have the causal and resemblance relations we happen to find there, the bundle would not be imperfectly unified. It would be a mere bundle. And Cottrell is right that I take Hume to treat its being a bundle as a brute fact (see HTS 264). The universe comes with different 'islands' of perceptions (HTS 264), each such island being a "universe of the imagination" (T 1.2.6.8; SBN 68) or "of thought" (T 1.4.5.21; SBN 242). Each person, when reflecting, cannot observe another person's perceptions; only by a thought experiment where we "see clearly into the breast of another" (T 1.4.6.18; SBN 260) could we cross the gap between different bundles. Thus, I take Hume's retraction in the "Appendix" to concern only his account of the imperfect unity of the mind, not the bundle view as such (see HTS 250).

Cottrell worries that taking the bundling of perceptions to be a brute fact conflicts with Hume's theory of relations, where 'co-bundling' does not fall into the seven categories of relations he gives: "If it were a brute fact that several perceptions compose a mind, then composition would have to be a basic or fundamental kind of relation, i.e., one that is not explained in terms of any further relations." Because Cottrell seems to take Hume's starting point to be a universe of free-floating perceptions, he needs something that would bring some of them together to compose minds. But once we distinguish between the issues of bundling and of mental unity, I can accept Cottrell's point about composition. The perceptions within a bundle *compose a mind* when they have the relations that cause us to associate our secondary ideas of them. That these perceptions are in the bundle in the first place remains a brute fact; equivalently, given Hume's reliance on introspection to understand the mind,[19] it is a brute fact that, when we reflect, we observe only a subset of perceptions, not all of those in the universe. If a relation is needed to characterize the perceptions in the bundle, their availability to introspection would suffice—with introspection being understood causally and thus having a place in Hume's taxonomy of relations (albeit the relation of any perception to the object it represents is a complex matter for Hume; see HTS 204).[20]

NOTES

1 References to the *Treatise* are to Hume, *A Treatise of Human Nature*, ed. Norton and Norton, hereafter cited in the text as "T" followed by Book, part, section, and paragraph number, and to Hume, *A Treatise of Human Nature*, ed. Selby-Bigge and Nidditch, cited in the text as "SBN" followed by the page number.

2 Karl Schafer also emphasizes the role of language and artifice in Hume's theory of representation; see "The Artificial Virtues of Thought," 1–20. But where Schafer takes the relevant kind of normativity here to be moral, I take Hume to allow for a kind of rule-governed normativity in a given domain that is non-moral. Note that he establishes the conventional nature of property first (T 3.2.2.1–22; SBN 484–98), and only then (T 3.2.2.23ff; SBN 498–501) considers that conformity to those rules is morally relevant because of the "sympathy with public interest" that respect for property makes possible (T 3.2.2.24; SBN 500).

3 Butler also worries that T 1.1.1.11 (SBN 6) seems to concern only secondary ideas *of ideas*, not secondary ideas *of impressions*. I acknowledge this point at HTS 122, where I note that he also recognizes (secondary) ideas of impressions at T 1.3.8.17 (SBN 106). Moreover, given that T 1.1.1.11 (SBN 6) concerns how he has been engaging in "this very reasoning concerning" perceptions – his establishment of his principle that almost all simple ideas are copies of prior simple *impressions*—he has been using secondary ideas of *both* ideas and impressions throughout T 1.1.1, even if T 1.1.1.11 overtly addresses only secondary ideas of ideas.

4 Wayne Waxman, *Hume's Theory of Consciousness*, is the clearest defender of this view.

5 As David Norton suggests in the "Introduction" to *A Treatise of Human Nature*, I23.

6 This is not to say that Hume's treatment of distinctions of reason is without its issues; see especially Donald Baxter, "Hume, Distinctions of Reason, and Differential Resemblance," and Taro Okamura, "Hume on Distinctions of Reason: A Resemblance-First Interpretation."

7 See my "Sympathy and the Unity of Hume's Idea of Self."

8 I use the word 'aware' in part because it is suitably generic and less freighted with philosophical theory than, say, 'conscious.' Hume uses it only once in the *Treatise* (T 1.4.6.6; SBN 254).

9 See HTS 53n18.

10 Phillip Cummins, "Hume's Diffident Skepticism."

11 Annette Baier, *A Progress of Sentiments*; W. E. Morris, "Hume's Conclusion."

12 Section 12 of *An Enquiry concerning Human Understanding.*

13 "My Own Life," in *Essays: Moral, Political, and Literary*, xxxv; "Letter to Gilbert Eliot," in *Letters of David Hume*, 1:158.

14 See Miriam McCormick, "A Change in Manner: Hume's Scepticism in the *Treatise* and the first *Enquiry*"; Hsueh M. Qu, *Hume's Epistemological Evolution.*

15 *Epistemological Evolution*, 103.

16 See his "Minds, Composition, and Hume's Skepticism in the Appendix."

17 Cottrell takes T App. 10 (SBN 633) to favour a metaphysical interpretation. Hume proposes there to review the arguments "on both sides, beginning [and lasting until T App.19, SBN 635]

with those that induc'd me to deny the strict and proper identity and simplicity of a self or thinking being" and thus, to Cottrell, suggesting that the second side (T App. 20–21; SBN 635–36) should be similarly metaphysical. But, because my view has a stronger metaphysical element that Cottrell acknowledges, it can take this point on board. T App. 20 (SBN 635) starts with Hume's retelling of his treatment of the imperfect unity of the mind (brought about by the fact that "when reflecting on the train of past perceptions, that compose a mind, the ideas of them are felt to be connected together, and naturally introduce each other" [see HTS 254–55 for a discussion of the significance of the word 'past' here]). But then he comes to recognize that his earlier account cannot explain his belief in mental unity and derivatively the mind's imperfect unity.

18 "Minds, Composition," 552.

19 His attitude on this point is conflicted. See HTS 62, 132–34.

20 Yumiko Inukai also notes that Hume treats the occurrence of perceptions in a bundle as a "brute fact" and argues that the problem he identifies in the "Appendix" arises as a consequence ("Hume's Labyrinth," 267). She takes him to hold that the perceptions in the bundle are "unified" (268ff.) but is unable to account for the connections between perceptions she takes such unity to require (Cottrell's concern that brute bundling would require a relation not included in Hume's taxonomy at T 1.1.5 is similar). I think, in contrast, that there is no unity in the bundle unless the perceptions display the relations that trigger the association of (secondary) ideas of them. Inukai concludes that "Hume's problem is more fundamental than most of the commentators have made it to be, for it is not specific only to his account of the generation of our idea of a persisting self, but it is with his primary presupposition on which his psychological account is based" (270). The interpretation thus conflicts with Hume's statement that the personal identity Section contains his single mistake in Books 1 and 2 (T App. 1; SBN 623) and with the insulation of the "Appendix" problem from other appearances of the bundle theory (for example, T 1.4.2.39; SBN 207).

WORKS CITED

Ainslie, Donald C. *Hume's True Scepticism*. New York: Oxford University Press, 2015.

Ainslie, Donald C. "Sympathy and the Unity of Hume's Idea of Self." In *Persons and Passions*. Edited by Joyce Jenkins, Jennifer Whiting, and Christopher Williams, 143–73. South Bend, IN: University of Notre Dame Press, 2005.

Baier, Annette. *A Progress of Sentiments*. Cambridge, MA: Harvard University Press, 1991.

Baxter, Donald. "Hume, Distinctions of Reason, and Differential Resemblance." *Philosophy and Phenomenological Research* 82 (2011): 156–82. https://doi.org/10.1111/j.1933-1592.2010.00411.x

Cottrell, Jonathan. "Minds, Composition, and Hume's Skepticism in the Appendix." *The Philosophical Review* 124 (2015): 533–69. https://doi.org/10.1215/00318108-3147021

Cummins, Phillip. "Hume's Diffident Skepticism." *Hume Studies* 25 (1999): 43–65.

Hume, David. *Enquiry Concerning Human Understanding: A Critical Edition*. Edited by Tom Beauchamp. Oxford: Clarendon Press, 2000.

Hume, David. *Enquiries Concerning Human Understanding and Concerning the Principles of Morals*. Edited by L. A. Selby-Bigge, revised by P. H. Nidditch, 3rd ed. Oxford: Clarendon Press, 1975.

Hume, David. "Letter to Gilbert Eliot." In *Letters of David Hume*. Volume 1. Edited by J. Y. T. Grieg. Oxford: Clarendon Press, 1932.

Hume, David. "My Own Life." In *Essays: Moral, Political, and Literary.* Edited by Eugene F. Miller. Indianapolis, IN: Liberty Fund, 1987.

Hume, David. *A Treatise of Human Nature*. Edited by David Fate Norton and Mary J. Norton. Oxford: Clarendon Press, 2000.

Hume, David. *A Treatise of Human Nature*. Edited by L. A. Selby-Bigge and P. H. Nidditch. Oxford: Clarendon Press, 1978.

Inukai, Yumiko. "Hume's Labyrinth: The Bundling Problem." *History of Philosophy Quarterly* 24 (2007): 255–74.

McCormick, Miriam. "A Change in Manner: Hume's Scepticism in the *Treatise* and the first *Enquiry*." *Canadian Journal of Philosophy* 29 (1999): 431–48. https://doi.org/10.1080/00455091.1999.10717520

Morris, W. E. "Hume's Conclusion." *Philosophical Studies* 99 (2000): 89–110. https://doi.org/10.1023/A:1018783526215

Okamura, Taro. "Hume on Distinctions of Reason: A Resemblance-First Interpretation." *Australasian Journal of Philosophy* 97 (2019): 423–36. https://doi.org/10.1080/00048402.2018.1529047

Qu, Hsueh M. *Hume's Epistemological Evolution*. Oxford: Oxford University Press, 2020. https://doi.org/10.1093/oso/9780190066291.001.0001

Schafer, Karl. "The Artificial Virtues of Thought: Correctness and Cognition in Hume." *Philosophers' Imprint* 19, no. 7 (2019): 1–20.

Waxman, Wayne. *Hume's Theory of Consciousness*. Cambridge: Cambridge University Press, 1994.

Hume Studies
Volume 45, Number 1–2, 2019, pp. 143–145

Précis of *Reflecting Subjects: Passion, Sympathy, and Society in Hume's Philosophy*

JACQUELINE A. TAYLOR

In chapter 1, I argue that Hume well understands the experimental method and its role as what Geoffrey Cantor refers to as "a discourse of power," insofar as establishing facts in terms of efficient causation properly delimits what counts as a science, which is, in Hume's case, a science of human nature. With respect to the passions, I focus on parts 1 and 2 of *Treatise* Book 2, as an extended set of experiments meant to explain the origin, nature, and effects of the passion of pride, an indirect passion that reflects a person's self-worth in virtue of her valuable qualities. Beginning with the observable phenomena of pride, Hume identifies various theoretical entities that constitute aspects of the cause and effect of pride, after which he examines the evidence that proves his hypothesis regarding the double relation of ideas and impressions as the cause of pride. His explanation in terms of efficient causes displaces the traditional appeal to final causes, especially to explain human agency. I argue that the experimental approach to explaining the indirect passions is a first stage that allows us to look more closely at the attention Hume pays to how institutions and conventions, and the social roles and relations they engender, profoundly affect how we experience and understand those passions.

In chapter 2, I begin to reconstruct a Humean social theory. The principle of sympathy plays a crucial role in transmitting meaning and values as these are reflected in our beliefs, passions, and sentiments. Our understanding and evaluative attitudes towards ourselves and others are, I argue, socially constituted, and our practical identities are formed within a system of dynamic social relations. Hume's account of the principle of sympathy is an innovation in the modern period, and in this chapter, I focus particularly on its role with respect to belief and the formation of social knowledge.

Jacqueline A. Taylor is Professor in the Department of Philosophy, University of San Francisco, San Francisco, CA..
Email: jtaylor2@usfca.edu.

Chapter 3 takes the account of social relations constituted by the sympathetic transmission of meaning and values, and places it in the context of Hume's detailed account of social power. This neglected part of Hume's *Treatise* is important as it explains why we ascribe various forms of social power to persons, and the influence of social power on the passions. I reconstruct Hume's account of social power, especially with respect to the person-evaluative passions of pride and humility, the passions of respect and contempt, and of fear. The power relations to which these passions are responsive inform our understanding of social identities, and of our own place in a nexus of social relations.

When we turn from Hume's social theory and moral psychology to his Book 3 system of ethics in the *Treatise*, it is striking how Book 2's deep and detailed account of social difference and division does not find a place in Hume's account of the moral sentiments and moral evaluation. Chapter 4 provides a critical analysis of *Treatise*, Book 3, pointing to a central problem with Hume's characterization of the common point of view from which we are supposed to calibrate our moral evaluations and sentiments. I argue that the more sophisticated account of moral evaluation in Hume's *Enquiry concerning the Principles of Morals*, with its emphasis on a shared moral discourse regarding praiseworthy and blameworthy traits of persons, has a considerable advantage over the *Treatise*. In EPM, Hume emphasizes the importance of the virtues required for accurately assessing and responding to merit or demerit. By introducing the sentiment or principle of humanity, Hume puts an emphasis on active participation in striving for shared agreement.

In the *Treatise,* Hume gives a central place to the passion of pride. While the principle of humanity has the central place in EPM, Hume clearly continues to regard pride as important for a sense of confidence and competence. Secular accounts of pride as a vice, or frailty, had currency in the modern period, most notably in the works of Hobbes and Mandeville. Chapter 5 begins with an examination of the troublesome forms of pride as discussed by Hobbes and Mandeville. Understanding their views on the dangers of pride, and the solutions they offer to mitigate pride's effects, helps to highlight the importance of pride as a virtue in Hume's moral theory. Hume attempts to restore the dignity of the virtue of pride by arguing for the importance of modesty, as well as the essential role that a "due" pride plays in the formation of our moral identity.

Reconstructing Hume's account of humanity reveals a powerful moral concept that makes Hume's later ethics in EPM a crucial achievement of the Enlightenment. Chapter 6 gives a detailed account of our capacity for humanity, both as a moral sentiment that approves of useful character traits that contribute to well-being, while blaming pernicious traits, and as a motive to the decent treatment of others. Hume's "Of the Standard of Taste" and "A Dialogue" show that confronting and overcoming prejudice is an important component of humanity. The chapter also draws together the strands of Hume's discussions of humanity in his *Essays*, and considers how humanity and justice are mutually supporting virtues.

WORKS CITED

Cantor, Geoffrey. "The Rhetoric of Experiment," in *The Uses of Experiment: Studies in the Natural Sciences*. Edited by David Gooding, Trevor Pinch, and Simon Schaffer. Cambridge: Cambridge University Press, 1989.

Hume, David. *An Enquiry concerning the Principles of Morals*. Edited by Tom L. Beauchamp. Oxford: Clarendon Press, 1998.

Hume, David. *Essays: Moral, Political, and Literary*. Edited by Eugene F. Miller. Indianapolis: Liberty Fund, 1985.

Hume, David. *A Treatise of Human Nature*. Edited by David Fate Norton and Mary J. Norton. Oxford: Clarendon Press, 2007.

Taylor, Jacqueline A. *Reflecting Subjects: Passion, Sympathy, and Society in Hume's Philosophy*. Oxford: Oxford University Press, 2015.

Hume Studies
Volume 45, Number 1–2, 2019, pp. 147–159

Hume as a Social Theorist: Comments on Taylor's *Reflecting Subjects*

WILLEM LEMMENS

Reflecting Subjects (abbreviated "RS") by Jacqueline Taylor is a book of genuine Hume scholarship and a delight to read. Central to this monograph is a reconstructive reading of Hume's moral philosophy, and of Hume's account of the way the indirect passions and sympathy shape the practical and social identities of human subjects. Starting from a meticulous analysis of Books 2 and 3 of the *Treatise*, Taylor integrates into her reading a challenging interpretation of Hume's *Enquiry concerning the Principles of Morals* and some of his essays. Taylor presents us a Hume who is at the same time an anatomist and painter of human nature. In Hume's hands, Taylor argues, a naturalist account of the human mind and its reflective capacity transforms into an innovative modern sentiment-based ethics of human dignity. For Taylor, the Second *Enquiry* forms the pitch of Hume's reformative and emancipatory moral discourse, from which we can still learn, despite its eighteenth-century prejudices and unavoidable blind spots.

1. Hume's Social Theory

There is much in this book to admire. Taylor highlights in a first chapter how Hume's *Treatise* reflects his revolutionary explanatory intentions. Hume, we learn, transcends the half-baked empiricism and naturalism of Locke and Hutcheson, still reminiscent of teleological conceptions of human agency and virtue, by developing his own experience-based, mechanistic moral psychology.

Chapter 2 derives from Hume's account of the indirect passions a "social theory," by which Taylor means: "an explanation of the indirect passions in relation to the distribution of wealth and property, and other forms of social power (typically grounded in government and other

---

Willem Lemmens is Professor for Modern Philosophy and Ethics at the University of Antwerp. Address: R214, Prinsstraat 13, B-2000 Antwerp.
Email: Willem.lemmens@uantwerpen.be

social institutions), as well as styles of living, learning, and working, and the commitment to various values" (RS 34). Taylor is original when she shows how for Hume, passions such as pride and humility (but also love and hate) gain significance through a web of culturally formed beliefs and values. Next to the natural hardware of the mind (for example, the double association of impressions and ideas), culturally transmitted beliefs and values determine *why* and *how* we feel pride when contemplating our achievements and social status, or *why* and *how* the poor feel a mixture of shame and respect for the wealthy to whom they are connected by rules of civil obedience through the institutions of property and government. Taylor stresses, following Duncan Forbes, that for Hume, our social and moral identities are the product of both nature *and* nurture: the human mind is "socially plastic" (RS 35). Indirect passions, in other words, have (formally) natural causes: an achievement based on the strength of character or the beauty of our body, for example, will universally cause pride in the self that exemplifies this achievement, and this self will be the object of love in the community that identifies with his or her achievement. But this causal relation always depends on social context and education, and thus on values and beliefs that may vary from culture to culture, which determine in which sense and how exactly qualities of body, character, or social status become significant, structure our passions, and shape our behavior.

As Taylor further shows, the indirect passions gain this full significance and power through the remarkable mental mechanism of sympathy. For Hume, sympathy appears to be "a key principle that helps to explain the meaning and value of our passionate life" (RS 44). Hume, as Taylor points out, sees sympathy not only as a mirroring capacity of the mind through which emotions of person x reverberate in the psyche of person y: sympathy is also a general tendency for the "sympathetic communication of the interconnected schemes of beliefs and values, especially those related to the causes and the nature of the indirect passions, that reflect a particular sociocultural context" (RS 37). Taylor discerns a strong interdependence between sympathy and culturally transmitted customs and habits, which transform natural causal relations (for example of sex and procreation or first possession), into symbolic relations (such as relations of family and property). Those relations have existential significance and shape our "practical" identities.[1]

Sympathy thus becomes a principle of great complexity, whose proper functioning depends on both imagination and judgment. Hume makes a great deal, as we learn from Book 3 of the *Treatise,* of the need to overcome our partial sympathy, for example, when we "reflect on someone's circumstances and make an evaluative judgment about why she might deserve greater compassion or contempt" (RS 48). As Taylor stresses, this process of correcting our passions by taking on a more "general point of view" through conversation and reflection hinges crucially on general rules, education, and social discourse. In particular, as Taylor explores in chapter 4, the attribution of moral blame and praise, and the "guilding" of characters with the epithet of virtue or vice often requires subtle reflection and judgment, whereby extended sympathy replaces its more emotive ancestor.

This brings us to Taylor's pivotal third chapter, "Power and the Philosophy of our Passions." In this most innovative part of her study, Taylor fleshes out this outline of Hume's social theory.

While in metaphysics the idea of "causal power" may be a fiction in a "strict philosophical way of thinking," in what Hume calls "the philosophy of our passions," this concept reappears and has a mighty influence on our imagination (RS 80; T 2.1.10.4; SBN 312). In Book 2 of the *Treatise*, as Taylor reads Hume, power becomes the quality we ascribe in social life to any social relation where the causal influence of the agency of one over the other is apparent: for example, the dominance of the rich over the poor, men over women, governors over subjects, and the judge over the accused. Fear of the potential exercise of power is a decisive mechanism of social stratification: Thus, when in the grip of fear, the poor, the oppressed and weak also develop attitudes of shame (humility) and respect towards the rich, while this latter group feels strengthened in its social role by attitudes of pride and self-esteem.

Here we see, as Taylor skillfully points out, how Hume's theory of the indirect passions contains a genuine social theory that accounts for the creation of *rank* and *political power*. In what sounds like a preliminary version of the master-slave dialectic of Hegel and Marx, Hume not only discerns this form of social stratification in the sphere of production and labor, but also in gender relations and the artifice of politics. Families are structured around power relations between men and women, but also between parents and children. In the same sense, relations of obligation and a sense of duty are established in politics through the indirect passions and the workings of sympathetic identification.

Gaining and sustaining social status is thus a fundamental drive of human sociability. Social status constitutes the symbolic capital or "lustre" that supports great families, their properties, the respect for their members, and the beauty and talents of their sons and daughters. Hume considers these relations of rank and power, with their connotations of distance and contiguity, as *constitutive* of social life, but also as the source of inequality and possible oppression and conflict.

2. Hume on Moral Evaluation: from Pride to the Sense of Humanity

In the second part of her book, Taylor evaluates the relation between Hume's theory of social power and his moral philosophy proper. Chapters four to six are devoted, respectively, to an analysis of Hume's account of "moral authority and competence"; an assessment of his views on the "dangers and dignity of pride"; and, finally, a presentation of Hume's sentiment-based ethics of humanity and dignity. While highly inspiring and innovative, this last part of Taylor's book is also the most challenging and controversial.

In chapter four, Taylor argues, against mainstream Hume scholarship, that the second *Enquiry* is more than just an adaptation of the moral theory of the *Treatise*. In Taylor's view, the methodology and approach of the *Enquiry*, and, in particular, the introduction of the principle of humanity, forms a real amendment to the account of moral evaluation of the *Treatise*, where the concept of sympathy does not meet the universalistic and impartial requirements of Hume's sentimental humanism.

In chapter 5, Taylor convincingly explains that Hume's theory of pride should be distinguished from the dismissive accounts of pride given by Hobbes and Mandeville. Where Hobbes sees pride or "glory" as a potentially destructive source of cruelty, contempt, and arrogance, Mandeville identifies pride with a vain self-liking and a source of greed. Though socially a functional vice, pride is for Mandeville hardly a virtue. Hume, as Taylor explains, is not blind to pride's potential to slide into vanity and self-glorification, but, at the same time, regards a "well-regulated pride" a necessary virtue that "makes us confident and enterprising" (RS 140). Moreover, for Hume, shame (or humility) and pride, though self-regarding, are fundamentally social passions: our self-appraisal or lack of self-esteem is structurally dependent on the gaze and judgment of our social environment. Thus, stressing again the pivotal role of sympathy, Taylor concludes that pride is crucial for the development of our practical identity: pride gives us an intimate sense of our own dignity and standing as a moral subject.

The account of pride leads us to the daring last chapter of *Reflecting Subjects*. Here, Taylor returns to the role of the sentiment and principle of humanity in Hume's second *Enquiry*. She evaluates the meaning of Hume's use of the concept of humanity in this, "of all my writings . . . incomparably the best" ("My Own Life," *Essays* xxxvi),[2] and highlights its role in some of Hume's *Essays*. According to Taylor, *humanity* has for Hume two meanings: it is a sentiment or *virtue*—indeed, the pivotal virtue in the second *Enquiry*—and a *principle* by which we are able to discern which virtues and character traits are generally beneficial for mankind or useful for society (RS 160–61). With the *Enquiry*, so Taylor is convinced, Hume develops a mature ethics of human dignity that transcends the still parochial tincture of the sympathy principle in Book 2 of the *Treatise*. The second *Enquiry* presents nothing less than Hume's own version of an universalistic ethics of equal dignity that hints towards a possible "kingdom of ends" thanks to the establishment of a shared sense of humanity. Taylor contends that a defense of the "requirement" to treat all as humans with equal dignity is prominent in Hume's criticism of the institution of slavery in "Of the Populousness of Ancient Nations," and his propagation of the superiority of monogamy in "Of Polygamy and Divorces."

Taylor further ascribes to Hume the idea that opposing the cruelty of ancient slavery gives a voice to the resentment felt by those humans who are denied a place in the moral community. In the same vein, Hume maintains that a form of marriage where man and woman are equal friends is far superior to the oppressive institution of polygamy, where a man relates to his many wives as his property and in constant jealousy towards possible intruders of his extensive family. Hume therefore contends that polygamy blocks the possibility of the commerce of men and women as equals, as well as their cultivation of self-esteem and a proper sense of humanity crucial for the development of society and individual flourishing.

3. Some Critical Reflections

With *Reflecting Subjects*, Taylor has put us in her debt. However, I still feel the need for further clarification on some points. First, I am not wholly convinced by the presentation of Hume's moral philosophy as reformist and emancipatory; secondly, I think Taylor underestimates the ambivalent nature of Humean sympathy as a causal force in communication and social interaction; and thirdly, I doubt whether her critique of Hume's account of moral evaluation in the *Treatise* is accurate.

3.1. Hume: Pagan Elitist or Liberal Reformist?

In a certain sense, labeling Hume a *reformist* moral philosopher is unproblematic. He undoubtedly challenged his contemporaries with his secular, a-religious presentation of the life of virtue in both *Treatise* and second *Enquiry*. And his provocative contention that moral distinctions are derived from sentiment, not reason, was equally an assault on the received wisdom of his time. With good reason, Annette Baier described Hume's presentation of pride as a virtue as a form of "Christian-baiting," as Taylor reminds us (RS 132). And Peter Gay had good reasons to call Hume a pagan Enlightenment philosopher, whose secularism aimed at debunking a religious inspired ethics of self-denial and guilt.[3]

However, in *Reflecting Subjects*, Taylor defends a bolder thesis with regard to Hume's reformist intentions. In her view, especially in the second *Enquiry*, Hume "shows a keen awareness of the strategies people develop to bridge socially constructed divisions as well as intercultural differences" (RS viii). If so, Hume intended to defend a twentieth-century ethic of equal dignity, where "a warm concern for the interests of mankind" (RS 161) stands out as a moral ideal. And, on Taylor's reading of the essays, Hume was eager to overcome oppressive inequality by cultivating a modern form of "eloquence" and reflection so as to correct our more selfish and comparison-based passions and sentiments. The author of the second *Enquiry* and the essays should be applauded for propagating an anti-relativist ethics of humanity which mobilizes "the *party* of human kind against vice or disorder, its common enemy" (EPM 9.9; SBN 275; RS 163).[4] In particular the *Dialogue* that forms an appendix to the second *Enquiry* would defend this universalistic humanist ethics.

Some of the best pages of Taylor's book are devoted to Hume's predilection for a modern ethics of humanity versus the austere moral culture of magnanimity and the martial sublime prominent in antiquity. For Hume the moral climate of antiquity clearly exemplifies inhumanity and cruelty, and thrives on a culture of division between masters and slaves, men and women, common people and nobility, rich and poor: here, the resentment of the oppressed remains without a voice.

However, in my reading of the second *Enquiry*, Hume's account of the principle of humanity is not driven by such outspoken normative intentions. In *A Dialogue,* for example, Hume seems rather eager to show that, despite first appearances, a common human nature underlies differences in moral values and norms: but this explanatory device leaves open whether we can derive from this fact any normative moral system. After all, Hume reminds us at the same time in *A Dialogue* that moral standards might differ considerably from culture to culture. Moreover, as Taylor herself explains brilliantly, the moral life of humans depends on a larger social reality of social rank and differences (of gender, talent, power) that forms the solid ground on which moral evaluations thrive and from which we can only abstract to a limited extent. Of course, change and historical evolutions might gradually alter this ground: but this should not imply that an ethics of deliberate change and emancipation is most in tune with human nature, or that, from a normative point of view, this ideal should form the core of morality.

Therefore, I am not convinced that the introduction of the principle of humanity in the second *Enquiry* serves the normative ends Taylor ascribes to Hume. I think the principle is more explanatory than normative. As Hume stresses, his investigation of morality concerns more "the speculative than the practical part of morals" (EPM 2.5 SBN 177–78). In the same vein, I remain unconvinced that Hume was more aware in the *Enquiry* than in the *Treatise* of the dynamics of social inequality and the need for an enlarged vision of humanity and equal dignity. The explanatory starting point in both works is different, but the implicit social imaginaries that guide Hume's discourse and his theoretical presuppositions remain, in my view, overall the same.

Of course, the principle of humanity in the *Second Enquiry* reflects Hume's preference for a pagan ethics that values ordinary life and opposes religious zeal and enthusiasm. But I think the principle of humanity is less universalistic than Taylor suggests. It is a *sentiment* that is triggered by the specific evaluative context wherein the moral evaluator finds herself. It springs from a spontaneous, but limited affection for the woe and weal of the other, and in this sense, it is, after all, a product of sympathy. Over the whole second *Enquiry*, Hume is eager to stress the limited character of our spontaneous benevolence or love of mankind as a motive of action and evaluation of specific characters and institutions. On this point, he did not substantially change his mind from the *Treatise.*

In his essays, Hume also remains fairly elitist in his attitudes towards the traditional institute of marriage, when he claims that the intercourse of politeness and calm friendship should not be too much disturbed by reflective corrective attitudes towards distinction and rank. Taylor puts great weight on the practice of "making resentment felt" by the oppressed, but when Hume introduces this idea, it is not as part of an emancipatory practice, but merely an explanatory condition which accounts for the need for general rules of justice in civil society. Indeed, in light of his social theory of power in the *Treatise*, it appears even plausible that Hume would favor a society of rank and distinction, based on economic relations, but also gender, as most in tune with human nature. It might be, as Alasdair MacIntyre claims, that a web of typical eighteenth-century beliefs and presuppositions made Hume rather unaware of the parochial character of his moral theory.[5]

In the critique of the institution of slavery in "Of the Populousness of Ancient Nations," Hume does stress its inhumanity, but he contrasts without much ado the cruel life of "submission to a pretty prince" with the "obedience to a great monarch." As Hume observes: "The more the master is removed from us in plank and rank, the greater liberty we enjoy; the less are our actions inspected and controlled; and the fainter that cruel comparison becomes between our own subjection, and the freedom, and even dominion of another" ("Populousness of Ancient Nations," *Essays* 383). In other words, the ideal of equal liberty of the citizens is from a political and economic point of view much more valuable, and from a moral point of view more humane than the ancient institution of slavery: but for Hume it remains a fact that liberty should be in balance with authority, even of the monarchical kind. And in his political essays, as in his *History of England*, Hume is always very sensitive to the need for political authority and the rule of law as a bulwark against too much freedom and equality.[6] In that context, as James Harris argues, it comes as no surprise that Hume showed no real reformative zeal towards slavery in the colonies of his days.[7]

3.2. Sympathy's Many Faces

This brings me to a second point where I feel the need for some clarification: Hume's account of sympathy. The concept of "sympathy" has in Hume a notoriously broad meaning. As I sketched already, Taylor very effectively shows that sympathy is for Hume much more than a mental mechanism of quasi-spontaneous emotional transfer: it also refers to the, often deeply cognitive, reflective communication of values, beliefs and opinions within communities. Taylor further highlights the crucial role Hume reserves for sympathy in the mirroring of self and other in the indirect passions: sympathy here refers to the practice of mutual evaluation and self-evaluation of characters wherein reflection and judgment plays a crucial role.

Taylor compares Hume's broad and inclusive account of sympathy with contemporary social psychological and neuroscientific research on *empathy*. For example, Preston and de Waal, like Hume, consider empathy to be a sort of container concept, integrating various forms of mental activity whereby the self (his or her emotions, beliefs and opinions) undergoes a perspective shift through the direct enlivening of the mental perspective of another person. In this way, the mental state of the self merges with the mental state of another, causing—and this is the most important—the sympathizing self to integrate this perspective of the other into his or her own beliefs and opinions, and act in accordance with this shift in standpoint (RS 41, 41n14).

Preston and de Waal have been criticized for defending a too broad and vague concept of empathy.[8] One might wonder whether this critique could also be applied to Hume's concept of sympathy. There is, after all, a deep divide between the quasi automatic mirroring of mental states (empathy as a sort of emotional contagion) and the culturally and social mediated process of sharing ideas and values, let alone the conscious perspective taking in moral evaluation. Hume's official view appears to be that sympathy always involves a form of emotional transfer, but Taylor defines Humean sympathy so broadly that it encompasses any form of sharing and transferring mental states: even the identification with values and cultural meanings. Humean sympathy becomes in Taylor's terms "*the* means of reproducing and sustaining forms of social life and schemes of values" (RS 70). This is a very broad conception of sympathy. It might be Hume's, but it remains unclear whether he really succeeds in integrating all forms of sympathy in a coherent explanation.

But even if one grants Hume this conceptual vagueness, it remains a fact that sympathy might not be that unequivocal *positive* social force that Taylor derives from Hume's account. As Taylor points out, Hume observes in the *Treatise* how sympathy can yield an attitude of resentment through the uncanny principle of comparison—a sort of equivalent of Nietzschean resentment. And in the second *Enquiry* Hume mentions "popular sedition, party zeal, a devoted obedience to factious leaders" as "some of the most visible, though less laudable effects of this social sympathy in human nature" (EPM 5.35; SBN 224). Moreover, when it comes to the way pride is formed and sustained by sympathetic mirroring, Taylor herself stresses that Hume considers self-deceit and vanity as typical products of the "love of fame" so typical for humans. Not only does this remind us of the less rosy features of Hobbes's "sense of glory" or Mandeville's "self-liking": it also indicates that Hume's account of sympathy might be more ambivalent in its practical outcomes than it might at first seem. Sympathy or the empathic mirroring of self and other might be potentially more disruptive and less socially harmonious than Hume himself suggests.

Taylor shows a great sensitivity to some of the dark sides of Humean sympathy when she analyses the notion of social power in the *Treatise*. But here, it seems that, for Hume, the social stratification of gender relations, family life and economic and political rank through sympathetic mirroring is a necessary, constructive mechanism for the sustenance of society. In fact, one wonders how Hume could account for the turning point where the productive and positive influence of sympathy and mental mirroring turns into a disruptive force? When, for example, is the "reverential fear" of the servant for his master a factor of social cohesion and a source of due esteem for the rich, in contrast with a fear that engenders hatred, resentment and possible turmoil and political sedition (RS 89)? I think Taylor analyses Hume's account of sympathy in a way that brings forward these pressing questions, but also leaves them largely unanswered.

As pointed out, a central contention of Taylor's book is that Hume elaborates a social theory from which one could derive an ethics of social justice and equality. Perhaps this emancipatory ethics is *implicit* in Hume's account, proposing in an indirect way strategies and correctives to remedy the social hierarchies and inequalities in social life caused by the particularist workings of sympathy. But is this Hume's view? Or did he rather consider the maintenance of social rank and distinction to be a *constitutive* and unavoidable factor of political society and human sociability? I would rather think that Hume feared that a too egalitarian society would ignite an emancipatory zeal and undermine political authority.

3.3 Sense of Humanity and the Judicious Moral Spectator

A last point in *Reflecting Subjects* that puzzles me is the analysis of Hume's account of moral evaluation in the *Treatise*. Sympathy, so we learn from chapter four, is a major structuring force in moral evaluation that needs amendment through reflection and general rules. Taylor recognizes that the *Treatise* account of this process of amendment of sympathy has its merits, but she sees also some serious flaws: by introducing the "sense of humanity," so she argues, Hume succeeds in the second *Enquiry* in better explaining the dynamics of moral evaluation and the creation of a corrective moral point of view.

Through Book 3 of the *Treatise* Hume shows how the partiality and bias of our natural sympathy should be overcome to arrive at a correct, more or less objective moral judgment.[9]

With his account of corrected or extended sympathy, Hume explicitly introduces the idea that our moral judgments, in order to be appropriate, often require reflection and a sort of calibration of our moral feelings or sentiments. The judicious moral spectator is for Hume, as Taylor stresses, a "man of taste" who is able to judge characters and actions from some "common points of view" or a standard of vice and virtue that transcends somehow our immediate feelings of moral praise and blame.[10]

Following Henry David Aiken and Annette Baier, Jacqueline Taylor reminds us how for Hume, moral evaluation derives from *both* sentiment and reasoning: it depends, like all intersubjective evaluation, on socially and culturally shared values and norms, on customs and moral discourse.[11] In other words, Humean moral evaluation is *a form of social praxis* with both emotive and cognitive ingredients. I agree wholeheartedly with this.

However, commenting on the *Treatise* account of moral evaluation, Taylor says: "I would argue that Hume's Book 2 account of how sympathy works—for example, of our tendency to be more influenced by those in position of authority or with the trappings of power, or to have contempt for those deemed socially inferior because of markers such as gender or socio-economic status—indicates rather that some voices will not be heard, or not given as much weight" (RS 116). Taylor further observes that Hume, in the *Treatise,* "neglects the importance of cultivating the virtues of good moral judgment" (RS 101). Indeed, he here allows for an account of moral evaluation whereby "persons with wealth and other forms of social power or authority are likely to regard themselves, and be so regarded by others, as having a greater *moral* authority" (RS 100). So, even when Hume comes to pay tribute to the need for the "common" moral point of view in Book 3 of the *Treatise*, his account remains flawed, in Taylor's view. She gives a specific citation to make her point. Towards the end of the *Treatise* Hume says:

> Every particular person's pleasure and interest being different, 'tis impossible men cou'd ever agree in their sentiments and judgments, unless they choose some common point of view, from which the might survey their object, and which might cause it to appear the same to all of them. Now in judgment of characters, the only interest or pleasure, which appears the same to every spectator, is that of the person himself, whose character is examine'd; or that of persons, who have a connexion with him. And tho' such interest and pleasures touch us more faintly than our own, yet being more constant and universal, they counter-balance the latter even in practice, and are alone admitted in speculation as the standard of virtue and morality. They alone produce that particular feeling or sentiment, on which moral distinctions depend. (T 3.3.1.30; SBN 391; RS 108)

For Taylor, with this account of the creation of a "common point of view," Hume's judicious spectator remains trapped in a shared perspective that might be too culturally determined and too biased given its dependence on social rank and position. For, in abstracting from his or her "interests," he or she appears to take the interests of the agent and his or her bystanders as *constitutive* of the standard of virtue. Hume appears confident that in so doing, a universally valid ethical point of view will come to undergird moral evaluation. But why, so Taylor asks, should the sympathetic feeling of agreement on the side of the spectator with the interests (the points of view) of the bystanders, be *normative* for our moral praise and blame? Suppose, so Taylor suggests, that the character we morally praise is of the proud and self-confident husband in a society that esteems polygamy? Suppose, furthermore, that the judicious spectator identifies impartially with the actual "interests" of the many women who live in humble obedience to this patriarch, unaware of their submission? Should we not say that these women lack the power to make their resentment felt, and that by implication, the judicious spectator lacks a genuine capacity or criterion for moral reflection? In short, should the common point of view not integrate a more objective perspective of morally relevant common interests?

In Taylor's view, Hume fails in the *Treatise* to account for such a more reflective and universal stance of moral evaluation and judgment. With the introduction of the principle of humanity, the second *Enquiry* appears more sensitive to these requirements. With this principle in hand, Taylor explains, Hume can account for the equal dignity of everyone concerned, irrespective of their partial involvements or interests. Through the principle of humanity, the second *Enquiry* opens a perspective upon Hume's universal humanist ethics, where the utility of virtue for the good of mankind forms the ground of the standard of virtue.

I am not convinced by this line of thought. As Taylor admits, the sketch of the way the general moral point of view is created through sympathetic identification in Book 3 might be vague, but there are other places in the *Treatise* where Hume offers more details about the requirements for genuine moral evaluation, for example when he stresses the role of "taste" in moral judgment (RS 113, 117) and the reliance on "strength of mind" on the side of the moral spectator to overcome not only his or her own interests, but also take in consideration "the commonality of interest among humankind" (RS 119).[12] In this sense, as Taylor quotes Hume, through an established practice of moral evaluation "we gradually form a "general inalterable standard" to which our moral sentiments should conform, so that our moral evaluations become correspondingly "constant and establish'd (T 3.3.3.2)" (RS 108–109).

But if the moral spectator, exemplifying an established practice, has thus a general moral standard to rely on, she is also in a position to take *distance* from the actual interests of the smaller circle affected by a character or institution judged. In other words, the citation by which Taylor justifies her critique of Hume's concept of extended sympathy as too partial and prejudiced could be read differently. As I read him, Hume wants to say that the stance taken by the judicious moral spectator *presupposes* a moral standard that is *independent* of any actual interests and which allows him to judge what *might* be appropriate interests of the people affected by a character or institution (these interests thus possibly being hypothetical). If you interpret this passage as part of a phenomenology of moral evaluation stressing the need for a "common point of view," Hume leaves open the possibility that the judicious moral spectator distances herself significantly from particular biases and interests shared by her narrow social circle.

In my reading of the *Treatise*, *what* Hume's account of moral evaluation highlights is exactly the always contextually and culturally embedded nature of our practice of moral evaluation. A fundamental correction of a particular standard of morality—that affects our own cultural values and norms and the way these relate to our social rank—is always possible and might over time be deemed necessary by a certain group or the majority of a moral community. But these factual historical shifts and turns cannot be regulated by a universalistic ethics that derives from a standard of virtue that is grounded in an abstract and generalized "sense of humanity." Moreover, the impartiality required in concrete moral evaluation does not rely on such a general and abstract perspective to judge the moral propriety of characters and actions. Even in the second *Enquiry*, as I read Hume, moral evaluation always implies the assessment of how we should *interpret* the requirements of our sense of humanity in particular settings and in relation to particular virtues and institutions, in order to really grasp what the good of mankind in this or that context might require from us.

Therefore, we should not misunderstand Hume's reference to the "interests" of mankind writ large when he contemplates the need for some "common point of view" as the ground of the standard of morality. Sometimes, of course, the concept of "mankind" might refer to all possible humans affected by, say, the general and abstract principles of justice—for example when it comes to climate change or the need for social justice. But sometimes, "the good of mankind" might just refer to the manner in which a certain virtue, or range of virtues, is exemplified by specific characters in a particular social role and the interests of the narrow circle to which these characters relate. In other words, the "impartiality" and "universalism" of Hume's common point of view is unavoidably—so I think—a view "from somewhere" and refers to a standard of virtue that is culturally dependent and embedded in the actual situation of the spectator. This embeddedness of the moral point of view is for Hume no failure, but an inevitable aspect, even a precondition, of the practice of moral evaluation.

In fact, the explanation of the creation of the moral point of view in the *Treatise* reflects a crucial feature of Hume's moral theory, highlighted elsewhere in *Reflecting Subjects*: namely, the idea that moral evaluation always hinges on an internal understanding of moral values and norms that is shaped by culture and custom. To return to the example of polygamy: a judicious spectator might have good reasons to integrate into her estimation of the patriarchal husband considerations about the undue submission of his many wives, and thus to criticize this character. Hume's account of moral evaluation clearly allows this. But it might, indeed, also be the case that the position of the moral judge remains positive about polygamy, for considerations that derive from an equally subtle "common point of view" that, influenced by a particular culture, proposes a different view of the situation judged. In a same vein, there is in Hume's moral theory no a priori *parti pris* in favor of a universalistic ethics that wants to overcome all forms of social division and inequality that might feature in a certain society or be taken for granted by particular groups in certain historical contexts.

In line with Taylor's analysis of Hume's social theory, I would therefore argue that for Hume, social distinction and rank play a role in our assessment of whom we consider to be appropriate moral spectators, and why we grant some among us greater moral authority than others. Of course, changes in social life and culture might make us suspicious about the moral authority claimed by some on the basis of their social status and power. We might also think that Hume was too much of an eighteenth-century conformist when he alludes, in specific examples, to characters of moral authority and virtue. But it would be very un-Humean, and in contradiction with the gist of his moral theory to believe that in his view our moral evaluations should radically transcend and reform the social structures and cultural practices which make us flourish as reflective moral subjects.

NOTES

1 Taylor is influenced here by Donald Ainslie who speaks of the importance of our "existential connections" following Hume's claim that the causes of pride and humility must be "connected with our being and existence" (T 2.1.8.8; SBN 302) (RS 58n49). References to the *Treatise* are to Hume, *A Treatise of Human Nature*, ed. Norton and Norton, hereafter cited in the text as "T" followed by Book, part, section, and paragraph number, and to Hume, *A Treatise of Human Nature*, ed. Selby-Bigge, rev. by Nidditch, cited in the text as "SBN" followed by the page number.

2 References are to Hume, *Essays, Moral, Political and Literary*, ed. Eugene F. Miller, hereafter cited in the text as *Essays*, followed by the page number and preceded by essay title.

3 Cf. Gay, *The Enlightenment. The Rise of Modern Paganism*, chapter 7.3: "David Hume: The Complete Modern Pagan."

4 References are to Hume, *An Enquiry concerning the Principles of Morals*, ed. Beauchamp, hereafter cited in the text as "EPM" followed by section and paragraph number, and to Hume, *Enquiries Concerning the Principles of Human Understanding and Concerning the Principles of Morals*, ed. Selby-Bigge, rev. by Nidditch, hereafter cited in the text as "SBN" followed by page numbers.

5 MacIntyre, *Whose Justice? Which Rationality?*, chaps. XII and XV.

6 Cf. EPM: "Perfect equality of possessions, destroying all subordination, weakens extremely the authority of the magistracy, and must reduce all power nearly to a level, as well as property" (EPM 3.26; SBN 194).

7 Harris, "Review of *Reflecting Subjects*" in *Intellectual History Review*.

8 Coplan, "Understanding Empathy: its Features and Effects."

9 Illustrative is the following passage from the beginning of Book 3: "An action, or sentiment, or character is virtuous or vicious; why? Because its view causes a pleasure or uneasiness of a particular kind. In giving a reason, therefore, for the pleasure or uneasiness, we sufficiently explain the vice or virtue. To have the sense of virtue, is nothing but to feel a satisfaction of a particular kind from the contemplation of a character. The very *feeling* constitutes our praise or admiration" (T 3.1.2.3; SBN 471).

10 Taylor is here influenced by Mary Mothersill (RS 113).

11 Baier, *A Progress of Sentiments*, chap. 8, "The Contemplation of Character"; Aiken, "An Interpretation of Hume's Theory of the Place of reason in Ethics and Politics."

12 Cf. also T 3.3.1.19 (SBN 584). Taylor further refers to the essay "Of the Standard of Taste," and the article of Mary Mothershill on this essay (cf. RS 113): Mothersill, "Hume and the Paradox of Taste."

WORKS CITED

Aiken, David Henry. "An Interpretation of Hume's Theory of the Place of Reason in Ethics and Politics." *Ethics* 90 (1979): 66–80. https://doi.org/10.1086/292134

Baier, Annette. *A Progress of Sentiments. Reflections on Hume's* Treatise. Cambridge, MA: Harvard University Press, 1991.

Coplan, Amy. "Understanding Empathy: Its Features and Effects." In *Empathy. Philosophical and Psychological Perspectives*. Edited by Amy Coplan and Peter Goldie, 3–18. Oxford: Oxford University Press, 2011.

Gay, Peter. *The Enlightenment. The Rise of Modern Paganism*. New York/London: Norton & Company, 1966.

Harris, James. "Review of *Reflecting Subjects*." *Intellectual History Review* May (2016). http://dx.doi.org/10.1080/17496977.2016.1168644

Hume, David. *An Enquiry Concerning the Principles of Morals*. Edited by Tom L. Beauchamp. Oxford: Oxford University Press, 1998.

Hume, David. *Enquiries Concerning the Principles of Human Understanding and Concerning the Principles of Morals*. Edited by L. A. Selby-Bigge, 3rd ed. Oxford: Clarendon Press, 1975.

Hume, David. *Essays, Moral, Political, and Literary*. Edited by Eugene F. Miller. Indianapolis: Liberty Fund, 1985.

Hume, David. *A Treatise of Human Nature*. Edited by David Fate Norton and Mary J. Norton. Oxford: Oxford University Press, 2007.

Hume, David. *A Treatise of Human Nature*. Edited by L. A. Selby-Bigge. Oxford: Clarendon Press, 1978.

MacIntyre, Alasdair. *Whose Justice? Which Rationality?* London: University of Notre Dame Press, 1988.

Mothersill, Mary. "Hume and the Paradox of Taste." In *Aesthetics: A Critical Anthology*. Edited by G. Dickie, R. Sclafani, and R. Roblin, 269–86. New York: St. Martin's Press, 1989.

Taylor, Jacqueline. *Reflecting Subjects*. Oxford: Oxford University Press, 2015.

Hume Studies
Volume 45, Number 1–2, 2019, pp. 161–168

The Social Aspects of Pride: Comments on Taylor's *Reflecting Subjects*

GENEVIEVE LLOYD

My comments on Jacqueline Taylor's rich and interesting study[1] will focus on a theme which I found particularly thought provoking: the discussion of Hume's treatment of pride. I think the topic of pride is central to the book's structure—closely integrated with the recurring consideration of what is distinctive in Hume's approach to the social significance of the passions.

I am going to come at this theme indirectly—through consideration of the differences between Hume and Spinoza on the nature and significance of pride. Taylor shows that Hume has made it possible for pride to be considered as a positive trait, perhaps even as a virtue. Spinoza's attitude to pride in the *Ethics* is, in contrast, quite negative. The differences between Spinoza and Hume here are of more than incidental scholarly interest. They go to the heart of what this book brings out so well: Hume's capacity to engage both with the social *effects* of emotions and with the ways in which emotions are themselves shaped—and sometimes transformed—by their social contexts.

One way of putting the point here is that the history of the emotions *reflects* their changing social conditions; and indeed, on my reading, that is one aspect of this book's engagement with the idea of *reflection*. Our understanding of an emotion is deepened by considering attitudes towards it which have prevailed in different places and times. In some cases, these variations can be seen as changes in attitude towards states which have remained fundamentally the same. Sometimes, too, an apparent change in attitude may in fact indicate a mere change in terminology, rather than a deep conceptual shift. However, in other cases, it can be argued that the emotion itself becomes something different from what it was. I want to suggest that Hume's treatment of pride—as it emerges in Taylor's discussion—involves that deeper kind

Genevieve Lloyd is Emerita Professor in Philosophy, University of New South Wales, Sydney, NSW, Australia.
Email: GenevieveLloyd@bigpond.com

of change; and that in this respect, *Reflecting Subjects* offers, more generally, an important engagement with conceptual issues about the philosophical history of emotions.

To clarify what is at stake here, let me refer briefly to a claim made by A. O. Hirschman in his book, *The Passions and the Interests,* published in 1977. Hirschman argued that there are *conceptual* shifts that happened throughout the seventeenth and eighteenth centuries, in relation to attitudes to money-making pursuits. On his account, what happened was not just a matter of a change in attitudes towards the acquisition of wealth. Rather, there was an underlying realignment in a cluster of concepts, that helped make activities related to such acquisition come to be perceived as honourable, after having been previously regarded as enacting shameful vices of greed or avarice. Hirschman talked of a "marvellous metamorphosis" of destructive passions into virtues, via the intervening concept of "rational pursuit of interest," which brought together what had previously been seen as opposed categories of "reason" and "the passions."[2]

Has Hume brought a comparable conceptual shift in the understanding of pride? If he has, then what is it about his philosophy that makes that shift possible?

In his discussion of pride in Book 2, section 5, of the *Treatise*, Hume reflects on the striking fact that pride not only presupposes the idea of the self, but also, in some ways, transforms and enriches it. Pleasure in a beautiful house, which one owns, passes into pleasure in oneself—as its owner. Pride changes us; and that productive process involves not just how we perceive ourselves, but how we are perceived by others—and, in turn, how we come to perceive ourselves differently.

In her illuminating discussion—in Chapter 2 of *Reflecting Subjects*—of the central role of pride in Humean social theory, Taylor stresses the role of "mirroring" in those productive aspects of pride. Sustained pride, reflected back to us by the reactions of others, brings an enduring sense of self-worth. "Mirroring" is here conceived as "a *social process* occurring *between human minds* and in which passionate experiences are communicated, responded to, and sustained, and in some instances also created and shaped" (Taylor, 69). Hume thus shows insight into the social dimensions of pride's productive power in relation to the formation and shaping of the sense of selfhood. The relation of ownership between person and house—which is presupposed by pride—is transformed by it to the sense of oneself as having the status of property owner, with a consequent place in a social system.

What I find interesting here is that Hume was able to articulate something which Spinoza seems unable to say. The difference is partly a consequence of the metaphysical framework which Spinoza brought to his treatment of pride. I want to argue that there is also a related difference which has to do with the changing genres of philosophical writing.

In defining pride, in his "Definition of the Affects" in Part III of the *Ethics,* Spinoza says that pride is thinking—out of love of oneself—more highly of oneself than one should. Pride, he explains, "is an effect or property of Self-Love."[3] It can, he continues, therefore also be defined as "Love of oneself, or Self-Esteem, insofar as it so affects a man that he thinks more highly of himself than is just" (Spinoza, 537). Pride is thus, for Spinoza, an excess of self-esteem—an *unjust* self-assessment—an error of judgment about our own qualities. A little earlier—at the

Scholium to Proposition 26 of Part III—he describes Pride as a form of self-delusion: "a species of madness." For the proud man "dreams, with open eyes, that he can do all those things which he achieves only in his imagination" (Spinoza, 508).

Spinoza suggests there, in effect, that pride rests on an inadequacy arising from flawed imagining. In a well-functioning rational mind, the imagining of one's own achievements would be accompanied by corrective ideas—ideas which exclude from existence those grand deluded imaginings about ourselves. So, pride arises from a flaw in imagination—uncorrected by the clear ideas of reason. This account of pride of course involves some reference to other people. They enter the analysis as objects of the erroneous unjust comparisons between self and others which are the core of pride. Those supposedly inferior others are objects of Scorn, which for Spinoza consists in wrongly considering ourselves as more worthy than them.

Those passages from the *Ethics* make it clear that Spinoza sees pride as a flaw. Yet, that does not of itself indicate that there is any deep conceptual difference between him and Hume. For Spinoza, after all, does not in these passages criticise *rightful* self esteem; he condemns self-esteem only in its excessive, *unjust* form. Might what seems at first a difference in attitude towards pride turn out to reflect merely a difference in terminology? There is, however, a deeper difference here which does seem to take us into the territory of conceptual difference.

To clarify the differences, we need just a little more from Spinoza. In elaborating his account of pride as "unjust over-estimation of self," he says something which may well seem counter-intuitive. Pride, he says, strictly "has no opposite." He acknowledges that this claim is at odds with common usage: for we are often accustomed to oppose Humility to Pride. But this, he insists, is because we are attending, not to the nature of the two states, but to their effects. "For we usually call him proud who exults too much at being esteemed . . . who tells of nothing but his own virtues, and the vices of others, who wishes to be given precedence over all others, and finally who proceeds with the gravity and attire usually adopted by others who are placed far above him. On the other hand, we call him humble who quite often blushes, who confesses his own vices and tells the virtues of others, who yields to all, and, finally, who walks with head bowed and neglects to adorn himself" (Spinoza, 538).

For Spinoza pride is a character flaw; and in describing it he seems to talk in the language of virtues and vices. Yet for him, pride does not—as we might have expected—have virtuous humility as its opposite. The rationale for Spinoza's insistence that pride and humility are not opposites is that, in his cartography of the emotions, they are derived from different, more basic passions. Pride is derived from Joy—via the pleasure of self-esteem. He argues that if pride really did have an opposite, it would have to be something derivable from sadness. Pride's opposite then would be, not a virtuous humility, but rather Despondency, which he defines as "thinking less highly of oneself than is just, out of sadness." "For as Pride is born of Self-Esteem so Despondency is born of Humility" (Spinoza, 538).

What is important for my purposes here is that, although Spinoza describes pride as a flaw, what passes in his social context as humility is also an unattractive trait—because of its associations with despondency. His discussion of humility and despondency concludes with a wry observation: these affects—humility and despondency—are both, in fact, very rare. "For human nature, considered in itself, strains against them, as far as it can. . . . So those who are believed to be most despondent and humble are usually most ambitious and envious" (Spinoza, 538).

When we read that passage now, it may well resonate with what we find unlikeable in the fawning "humility" of Charles Dickens's character, Uriah Heep, in *David Copperfield.* Hume, too, often offers ironic observations of the passions in action which still resonate with us. Spinoza and Hume share a distrust of the posturing at play in the public enactment of emotions. At the level of acute observation of behaviour, their insights can agree. Yet, there are significant theoretical differences. To clarify those differences, it is important first to note their shared appreciation of the role of imagination in shaping the emotions.

Spinoza stresses that a flawed *imagining* of our powers and capacities can have debilitating effects on the adequate *understanding* of them; and that this inadequate understanding can in turn come to limit the capacities themselves. It can, he says, happen that "while someone sad considers his weakness, he imagines himself to be disdained by everyone—even while the others think of nothing less than to disdain him" (Spinoza, 537–8). Moreover, it can happen that such a person "denies something of himself in relation to a future time of which he is uncertain." The despondent person comes to deny his own capacity to do, in the future, anything but what is wrong or dishonourable. Or, perhaps from too much shame, he becomes timid, so that he does not "dare things that others equal to him dare" (Spinoza, 538).

Spinoza's remarks about despondency are perceptive about its pathology as a negative emotion. Those insightful remarks come in the context of an insistence on the debilitating effects of imagination—despite the role it plays in the formation of the adequate ideas of reason, by allowing us to grasp what things have in common. For Spinoza, what allows us to overcome despondency is the exercise of the mind's powers of rational thought. Unlike Descartes, he does not attribute the "remedy" of the passions to the exercise of a virtuous will. But nor does he treat one emotion as able of itself to overcome the power of another, without the exercise of the mind's desire for better understanding of its passions. Pride and humility alike are, for Spinoza, products of flawed imagining. For Hume, in contrast, it is the emotion of pride itself that allows us to overcome the debilitating effects of the lack of confidence in our own abilities. Reason, he famously claims in Book 2, section 3 of the *Treatise,* is not the master of the passions, but their slave—fit only to serve and obey them.

Spinoza, despite his reputed "rationalism," recognised the importance of both imagination and emotion in the life of the mind. In many respects, his treatment of the interactions between reason, imagination, and emotion can be seen as foreshadowing Hume. Yet, his insight into the power of the passions in their own right falls short of Hume's; and that difference is particularly striking in Hume's treatment of the positive effects of pride. Taylor shows its relevance, for example, to understanding how pride can strengthen self-confidence, especially for those socialised not to believe in their abilities: women and marginalised minorities.

In comparison with Spinoza, Hume highlights the direct effects on emotions of the ways in which selves perceive one another. There are intimations, in the *Ethics*, of the idea that a well-lived human life thrives on the perception of the virtues of others. Yet, Spinoza's system cannot really capture the powerful effects of the intersubjective connections which Hume describes as "sympathy." Taylor presents Humean sympathy as a principle of communication between selves—captured in the metaphor of dynamic, reciprocal "mirroring."

As I said earlier, Spinoza of course recognised that pride involves thinking about others—making comparisons between them and ourselves. He did not treat pride as capable of existing in absolute solitude. He also recognised—as we have seen in his discussion of despondency—that our emotions can be affected by how we think (rightly or wrongly) others think of us. Yet, when we compare it with Hume's, Spinoza's version of pride is strikingly "internal." It pictures the mind as taking notes, as it were, on the basis of which it makes judgements on the comparative worth of itself in relation to others. Under the influence of inadequacies in imagining, it often gets those judgements wrong—thus falling into the flawed conditions of pride or despondency. For Hume, in contrast, sympathetic "mirroring" can make pride of itself a sustaining force in the shaping of selfhood. Put briefly, Humean sympathy opens up space for the productive social role of pride to be articulated.

So far, I have focused on the differences in content between Spinoza and Hume on pride. Let me now make a few brief remarks about what I think are relevant differences between them, in relation to genres of philosophical writing. I want to suggest that Spinoza's insights into the emotions are in tension with the rigid deductive structure of the *Ethics*—that his thought strains at the limits of the genre in which it is expressed. Thus, although he mentions the social dimensions of pride, those observations can seem at odds with the static cartography of the emotions, laid out in the *Ethics.* Spinoza cannot readily capture in that form the dynamism which Hume encapsulates in his treatment in the *Treatise* of the *productive* power of the passion of pride.

The subtlety—and at times the obvious irony—of Spinoza's observations pulls against the rigidity of form imposed by the structure of the *Ethics.* The relatively free flowing *Corollaries*—in which Spinoza adds general observations to his logical deductions—are sometimes able to escape that restraint; and it is in those sections that the affinities between Spinoza's insights and Hume's become most apparent. It is also worth noting here that the prose of the *Tractatus-Theologico-Politicus*—whatever its title might suggest—is more free-flowing. There, Spinoza is able to talk more directly about the constructive interplay of imagination, emotion, and understanding, offering an integrated view of the human mind, the theoretical basis for which is formulated in the *Ethics.*

Issues of genre cannot always be sharply separated out from the philosophical insights expressed through them. Yet, it is interesting to reflect on their relevance here. Hume did not write about the emotions in in a rigid geometrical mode. Yet, in his early writing, he did try to conform his observations to what he took to be an emerging "science of human nature"—appropriately expressed in the genre of *Treatise.* In keeping with his self-imposed task of laying bare the intricacies of human nature, the work evokes a unitary structure of the mind, within which all the interactions of "impressions" and "ideas" goes on.

In an intriguing section in his Appendix to the *Treatise*, reflecting on his treatment of personal identity, Hume seems to express his own sense of dissatisfaction with the restraints of that model of the mind. On reviewing his treatment of personal identity, he says, he finds himself in a "labyrinth" from which he can find no escape. There would be no difficulty if it were the case either that our perceptions inhered in something simple and individual, or that the mind perceived some real connection among them. But, having rejected both those possibilities, he disarmingly acknowledges, he must "plead the privilege of a sceptic" and confess that the difficulty is too hard for his understanding[4] (T App. 21; SBN 636). Hume articulates his "labyrinth" as a perplexity about the conditions of personal identity. But there is a deeper issue which relates to the underlying model of the self as the "theatre" within which the whole show can go on.

I want to suggest that the perplexity Hume expresses in the Appendix concerns the difficulty of adequately conceptualising the social world—the world of inter-acting selves—within a frame set by the model of an individual mind inspecting its own contents. In the case of the passion of pride, Hume's insights into the fluid social dimensions of selfhood are especially difficult to fit into the fixity of the model of a mind inspecting its mental contents. Perhaps Hume came to see that he had a difficulty in articulating—within the genre of *Treatise*—philosophical insights into the dynamic changeability of sociable selves, whose identities are formed and shaped by interactions with one another.

It may be helpful here to try to bring *Reflecting Subjects* into relation with issues about philosophical writing raised in another important recent book on Hume, James Harris's intellectual biography.[5] Discussing the evolution of Hume's writing style, Harris argues against the common view that he had, in effect, already reached all his main philosophical conclusions in the *Treatise,* so that the later writings amount to little more than a process of reformulating ideas for purposes of more accessible communication. On Harris's account, Hume developed in his later works a more nuanced idea of what it was to write philosophy, and of what it was for a philosopher of his times to engage in an "objective" study of human nature. Thus, Hume developed as a curious, observant, philosophically informed "man of letters"—rather than as a would-be "scientist of human nature." Instead of continuing to model his writing on the concerns of a systematic "experimenter," he became progressively a detached observer of human ways, as they were played out in the social context of his times. As Harris describes it, that change amounts, not so much to a repudiation of the ideal of a "science of human nature," as to a different way of pursuing it. Thus, the philosophy Hume came to write is best seen not as a specific subject matter or body of doctrine, but rather as a habit of mind, which could be applied to a range of subjects.

Harris's approach to the sequence of Hume's works allows a new emphasis to be put on the significance of Hume's shift away from the model of formal *treatise* to the genre of *essay.* Hume himself celebrated that free-flowing form of writing in his essay "On Essay Writing." Already in the *Treatise,* his insights sometimes take off in ways that can seem a digression—or at any rate a detour—from the main business, just as Spinoza's *Corollaries* do. There is, for example, the chapter on "Curiosity or the Love of Truth," which marks the end of part 2—with its playful comparison of intellectual inquiry to hunting and gaming. That section reads like a mini essay; so, too, does the matching "Conclusion to this Book" in part 1—with its moving descriptions of the "careless scepticism" appropriate to the life of the contemporary man of letters. Rather than confirming to a model of ordered sub-sections in a systematic *Treatise*, those chapters seem close—both in content and in mood—to his later essays on the "Platonist," the "Epicurean," the "Stoic," and the "Sceptic." In that set of essays he sketched divergent forms of intellectual character, as enacted by contemporary men of letters, through the prism of classical ideas of the philosophical life.

I have argued that the consideration of modes of writing can enrich our understanding of Hume's insights into the social dimensions of emotion. At the level of theoretical content, he provides a basis for recognising the productive force of pride within the structures of sociability operating in his time and place. His observations on the passions are grounded in philosophical insights into their social roles. Yet, that shift in content is also in tune with the evolution of his writing practice. He comes to write philosophy in ways attuned to modern lives of philosophically inclined *men*—as they mostly were—*of letters*.

Thus understood, Hume's later writings are not just a popularisation of what he had already done in the *Treatise*. On this way of looking at Hume's intellectual trajectory, the shift away from the *Treatise* genre gave him more flexibility and freedom for direct engagement in observing the passions in action. His writing remained informed by an understanding of the systematic methods of scientific investigation. Yet, if we want to see him as a precursor of contemporary ways of understanding the emotions, it may be that we will find him personified more fully in the spirit and style of the essay writer, rather than that of a contemporary cognitive scientist.

These issues of genre bear also, I think, on Taylor's interesting discussions of Hume's insights into the status of *humanity* as a modern virtue. Perhaps it is partly his concern with issues of philosophical writing that allows Hume to identify a general positive trait, describable as *humanity*—though that trait can take different forms, in different contexts. In Hume's intellectual trajectory, perhaps, that fluid construct comes to replace the comparative fixity of the notion of a unitary "human nature" discoverable through systematic methods of inquiry. Perhaps the open-ended world of social interaction, in which emotions take different forms in changing contexts, came for Hume to provide an escape from the "labyrinth" imposed by the inward "theatre" of the self.

Humanity—thus construed as a virtue of sociability, arising within inter-subjective relations—might prove, in our contemporary social contexts, a less contentious virtue than Pride.

NOTES

1 Taylor, *Reflecting Subjects*, hereafter cited in text by page number.

2 Hirschman, *The Passions and the Interests*, 17.

3 Spinoza, *Ethics*, 537, hereafter cited in text by page number.

4 References to the *Treatise* Appendix are to Hume, *A Treatise of Human Nature*, ed. Norton and Norton, cited in text as "T App." followed by page number, and to Hume, *A Treatise of Human Nature*, ed. Selby-Bigge, rev. by Nidditch, cited as "SBN" followed by the page number.

5 Harris, *Hume: An Intellectual Biography*.

WORKS CITED

Harris, James. *Hume: An Intellectual Biography*. Cambridge: Cambridge University Press, 2015.

Hirschman, Albert O. *The Passions and the Interests: Political Arguments for Capitalism before its Triumph*. Princeton: Princeton University Press, 1977.

Hume, David. *Treatise of Human Nature*. Edited by L. A. Selby-Bigge, revised by P. Nidditch. Oxford: Oxford University Press, 1978.

Hume, David. *A Treatise of Human Nature*. Edited by David Fate Norton and Mary J. Norton. Oxford: Oxford University Press, 2007.

Spinoza, Benedict de. "Ethics." In *The Collected Works of Spinoza*. Edited and translated by Edwin Curley, vol. I. Princeton: Princeton University Press, 1985.

Taylor, Jacqueline A. *Reflecting Subjects: Passion, Sympathy, and Society in Hume's Philosophy*. Oxford: Oxford University Press, 2015.

Hume Studies
Volume 45, Number 1–2, 2019, pp. 169–178

Social Theory, Ethics, and Autonomy: Comments on Taylor's *Reflecting Subjects*

DARIO PERINETTI

Reflecting Subjects offers a bold and original reading of Book 2 of the *Treatise,* and presents a problem that has been little explored by Hume scholarship. Jacqueline Taylor's book argues that we can reconstruct what she calls a "social theory" out of Book 2 of the *Treatise.* Based on a detailed account of the passions that constitute social selves, the social theory of the *Treatise* offers, according to Taylor, rich and fine-grained explanations of the causes of difference and inequality among human beings, based on understanding the characters of individuals, their social statuses, and their differences in power. However—and this is one of the central problems that *Reflecting Subjects* seeks to tackle—in Book 3 of the *Treatise,* Hume uses the same moral psychology developend in Book 2 to build an account of ethics, in which human beings are to be considered as equals. In her reading, this generates a tension between the moral psychology of Book 2, which is particularly sensitive to the way emotions are related to the variability of social practices and social statuses, and the account of morals in Book 3, which seems to disregard this social complexity in explaining moral judgment. As she puts it, in the third Book of the *Treatise,* "Hume neglects the social inequalities he has examined and instead appears to regard all persons as having more or less equal moral standing."[1]

Taylor argues that Hume eases this tension in his mature work. She claims that, in the second *Enquiry* and the *Essays,* Hume makes fundamental changes to his earlier moral theory, in order to produce a "more sophisticated" account of morals that take too moral evaluations as a kind of social practice (ibid). *Reflecting Subjects* sees the mature Hume as perfecting his earlier social theory by producing a more coherent account of the connection between social theory, moral psychology, and ethics.

Dario Perinetti is Professor of Philosophy at University of Quebec in Montreal: Département de philosophie, Université du Québec à Montréal, Case postale 8888, succursale Centre-ville, Montréal (Québec) H3P 3P8.
Email: perinetti.dario@uqam.ca

In the first chapter, Taylor argues that Hume abandons a common early-modern strategy of providing teleological explanations of the passions, and embraces an account solely based on an analysis of their efficient causes. She carefully shows that, once we properly understand what methodological experimentalism meant in the early-modern period, we can see that Hume's account of the passions was faithful to the project announced in the title of the *Treatise*: that of introducing "the experimental method of reasoning into moral subjects." In this initial chapter, Taylor reaches the central conclusion that the elimination of teleological explanations and the adoption of experimentalism turn Hume's account of the passions into something that goes well beyond the limits of moral psychology and can be appropriately labelled a "robust social theory" (*Reflecting Subjects*, 31). Hume's robust social theory is one that focuses on how social institutions, understood as historically and culturally determined, are crucial for shaping human nature and engendering social roles and relations.

Chapters 2 and 3 are devoted to present in detail the social theory that Taylor sees as pivotal to Book 2 of the *Treatise*. These chapters provide a fascinating analysis of how the indirect passions, together with the mechanism of sympathy, serve to explain a great number of significant social phenomena: the generation of social statuses, the production of wealth, the distribution of property, the transmission of cultural values and attitudes, and the existence of different forms of social power. In this short piece, I cannot begin to do justice to the richness of Taylor's work in these chapters. But I would like to underscore here the originality and the importance of her reconstruction of Hume's social theory. This reconstruction provides a new and refreshing angle for reading Book 2 of the *Treatise;* and the meticulous analysis of a wide range of social phenomena will provide future scholars with very useful materials to further advance this kind of reading.

Two other important claims are put forward in these two chapters. The *first* is that the theory of sympathy cannot be reduced to Hume's associationism. There is much more to it (*Reflecting Subjects*, 48). For example, Taylor rightly draws attention to the importance of the process of mirroring that the mechanism of sympathy makes possible. As Hume puts it: "In general we may remark, that the minds of men are mirrors to one another, not only because they reflect each other's emotions, but also because those rays of passions, sentiments and opinions may be often reverberated, and may decay away by insensible degrees" (T 2.2.5.21; SBN 365). The mirroring process is what turns us not only into the social creatures that we are, but, most importantly, into the *reflective subjects* that we become in our social interactions. The mirroring process is responsible for the kind of reciprocal relations that Taylor sees as constitutive of selves. Reflective subjects are the ones who aquire reflective awarenes of themselves in virtue of the fact that they see themselves reflected in others and that they, in turn, serve as mirrors for other subjects.

The importance of the mirroring process can be fully appreciated in the details of Hume's explanation of the "indirect passions," or the passions directed at persons. These passions are all forms of pleasure or displeasure about ourselves or about others; and they are caused by some pleasant or unpleasant quality or object. Pride, for instance, obtains when "*agreeable objects* [are] *related to ourselves by an association of ideas and of impressions*" (T 2.1.6.1; SBN

290). If agreeable objects are related to another person, the double relation of impressions and ideas begets love. When the objects that cause the passions are disagreeable, the passions produced are, respectively, humility and hate. So, self-regarding and others-regarding passions are dependent on a) evaluative attitudes directed at objects that are b) judged to be somehow related to oneself or another person.

So far, this looks like a strictly psychological account. But Hume stresses that the psychology of indirect passions is crucially sensitive to social factors. Pride can only arise when the agreeable object is *closely related*, as opposed to loosely related to us (T 1.2.6.3; SBN 66). I can enjoy myself by attending to a great party, but only the person that threw the party can properly be proud of it (T 2.1.6.2; SBN 290–91). A close relation to a valuable object or quality needs also be *peculiar to us* to produce pride (T 2.1.6.4–5; SBN 291–92). Thus, the positive (or negative) value of an object or quality is, to a great extent, a function of its scarcity. I can enjoy, for instance, being considerate and sensible, but it is only when these personal qualities are both prized and scarce, that they can be a source of pride. For only then, our being related to this quality becomes a way of distinguishing ourselves (positively or negatively) from others. Similarly, it is not sufficient for pride that I value positively a scarce quality or object that is closely related and peculiar to me. It is also required that its value be publicly recognized (T 2.1.6.6; SBN 292). No matter how much pleasure we might retire from something we possess, or a quality we have, it will hardly produce pride if we cannot imagine anyone concurring in our positive assessment of it.

Thus, indirect passions are more than mere ways of experiencing pleasure or displeasure about persons. They also serve to evaluate oneself or others, they involve beliefs, assessment of what others believe, and reliance on social norms. Indirect passions are shaped by and dependent on socially determined evaluative attitudes and judgments. Hence, indirect passions are social passions because—unlike joys or mere dislikes—they simply cannot exist in the absence of social relations and the sympathetic communication of passions in society. The mirroring process is, thus, characterized by the way our own self is reflected in the evaluative attitudes of others, and by the way other selves are reflected in our own evaluative attitudes. Hence, Taylor is correct in stressing that the mirroring process plays a fundamental role in our acquiring the competence of evaluating oneself and others epistemically, socially and morally (*Reflecting Subjects*, 55, 59).

The *second* important claim that emerges from Taylor's reconstruction of Hume's social theory is that there is a two-way direction of explanation between indirect passions and social institutions. On the one hand, our natural sentimental responses are at the origin of social attitudes and generate the need for institutional arrangements. On the other hand, through the same mirroring process, social institutions and conventions play a fundamental role in shaping the character and emotional bent of our individual selves.

Chapters 4, 5 and 6 are devoted to show how the same mechanisms that explain the emergence of our social attitudes are also responsible for the existence of our moral attitudes. In these chapters, Taylor seeks to explain how Hume's social theory connects with his sentimentalist ethics. She argues too that Hume's strategy for connecting his social theory with his ethics was unsuccessful in the *Treatise*. The reason is, in her opinion, that Hume's excessive reliance on psychological explanations and on the mechanism of sympathy results in a neglect of "the importance of good judgment and . . . of cultivating the virtues of good moral judgment." The focus on the psychology of sympathy has also the side-effect of masking the implications that social inequalities have for the moral authority of agents in actual practices of moral judgment (*Reflecting Subjects*, 101). In her view, Hume only managed to solve this problem in his mature work, particularly in the second *Enquiry* and in the *Essays*. The solution comes when Hume decides a) to abandon explanations that are exclusively based in the psychology of sympathy and; b) to give a central role to the sentiment of humanity, to moral reasoning, and to discursive practices in regulating our moral attitudes.

Let me focus here on the problem of connecting Hume's social theory with his ethics. One of the great merits of *Reflecting Subjects* lies in shedding light on a tension between Hume's sentimentalist account of social relations and his sentimentalist ethics. The problem is the following: does Hume have the resources for explaining how the same sentimental mechanisms that are responsible for social inequalities and differences in power also underlie the adoption of impartial moral attitudes that suppose accepting the equal worth and moral autonomy of human beings? In Book 2 of the *Treatise*, the indirect passions and the mechanism of sympathy serve to explain how we acquire the competence to identify and to evaluate the social significance of objects and persons. But Hume's social theory shows that the passions and sympathy generate unequal and asymmetrical relations between human beings. How can this theory also explain our capacity to identify and evaluate the moral significance of persons, a capacity that crucially depends on our seeing each other as equals?

This is an interesting question, and, as pointed out above, Taylor's answer is that Hume failed to give a satisfactory answer to it in the *Treatise*, but succeeded in the second *Enquiry* and the *Essays*, where his account of moral evaluation gives more room to the sentiment of humanity, to social practices of moral regulation, and to moral reasoning. Hume's account of moral evaluation in the *Treatise* is defective because, Taylor argues, it is exclusively based on the psychological mechanism of *extensive* sympathy. Extensive sympathy is the capacity to experience pleasure or pain regarding the actions of people that are not closely related to us, by imagining the effects that their actions tend to have on people close to them. Unlike it, *limited* sympathy is determined by the way someone's actions affect us or people in our circle. Extensive sympathy results from imaginarily projecting ourselves in social circles that have no close connection with us or, even, with groups or persons whose interest are in conflict with ours (see, for example, T 2.2.9.14–15, T 3.3.1.23 and T 3.3.6.3; SBN 386–87, 586–87, 615). This imaginary projection establishes what Hume calls a "common point of view," that is, a point of view in which, by disregarding our own interest, we can understand and experience the emotions of persons distant from us, in time, space, culture, or interests.

The problem that Taylor sees in the *Treatise* account is that the theory of sympathy forces Hume to adopt an implausible view of moral evaluation. Moral evaluation occurs when, failing to immediately sympathize with the observed agent, the moral observer places herself in the common point of view and sympathizes instead with the effects that the agent's actions have on her own circle. In this point of view, we consider how the agent is evaluated by the persons belonging to her circle and we sympathize with these evaluations. For Taylor this account turns the responses of people in the agent's circle in *our* criterion for evaluating the agent's virtue. This leads, in her view, to "*assume* that the circle's responses will be appropriate ones, and that sympathy with the agent's circle is therefore sufficient to guide the approval or blame of those adopting the common point of view." Thus, "the *Treatise* account depicts the responses of an agent's circle as reliably attesting to her character" (*Reflecting Subjects*, 113).

Now, if the common point of view is supposed to correct or neutralize *our* personal interest so that our evaluations of characters become genuinely *moral* evaluations, how can this procedure neutralize the interests and biases of the persons in the observed agent's circle? If extensive sympathy is merely sympathy with the emotions and responses of those who are close to the observed agent, then adopting the common point of view is tantamount to always legitimizing the situated and interested evaluations produced by the persons in the observed agent's circle. There is no room in this account for assessing the correctness of *their* evaluations.

Taylor contrasts this view of moral evaluation with the one that Hume presents in the second *Enquiry* and in "Of the Standard of Taste." She claims that "in the *Enquiry*, Hume stresses the importance of general conversation and good reasoning to establish a standard of virtue, rather than appealing to sympathy with the responses of an agent's associates" (*Reflecting Subjects,* 121–23). Taylor sees the *Enquiry*'s appeal to the *sentiment of humanity* as the source of moral responses as symptomatic of this shift in focus. Although ultimately based on the psychological mechanism of sympathy, the sentiment of humanity is, in her view, more than mere extensive sympathy. She argues that "the sentiments arising from the principle of humanity *require* reason and reflection" (ibid., 128, see also 122), and imply a general concern with society, rather than a more narrow sympathetic connection with specific social circles.

The close connection between the sentiment of humanity and moral reasoning leads Hume to an alternative understanding of the standard of virtue. Taylor argues that this alternative account can be found in "Of the Standard of State," where "Hume argues that the standard is the collective verdict of those who exercise certain virtues of good judgment" rather than, simply, anyone in the close circle of the observed agent (*Reflecting Subjects*, 113). In the mature view, moral reasoning makes us sympathize with the evaluations of judges closer to the agent than we are, but only on the condition that they be good judges, namely, that they too adopt the common point of view. This is, in Taylor's reading, a major improvement with respect to the "weakness" of the *Treatise* account. For the mere mechanism of extensive sympathy "renders us impartial but not necessarily reflective" (*Reflecting Subjects*, 129).

I am not convinced that Taylor is right in suggesting such an important change between the *Treatise* and later work in Hume's account of moral evaluation. Furthermore, I think that if she were right, her own account of how Hume solves the tension between the inequality proper to social relations and the equality required for moral evaluations would be weakened as a result. Let me explain. In the *Treatise,* Hume does not say that extensive sympathy is merely a way of endorsing the evaluations of persons in the observed agent's circle. What Hume says is that when evaluating the character of someone not related to us:

> we confine our view to that narrow circle, in which any person moves, in order to form a judgment of his moral character. When the natural tendency of his passions leads him to be serviceable and useful within his sphere, we approve of his character, and love his person, by a sympathy with the sentiments of those, who have a more particular connexion with him. (T3.3.3.2; SBN 602)

True, extensive sympathy, here, is sympathy with the sentiments of the persons immediately affected by the character of the observed agent. But that sympathy is based on *our own* evaluation of the passions that are durable traits of the agent's character. We have to judge that the character traits of the observed agent turn her into someone "serviceable and useful within his sphere." This judgement is based on a reasoned assesment of the effects that the agent's actions have on people on her circle, and on the sentiments these actions might generate in them. The idea we form of these sentiments, converts by sympathy into a moral sentiment, and we approve or disapprove the character of the person under observation. It is not sympathy with *their* assessment of the same character. Our attitude towards the agent's character rests on our evaluation of her durable traits of character and their imagined effect on the sentiments of persons in her circle. *We* are the ones who "consider the tendency of any passion to the advantage or harm of those, who have any immediate connexion or intercourse with the person possess'd of it" (T 3.3.3.2; SBN 602–603). This is something we can only do by reasoning. And it is only when *we* do that, that "our sentiments *concur* with those of others" (ibid., italics added). In other words, we are not deferring to the judgments of people in the agent's circle. We reason and judge, and our judgments count as a moral evaluation of the agent's character, only insofar as we abandon our own point of view and consider the effects of this character on her circle. The crucial point here is that *our* judgment must "concur" with that of anyone adopting the same perspective, that is, with anyone who impartially considers the effects of this character on other people. This view is quite consistent with rejecting the partial or biased evaluations of those in the narrow circle of the observed agent. To put it briefly, it is not a consequence of the *Treatise* account, that we must approve the dreadful character of someone because the equally dreadful people in his circle find him praiseworthy and benefit from his actions. The standard of virtue remains the reasoned judgment of an observer adopting the common point of view, not the one passed by the people in the observed agent's circle.

I agree that there certainly are significant differences in emphasis between the *Treatise* and Hume's later works. But I do not see sufficient evidence of an important shift in Hume's views here.[2] Even Taylor acknowledges that there are many passages in the *Treatise* that suggest a view quite similar to the one she thinks Hume developed only in his mature work.[3] But she claims that although those passages "point to the possibility of a more complex account of moral evaluation," they "do not square with the official *Treatise* line grounding the standard of virtue in the responses of those on the agent's sphere of influence" (*Reflecting Subjects*, 117). My previous remarks show that I do not think that this was Hume's "official line" in the *Treatise*.

In the absence of any decisive passage backing Taylor's interpretation, I think it safer to assume that Hume already had this more complex account in the *Treatise*. Actually, I believe that assuming the continuity of Hume's views on moral evaluation would serve to strengthen, rather than to undermine, what I see as Taylor's most important claim, namely, that in the mature works, Hume was primarily concerned with explaining the role that reasoning and discursive practices play in shaping our social and moral attitudes. For if it is true, as Taylor claims, that Hume's account of moral evaluation in the mature works does not rely on the *Treatise's* detailed psychology of sympathy and is, instead, based on the sentiment of humanity; and if it is also true that the sentiment of humanity is not just shorthand for sympathy, then Hume will be in trouble. For, Hume's account of moral judgment in terms of the theory of extensive sympathy in Book 3 of the *Treatise* is supported by the robust and detailed moral psychology developed in Book 2. But, if we were to suppose that, in the second *Enquiry,* Hume replaced the theory of sympathy by an appeal to the sentiment of humanity, Hume's sentimentalist ethics would be weakened as a result. For Hume's treatment of the sentiment of humanity in the EPM is too brief, if not sketchy, with respect to the psychology that underlies it. On Taylor's reading, the mature work strengthens the connection between the social theory and the moral theory. But, if I am correct, it would do so by losing the connection with Hume's moral psychology. On the contrary, assuming the continuity of Hume's views on moral judgment will be better to Taylor's more general aim of explaining the connection between these three aspects of Hume's thought. Assuming continuity will also be consistent with Taylor's claim that there is a significant evolution in Hume's mature works. The story, as I see it, would go as follows. Having achieved a consistent account of the connection between moral psychology and ethics in the *Treatise,* Hume became increasingly interested in giving a more detailed account of the role of social practices and moral reasoning in shaping our moral attitudes and evaluations. This would explain the change of focus in the second *Enquiry* and much of the content of his *Essays.* The shift of focus will also explain Hume's increasing interest in providing historical explanations for social practices and moral attitudes, such as we find them in the *Natural History of Religion,* some of his essays and, of course, in the *History of England.*[4]

Let me now return to the general problem of connecting the inequality that is assumed in Hume's social theory with the equality required for his ethics. In several passages of chapters 5 and 6, Taylor advances an important contention that may otherwise pass unnoticed. She argues that Hume offers a substantial account of moral autonomy that importantly differs from the usual Kantian one (*Reflecting Subjects*, 182). The advantage of a Kantian approach to autonomy (assuming for the sake of argument that it offers a coherent one) is that, given that autonomy is taken as the offspring of human practical reason, individuals are not required to be socially equal in order to be morally equal. In his writings on history and perpetual peace, Kant certainly shows awareness that the full exercise of the moral autonomy of human beings depends on their being able to create in history a rationally governed commonwealth.[5] But it remains true that human beings are autonomous irrespective of whether their social environment is optimally adapted to the exercise of their autonomy. In the case of Hume, the situation is more complex. Taylor's contribution here lies in underscoring that Hume has a view on moral autonomy, but that he considers it to be *acquired* in social interactions and, hence, *dependent* on them. This contention is consistent with her claim that the sympathy-based mirroring process plays a pivotal role in constituting selves. The interesting point is that she argues, both by referring to Hume and to contemporary works in psychology, that interconnectedness is integral to having a self. But interconnectedness does not, as some Kantians might fear, turn agents into heteronomous individuals. As Taylor puts it, a "connected self has received the kind of mirroring that allows her to make independent judgments" (*Reflecting Subjects*, 156).

If that is true, and I think Taylor is on the right track here, it seems that Hume faces the problem of explaining how moral attitudes that suppose recognizing each other as equals can emerge amid institutional settings and cultures that are based on social and political inequality. To put it otherwise, interconnected Humean agents are shaped by the inequalities characterizing their social connections that constitute them. In the absence of any Kantian noumenal standpoint—the one provided by the categorical imperative—how can such agents be brought to recognize each other as equals? The only route available for Hume seems to be to add an account of the historical progression of morality and autonomy to his social theory.

On this issue Taylor credits Hume with what I think is a weak (and Whiggish) conception of moral progress in history. The basic story will be the following: the more people interact and the more different countries enter into mutual commerce, the more a common human point of view develops and makes possible the flourishing of genuinely moral attitudes in society. The progress of industry, the arts, and knowledge fosters all sorts of social commerce and exchanges and, so, is instrumental in nurturing the development of moral attitudes. As Hume puts it in "Of Refinement in the Arts" (1752) : "Industry, knowledge, and humanity, are linked together by an indissoluble chain, and are found, from experience as well as reason, to be peculiar to the more polished, and, what are commonly denominated, the more luxurious ages" (E-RA 271). Now, it is not obvious to me that Hume espoused this rather simple-minded conception of moral progress. At least later in his life, Hume must certainly have been aware that people like Rousseau or Adam Ferguson, had compellingly argued that the development of complex commercial societies does not necessarily result in a parallel development of human moral attitudes. Rousseau argued for the contrary view, and Ferguson claimed that social progress implies moral progress only for the privileged people who possess the leisure necessary to cultivate their moral virtues. Here is where I regret that Taylor has not devoted more time to understanding Hume's social theory and its connection to morality in their historical dimension. The *History of England,* which is the place to go for investigating Hume's view on these matters, is remarkably absent in Taylor's book.

Let me close my comments by stressing again what I see as Taylor's major contributions in *Reflecting Subjects*: a) a truly novel reading of Hume on the passions that uncovers a rich and complex social theory, b) the discussion of an important but neglected problem: the connection between Hume's social theory and his ethics, and c) the stress on the evolution of Hume's thinking about these issues. Taylor's layered discussion of these important topics leads her to raise important questions about the moral autonomy that essentially social beings can expect. Thus, *Reflecting Subjects* is not only a significant achievement in Hume's studies. It also opens very promising research paths for future scholarly endeavours.

NOTES

1 Taylor, *Reflecting Subjects*, 100. Hereafter cited in text by page number.

2 This is a vexed issue in Hume's scholarship. It mostly turns on whether Hume abandoned in the second *Enquiry* the sympathy-based account of moral sentiments that he adopted in the *Treatise*. Norman Kemp Smith argues that the sympathy-based account of ethics is incompatible with a moral sense theory. He also claims that, in EPM, Hume abandoned the theory of sympathy in order to adopt a Hutchesonian moral sense theory. See Kemp Smith, *The Philosophy of David Hume*, 150–52. Kate Abramson agrees that a sympathy-based account is incompatible with moral sense theory, but she claims that Hume did not give up sympathy and, hence, that he never held a moral sense theory. See Abramson, "Sympathy and the Project of Hume's Second Enquiry," 52. Remy Debes agrees that Hume did not abandon the theory of sympathy, and that Hume's use of the sentiment of humanity in the *Enquiry* is "shorthand" for the principle of sympathy. See Debes, "Humanity, Sympathy and the Puzzle of Hume's Second *Enquiry*" and "Has Anything Changed?" In chapter 4 of *Reflecting Subjects*, Taylor claims that, on the contrary, the principle of humanity, which Hume introduces in his mature works replaces the sympathy-based account. See also Jacqueline Taylor, "Hume's Later Moral Philosophy." I have discussed the issue in Perinetti, "Moral Pluralism and the Historical Point of View."

3 See *Reflecting Subjects*, 117–20, where she comments on Hume's remarks in T 3.2.7.2, 3.3.1.13, 3.3.2.15–17 ; 534–35, SBN 580, 600–601, among other passages.

4 I have discussed that connection in Perinetti, "Moral Pluralism and the Historical Point of View."

5 See, for example, Kant, "Idea for a Universal History with a Cosmopolitan Aim" and "Toward Perpetual Peace."

WORKS CITED

Abramson, Kate. "Sympathy and the Project of Hume's Second *Enquiry*." *Archiv für Geschichte der Philosophie* 83, no. 1 (2001): 45–80. https://doi.org/10.1515/agph.83.1.45

Debes, Remy. "Has Anything Changed? Hume's Theory of Association and Sympathy after the *Treatise*." *British Journal for the History of Philosophy* 15, no. 2 (2007): 313–38. https://doi.org/10.1080/09608780701240040

Debes, Remy. "Humanity, Sympathy and the Puzzle of Hume's Second *Enquiry*." *British Journal for the History of Philosophy* 15, no. 1 (2007): 27–57. https://doi.org/10.1080/09608780601087954

Hume, David. *Dialogues Concerning Natural Religion, and Other Writings*. Edited by Dorothy Coleman. Cambridge: Cambridge University Press, 2007.

Hume, David. *An Enquiry Concerning the Principles of Morals*. Edited by Thomas L. Beauchamp. Oxford: Clarendon Press, 2003.

Hume, David. *Essays Moral, Political, and Literary*. Edited by Eugene F. Miller. Indianapolis: Liberty Fund, 1987.

Hume, David. *A Treatise of Human Nature*. Edited by David Fate Norton and Mary J. Norton Oxford: Oxford University Press, 2011.

Kant, Immanuel. "Idea for a Universal History with a Cosmopolitan Aim." In *Kant's Idea for a Universal History with a Cosmopolitan Aim: A Critical Guide.* Translated by Allen W. Wood. Edited by Amèlie Rorty and James Schmidt, 10–23. Cambridge: Cambridge University Press, 2009.

Kant, Immanuel. "Toward Perpetual Peace." Translated by Mary J. Gregor. In *Practical Philosophy.* Edited by Mary J. Gregor and Allen Wood. Cambridge Edition of the Works of Immanuel Kant. Cambridge: Cambridge University Press, 1996.

Kemp Smith, Norman. *The Philosophy of David Hume.* 1941. London: Palgrave Macmillan, 2005.

Perinetti, Dario. "Moral Pluralism and the Historical Point of View: Reading 'A Dialogue.'" In *Reading Hume on the Principles of Morals.* Edited by Jacqueline Anne Taylor, 196–218. Oxford: Oxford University Press, 2020.

Taylor, Jacqueline. "Hume's Later Moral Philosophy." Chap. 10 in *The Cambridge Companion to Hume, 2nd Edition.* Edited by David Fate Norton and Jacqueline Anne Taylor, 311–40. Cambridge: Cambridge University Press, 2009.

Taylor, Jacqueline. *Reflecting Subjects: Passion, Sympathy, and Society in Hume's Philosophy.* Oxford: Oxford University Press, 2014.

Hume Studies
Volume 45, Number 1–2, 2019, pp. 179–186

Reply to My Critics

JACQUELINE A. TAYLOR

I

I thank Genevieve Lloyd for her generous and thought-provoking comments and questions. She raises two distinct issues: one regarding how to think about the way in which Hume's account of pride might be innovative, and the other about how a genre of philosophical writing limits or opens up what and how an author might discuss the subject at hand. She sets both issues in the context of comparing Spinoza with Hume.

Lloyd reminds us that A. O. Hirschman, in *The Passions and the Interests*, charts a conceptual shift between the seventeenth and eighteenth centuries, such that the change in political and economic conditions, heralding the rise of capitalism, led to the deposing of the traditional opposition between reason and passion in favor of their alliance in the form of rational interest. Is Hume effecting a similar conceptual shift with pride? This is an excellent question, and one I had not explicitly addressed in the book. In the *Treatise* account of pride, Hume purports to be critically examining the "nature, origin, causes, and effects" of the indirect passions" (T 2.1.1.3; SBN 276).[1] In establishing the origin of pride by way of a double association of ideas and impressions, we see Hume at his most experimental, finding the general causes and effects that characterize every occurrence of pride. But, when he turns to the particular occasioning causes of pride, an account meant to provide evidence for the hypothesis regarding the double association, Hume presents general categories of causes, such as qualities of mind and of body, or wealth, that reflect the facts about what people take pride in, or are esteemed for, in the observation of "common life." Hume does here differ from Spinoza's more traditional (and in a sense Christianized) view of pride as an unjust estimation

Jacqueline A. Taylor is Professor in the Department of Philosophy, University of San Francisco, San Francisco, CA.
Email: jtaylor2@usfca.edu

of oneself, or a putting of oneself above others (including God). For Hume, people justly take pride in their talents or virtue, their beautiful or talented children, as well as their beautiful house. He had also described these causes as non-original insofar as what counts as, say, virtue or a fine house will track such things as custom or trends, technological innovation or deprivation, and in particular the way in which sympathetic communication and mirroring help to create and sustain the contours of shared values.

I agree with Lloyd's point that Spinoza's distinction between the proud person's imagination-based inadequate idea of himself and someone whose rightful self-esteem is based on a true understanding of his capacities differs from the role that Hume assigns the imagination, especially with respect to the production of pride, and the sympathy-based shaping of pride's contours. As a naturalist, Hume takes an interest in what Lloyd terms sympathy's darker side, such as how sympathetic communication between those in a community with an extreme imbalance of power can enhance the pride of the powerful or the humility of the powerless. In his later work, especially the study in the *Essays* of moral causes, both fixed and accidental, we can reconstruct a broader and more in-depth account of the different kinds of institutional and less formal arrangements that can lead to greater or lesser sociability and society-wide flourishing. In the essay genre, and in the later moral philosophy of the *Enquiry*, Hume attends more fully to the social mores of common life, setting aside the detailed mental associationism of the *Treatise* in favor of locating the foundation of morals and the markers of social flourishing (knowledge, industry and humanity) in an observable human nature embedded in social contexts and linguistic conventions (for example, that of morality rather than self-interest, or of gallantry and politeness).

II

Willem Lemmens has been a friend and fellow Hume researcher for a number of years, and I have valued the opportunities to visit beautiful Antwerp to discuss sympathy and Hume, and to work with some of his graduate students. In his remarks, Lemmens denies that Hume has reformist or emancipatory aims that would impart a normative dimension to his moral philosophy. For example, Hume's discussion of humanity is part of his speculative philosophy regarding morals, not an endorsement of the power of humanity to promote sociability and social flourishing. Similarly, resentment, as part of human nature, is one of the conditions that make justice necessary and possible for us. In interpreting Hume's moral philosophy, the notion of normativity is a vexed one (I do not believe I mentioned the word in my book). I did not claim that Hume has emancipatory aims akin to those, for example, of the late eighteenth- and ninenteenth-century English radicals and reformers, or the campaigns for civil and other rights. Rather, I pointed to Hume's evident awareness in his discussion of gallantry and politeness of the value of a specific discourse, where a speaker may "yield the superiority" to the otherwise socially or politically disadvantaged, such as strangers or women, through the public enactment of civility and respect, to promote a more equal "intercourse of minds."[2] Hume specifically contrasts politeness and gallantry with ancient rusticity, and aligns the former with virtues such as generosity, wisdom, and prudence, while the ancient men reduce "their females to the most abject slavery; by confining them, by beating them, by selling them, by killing them."[3] Hume may of course be *describing* the difference between two kinds of societies, but since he is in this essay charting the rise and progress of arts, sciences, economies, and manners that lead to the flourishing of more rather than fewer members of a society, I read him as also *endorsing* modern manners, virtues, and the cultivation of humanity, and *condemning* the vices, including the treatment of women, of the ancients. A main implication, in my view, is that Hume's insights provide resources for those of us interested in analyzing and charting ways to bridge more invidious socially constructed divisions.

Regarding resentment, Lemmens is right that Hume presents as a condition of justice our having the capacity to make felt the effects of resentment by those who injure, insult, or oppress us. But Hume is also making the point that the society of human beings, their association together based on a shared nature, "supposes a degree of equality" (EPM 3.18; SBN 190).[4] It is then, according to Hume, a fact about human beings that they stand in relation to one another in terms of some degree of equality, namely, that which is a ground for rights. This contrasts with a relation such as that between man and other animals, which is characterized by "absolute command on the one side, and servile obedience on the other," that would place us under a duty of compassion rather than justice (EPM 3.18; SBN 190). A person's resentment, even if it goes unanswered, thus functions as a complaint against injustice, or demand for more just treatment.

Lemmens suggests that for Hume, human nature is perhaps best realized through a society characterized by rank and other social distinctions such as that of gender, and that this is a reason for Hume to favor such distinctions. I put the point differently. According to Hume, government, which is needed for our continued association, in making "a distinction in property . . . establishes the ranks of men," which in turn produces physical differences ("the skin, pores, muscles, and nerves of a day-labourer")—differences to the mental fabric and our passionate makeup, as well persons' sense of who they are in terms of social standing, and their understanding of who has claims to social authority (T 2.3.1.9; SBN 402). In the chapter of my book on power and "the philosophy of our passions," I drew attention to Hume's explanation of how comparison and mutual sympathetic mirroring worked to show how "the vanity of power, or shame of slavery, are much augmented by the consideration of the persons, over whom we exercise our authority, or who exercise it over us" (T 2.1.10.12; SBN 315). I take him here to be *describing* how an extreme imbalance of power informs a person's sense of herself, based on her sympathetic communication of her own passions or sentiments and the reception of those of others, as well as their responses to them. The influence of mirrored sentiments shows how an initial sense of humility becomes an abject humility, while pride, in turn, becomes pride in having power over the abject. The ongoing mirroring of passionate responses contributes to a sense of identity in relation to others. Nevertheless, in his later works, there is no doubt that Hume regards the influence of the extreme imbalance in social relations, such as that between ancient men and women, or masters and slaves, and the production of a power-enhanced pride or an abject humility in response to that pride and power, as the darker workings of sympathy. Moreover, in the *Enquiry*, the government-established ranks in the more robust and healthy economy (for example, day-laborer, vassal, and lord, in contrast to that of the slave-holding society) are not wholly constitutive of our passionate or sentimental attitudes towards one another. Hume writes:

> A man, who has cured himself of all ridiculous prepossessions, and is fully, sincerely, and steadily convinced, from experience as well as philosophy, that the difference of fortune makes less difference in happiness than is vulgarly imagined; such a one does not measure out degrees of esteem according to the rent-rolls of his acquaintance. He may, indeed, externally pay a superior deference to the great lord above the vassal; because riches are the most convenient, being the most fixed and determinate, source of distinction: But his internal sentiments are more regulated by the personal characters of men, than by the accidental and capricious favours of fortune. (EPM 6.34; SBN 248)

The point Hume makes, and it is an important one, is related to the account I give of the discourses of politeness or gallantry in effecting a greater semblance of equality. In the example above, the norms associated with the social roles, such as that of lord and vassal, require the public performance of respect and deference to the lord. While it may sound as if the internal sentiments that value the character of the vassal over that of the lord find no public expression, we know, and I believe Hume knew, that there are more or less subtle ways of indicating one's internal sentiments (see *Reflecting Subjects*, 174–75, 179). My point, in response to Lemmens, is that even if social stratification is inevitable, Hume's description of our actual experiences of the expression of moral attitudes, which in some circumstances may not be *fully* separable from attitudes that get expressed in response to wealth or power, carry some normative weight. Against the backdrop of the actual social contexts in which we find ourselves, we can respond to one another in various ways, to moral character as well as rank, to signal different levels of valuation or esteem. Hume's account of the complex ways in which we negotiate the values of persons suggests he favors some valuations more than others. While some of high rank may particularly value the due deference they receive based on their social standing, Hume indicates that a moral esteem for personal merit has as its object something with more worth.

Regarding Humean sympathy, I think Hume does offer a coherent, albeit quite complex explanation of its workings. It explains different sort of phenomena: the reinforcement of particular cultural meanings and values, for example, when there is "any peculiar similarity in our manners, or character, or country, or language" (T 2.1.11.5; SBN 318); the sustaining or undermining of pride; the production of moral sentiments, and so on. This is an area where much more work might be done to see how Hume's account meshes with contemporary work, say, in neuroscience. Consider contemporary work on fear as a central state: fear, anxiety, and panic stand on a continuum with respect to threat imminence, and there may be different fear circuits depending on kinds of stimuli. We might argue for something similar for sympathy as a central state: contagion, sympathetic identification regarding causes, manners, or temperament, and the cultivation of a sense of humanity all stand on a continuum with respect to the communication of opinions, passions, and sentiments, depending on what the sympathetic state is a response to.[5] I drew attention to Hume's recognition of sympathy's darker side, whether in the form of contagious sublime sentiments, or the zealous partiality of factions and seditions. That sympathy functions to create and sustain partialities does not militate against a more reason-informed sense of humanity that also has its source in sympathy. Hume develops his account of humanity in the *Enquiry*, emphasizing the need for reasoning, conversation, and negotiation, in order to form a general standard based on general views of useful or pernicious character traits.

III

Since Lemmens and Dario Perinetti offer similar criticisms regarding my argument for Hume's advancing different accounts of moral evaluation between the *Treatise* and the *Enquiry*, I will respond to both of them below. As I argue in chapter 4, Hume does provide some resources in *Treatise* Book 3 for an account of moral evaluation that gives some role to an independent and reason-informed judgment of the moral spectator; for example, in urging that virtue in rags is still virtue, Hume argues that we can in such cases rely on our understanding of the general tendency of character traits, even when someone cannot, due to circumstances, effectively exercise a trait she possesses. Nevertheless, Hume insists that we can bring a moral subject nearer, or evaluate his character impartially, "by a sympathy with those, who have any commerce with the person we consider," and that our sympathy with *their* pleasures, pains, or interests is the basis for *our* moral approval or blame (T 3.3.1.18; SBN 583). I pointed to several passages that suggest an over-reliance on the passions or sentiments of others as the basis for our own moral sentiment. Consider the following:

> Since every quality in ourselves or others, which gives pleasure, always causes pride or love; as every one, that produces uneasiness, excites humility or hatred: It follows, that these two particulars are to be consider'd as equivalent, with regard to our mental qualities, *virtue* and the power of producing love or pride, *vice* and the power of producing humility or hatred. In every case, therefore, we must judge of the one by the other; and may pronounce any *quality* of the mind virtuous, which causes love or pride; and any one vicious, which causes hatred or humility. (T 3.3.1.3; SBN 574)

The problem lies in the inference that Hume entitles one to draw in observing someone's love for a particular agent. My love for a partner's courageous daring and skill in stealing from or defrauding others is grounds for an observer to pronounce virtuous the quality that causes my love.

More problematic is Hume's argument for how we establish "the standard of virtue and morality" to correct the variable sentiments that arise when the moral subject is too distant from us to engage our natural sympathy:

> In judging of characters, the only interest or pleasure, which appears the same to every spectator, is that of the person himself, whose character is examin'd; or that of persons, who have a connexion with him. And tho' such interests and pleasures touch us more faintly than our own, yet being more constant and universal, they counter-ballance the latter even in practice, and are alone admitted in speculation as the standard of virtue and morality. They alone produce that particular feeling or sentiment, on which moral distinctions depend. (T 3.3.1.30; SBN 590)

Hume makes it quite clear: the interests and pleasures of the agent or those whom she affects are "more constant and universal," and "counter-ballance" our own natural response, and serve as "the standard of virtue and morality." That is, their interests and pleasures are those with which we sympathize in order to conform our own sentiments accordingly. Perinetti suggests that another passage shows that Hume thinks we make an independent judgment regarding someone's character. So, in judging the good qualities of the benevolent person, we:

> confine our view, to that narrow circle, in which any person moves, in order to form a judgment of his moral character. When the natural tendency of his passions leads him to be serviceable and useful within his sphere, we approve of his character, and love his person, by a sympathy with the sentiments of those who have a more particular connexion with him. (T 3.3.3.2; SBN 602)

According to Perinetti, this passage indicates that our evaluation relies on our own evaluation of the person's durable character traits. He acknowledges that we do sympathize with the sentiments of those in the agent's sphere, so that the idea we form of their sentiments converts into a moral sentiment. But our moral approval or blame does not arise from our sympathy with their sentiments. I read this passage differently. Hume writes explicitly that "we approve of his character, and love his person, by a sympathy with the sentiments of those who have a more particular connexion with him." The problem that this passage points to is Hume's eagerness to account for our moral sentiments arising through association, a process that is, in a sense, similar to that of indirect passions. The generation of our approval or blame requires an antecedent pleasure or pain for us to sympathize with, so Hume relies on the pleasures or pains of those affected by the agent's character. In contrast to Perinetti's view, I find these passages decisive for an account of moral evaluation that gives too great a role to the pleasures, pains, and interests of those in an agent's sphere. Hume sought to correct this account in the *Enquiry*.

In that work, Hume assigns good reasoning a considerable role in producing appropriate moral sentiments that accurately assess the tendencies of character traits. That accurate assessment is crucial for touching our humanity, a sense or principle that itself works to interest us in, and give us some concern for, the happiness and misery of others. I do not argue, as Perinetti suggests, that Hume abandons sympathy in favor of humanity. Rather, I argue that a broader conception of sympathy serves to generate different kinds of moral sentiments.

An immediate and unreflective sympathy produces through contagion, for example, the sentiment of sublime admiration in response to the immediately agreeable greatness of mind possessed by the ancient heroes and heroines. We cannot help but respond immediately to the charms of an agent's compassion in action. Humanity, Hume indicates, is grounded in the same sympathy; as he notes at the end of section 5 of the *Enquiry*, regarding the progress of his argument, consideration of qualities useful to ourselves and then qualities immediately agreeable to the self or others, "will bring a farther confirmation of the present theory, by showing the rise of *other sentiments* of esteem and regard from the *same or like principles*" (EPM 5.47; SBN 232, emphases added).

The principle of humanity produces reason-informed sentiments of approval or blame in response to the useful or pernicious tendencies of character traits. It does so not through our sympathy with the pleasures and pains of those affected by an agent's character. Rather, we establish a general standard of virtue by reasoning together (gathering facts, comparing cases, taking notes of relations, and so on regarding the tendencies of traits and policies) and conversing in terms of a specifically moral discourse, to arrive at (more or less shared) preferences for the qualities that make up personal merit.

Perinetti has advocated for an important historical dimension in Hume's *Treatise*, and I look forward to the monograph he is preparing on this. Regarding, however, his comments on my comparison between Hume and Kant on the possibility of autonomy (or independent judgment, as I put it), I do not ascribe to Hume a weak and Whiggish view of moral progress. Indeed, I make it clear that any such progress, for example, in a group securing a right that they were previously denied, while an achievement, may always be subject to the kinds of countervailing forces (tyranny or extremism, for example) that may gain hold and threaten to undo such accomplishments. Hume's position here, his comparison between a "party of humankind" and sympathetic yet factious partialities, is nuanced and subtle, and deserves further careful analysis and interpretation (EPM 9.9; SBN 275).

NOTES

1 References to the *Treatise* are to Hume, *A Treatise of Human Nature*, ed. Norton and Norton, hereafter cited in the text as "T" followed by Book, part, section, and paragraph number, and to Hume, *A Treatise of Human Nature*, ed. Selby-Bigge, rev. by Nidditch, cited in the text as "SBN" followed by the page number.

2 Hume, "Rise and Progress of the Arts and Sciences," in *Essays*, 132.

3 "Rise and Progress," 133.

4 References are to Hume, *An Enquiry concerning the Principles of Morals*, ed. Beauchamp, hereafter cited in the text as "EPM" followed by section and paragraph number, and to Hume, *Enquiries Concerning the Principles of Human Understanding and Concerning the Principles of Morals*, ed. Selby-Bigge, rev. by Nidditch, hereafter cited in the text as "SBN" followed by page numbers.

5 See Adolphs, "The Biology of Fear."

WORKS CITED

Adolphs, Ralph. "The Biology of Fear." In *Curr. Biol.* 23, no. 2 (2013): 79–93. https://doi.org/10.1016/j.cub.2012.11.055

Hume, David. *An Enquiry Concerning the Principles of Morals*. Edited by Tom. L. Beauchamp. Oxford: Oxford University Press, 1998.

Hume, David. *Enquiries Concerning the Principles of Human Understanding and Concerning the Principles of Morals*. Edited by L. A. Selby-Bigge, revised by P. H. Nidditch, 3rd ed. Oxford: Clarendon Press, 1975.

Hume, David. *A Treatise of Human Nature*. Edited by David Fate Norton and Mary J. Norton. Oxford: Oxford University Press, 2007.

Hume, David. *A Treatise of Human Nature*. Edited by L. A. Selby-Bigge, revised by P. H. Nidditch. Oxford: Clarendon Press, 1978.

Taylor, Jacqueline. *Reflecting Subjects: Passion, Sympathy, and Society in Hume's Philosophy*. Oxford: Oxford University Press, 2015.

Hume Studies
Volume 45, Number 1–2, 2019, pp. 187–189

Erratum

The following "works cited" section was inadvertently omitted from the print version of *Hume Studies* 44.2. It should have appeared after p. 273 in the article by Emily Kelahan, "Naturalness and Artificiality in Humean Virtue Theory."

WORKS CITED

Abramson, Kate. "Correcting Our Sentiments about Hume's Moral Point of View," *The Southern Journal of Philosophy* 37 (1999): 333–61. https://doi.org/10.1111/j.2041-6962.1999.tb00871.x

Abramson, Kate. "Sympathy and the Project of Hume's Second Enquiry," *Archiv für Geschichte der Philosophie* 83 (2001): 45–80. https://doi.org/10.1515/agph.83.1.45

Abramson, Kate. "What's so 'Natural' about Hume's Natural Virtues?" In *The Cambridge Companion to Hume's* Treatise, edited by Donald C. Ainslie and Annemarie Butler, 333–68. Cambridge: Cambridge University Press, 2015.

Aristotle. *The Complete Works of Aristotle*. Edited by J. Barnes. Princeton: Princeton University Press, 1971.

Baceski, Tina. "Hume on Art Critics, Wise Men, and the Virtues of Taste," *Hume Studies* 39.2 (2013): 233–56. https://doi.org/10.1353/hms.2014.0002

Baehr, Jason. "Four Varieties of Character-Based Virtue Epistemology," The Southern Journal of Philosophy 46 (2008): 469–502. https://doi.org/10.1111/j.2041-6962.2008.tb00081.x

Baier, Annette. *A Progress of Sentiments*. Cambridge, MA: Harvard University Press, 1991.

Baron, Marcia. "Hume's Noble Lie: An Account of his Artificial Virtues," *Canadian Journal of Philosophy* 12.3 (1982): 539–55. https://doi.org/10.1080/00455091.1982.10716347

Battaly, Heather. "Virtue Epistemology," *Philosophy Compass* 3/4 (2008): 639–63. https://doi.org/10.1111/j.1747-9991.2008.00146.x

Boyle, Deborah. "The Ways of the Wise: Hume's Rules of Causal Reasoning," *Hume Studies* 38.2 (2012): 157–82. https://doi.org/10.1353/hms.2012.0011

Brown, Charlotte. "Hume on Moral Rationalism, Sentimentalism, and Sympathy." In *A Companion to Hume*, edited by Elizabeth S. Radcliffe, 219–39. Malden, MA: Wiley-Blackwell, 2011.

Brown, Charlotte. "From Spectator to Agent: Hume's Theory of Obligation," *Hume Studies* 20 (1994): 19–35.

Cohen, Alix. "The Notion of Moral Progress in Hume's Philosophy: Does Hume Have a Theory of Moral Progress?" *Hume Studies* 26.1 (2000): 109–27. https://doi.org/10.1353/hms.2011.0211

Cohon, Rachel. "The Common Point of View in Hume's Philosophy," *Philosophy and Phenomenological Research* 57.4 (1997): 827–50.

Cohon, Rachel. "Hume's Natural and Artificial Virtues." In *The Blackwell Guide to Hume's* Treatise, edited by Saul Traiger, 256–75. Malden, MA: Blackwell, 2006. https://doi.org/10.2307/2953805

Driver, Julia. "The Conflation of Moral and Epistemic Virtue," *Metaphilosophy* 34.3 (2003): 367–83. https://doi.org/10.1111/1467-9973.00279

Frykholm, Erin. "A Humean Particularist Virtue Ethic," *Philosophical Studies* 172 (2015): 2171–91. https://doi.org/10.1007/s11098-014-0404-y

Garrett, Don. "The First Motive to Justice: Hume's Circle Argument Squared," *Hume Studies* 33.2 (November 2007): 257–88.

Gauthier, David. "Artificial Virtues and the Sensible Knave," *Hume Studies* 18.2 (1992): 401–27. https://doi.org/10.1353/hms.2011.0388

Goldman, Alvin. *Liaisons*. Cambridge, MA: MIT Press, 1991.

Hickerson, Ryan. (2013). "What the Wise Ought to Believe: A Voluntarist Interpretation of Hume's General Rules," *British Journal for the History of Philosophy* 21.6 (2013): 1133–53. https://doi.org/10.1080/09608788.2013.821594

Hume, David. *Dialogues Concerning Natural Religion*. Edited by Dorothy Coleman. Cambridge: Cambridge University Press, 2007.

Hume, David. A Dissertation on the Passions: *The Natural History of Religion*. Edited by Tom L. Beauchamp. Oxford: Oxford University Press, 2007.

Hume, David. *An Enquiry Concerning Human Understanding*. Edited by Tom L. Beauchamp. Oxford: Oxford University Press, 2001.

Hume, David. *An Enquiry Concerning the Principles of Morals*. Edited by Tom L. Beauchamp. Oxford: Oxford University Press, 1999.

Hume, David. "Of the Standard of Taste." In *Essays, Moral, Political, Literary*, revised edition. Edited by Eugene F. Miller, 226–49. Indianapolis: Liberty Fund, 1987.

Hume, David. *A Treatise of Human Nature*. Edited by David Fate Norton and Mary J. Norton. Oxford: Oxford University Press, 2007.

Hursthouse, Rosalind. "Virtue Ethics and Human Nature," *Hume Studies* 25.1–2 (1999): 67–82.

Kail, P.J.E. "Understanding Hume's Natural History of Religion," *The Philosophical Quarterly* 57.227 (2007): 190–211. https://doi.org/10.1111/j.1467-9213.2007.479.x

Kopajtic, Lauren. "Cultivating Strength of Mind: Hume on the Government of the Passions and Artificial Virtue," *Hume Studies* 41.2 (2015): 201–29. https://doi.org/10.1353/hms.2015.0009

Korsgaard, Christine. "The General Point of View: Love and Moral Approval in Hume's Ethics," *Hume Studies* 25.1–2 (1999): 3–42.

Lottenbach, Hans. "Monkish Virtues, Artificial Lives: On Hume's Genealogy of Morals," *Canadian Journal of Philosophy* 26.3 (1996): 367–88. https://doi.org/10.1080/00455091.1996.10717458

McCormick, Miriam. "Why Should We Be Wise?" *Hume Studies* 31.1 (2005): 3–19. https://doi.org/10.1353/hms.2011.0262

McIntyre, Jane. "Strength of Mind: Prospects and Problems for a Humean Account," *Synthese* 152 (2006): 393–401. https://doi.org/10.1007/s11229-006-9005-4

Owen, David. *Hume's Reason*. Oxford: Oxford University Press, 1999.

Qu, Hsueh. "Hume's Practically Epistemic Conclusions?" *Philosophical Studies* 170 (2014): 501–24. https://doi.org/10.1007/s11098-013-0260-1

Qu, Hsueh. "Prescription, Description, and Hume's Experimental Method," *British Journal for the History of Philosophy* 24.2 (2016): 279–301. https://doi.org/10.1080/09608788.2015.1134438

Radcliffe, Elizabeth S. "Strength of Mind and the Calm and Violent Passions," *Res Philosophica* 92.3 (2015): 547–67. https://doi.org/10.11612/resphil.2015.92.3.1

Ridge, Michael. "Epistemology Moralized: David Hume's Practical Epistemology" *Hume Studies* 29.2 (2003): 165–204.

Sayre-McCord, Geoffrey. "On Why Hume's 'General Point of View' Isn't Ideal-And Shouldn't Be," Social Philosophy and Policy 11.1 (1994): 202–28. https://doi.org/10.1017/S0265052500004350

Schafer, Karl. "Curious Virtues in Hume's Epistemology," *Philosophers' Imprint* 14.1 (2014): 1–20.

Sosa, Ernest. "For the Love of Truth?" In *Virtue Epistemology: Essays on Epistemic Virtue and Responsibility*, edited by Linda Zagzebski and Abrol Fairweather, 49–62. Oxford: Oxford University Press, 2001.

Smith, Adam. *The Theory of Moral Sentiments*, edited by Knud Haakonssen. Cambridge: Cambridge University Press, 2002.

Swanton, Christine. *The Virtue Ethics of Hume and Nietzsche*. Malden, MA: Wiley-Blackwell, 2015.

Swanton, Christine. *Virtue Ethics: A Pluralistic View*. Oxford: Oxford University Press, 2003.

Taylor, Jacqueline A. "Hume on the Standard of Virtue," *Journal of Ethics* 6.1 (2002): 43–62.

Taylor, Jacqueline A. *Reflecting Subjects: Passion, Sympathy, and Society in Hume's Philosophy*. Oxford: Oxford University Press, 2015.

Vitz, Rico. "Contagion, Community, and Virtue in Hume's Epistemology." In *The Ethics of Belief*, edited by Jonathan Matheson and Rico Vitz, 198–215. Oxford: Oxford University Press, 2014.

Vitz, Rico. "Doxastic Virtues in Hume's Epistemology," *Hume Studies* 35.1–2 (2009): 211–29.

Wolf, Susan. "Moral Psychology and the Unity of the Virtues," *Ratio* 20.2 (2007): 145–67. https://doi.org/10.1111/j.1467-9329.2007.00354.x

Wright, Sarah. "Hume on Testimony: A Virtue-Theoretic Defense," History of Philosophy Quarterly 28.3 (2011): 247–65.

Zagzebski, Linda. Virtues of the Mind: An Inquiry into the Nature of Virtue and the Ethical Foundations of Knowledge. Cambridge: Cambridge University Press, 1996.